A SHORT HISTORY OF MATHEMATICS

BY

VERA SANFORD

Teacher of Mathematics, State Normal School, Oneonta, New York

UNDER THE EDITORSHIP OF
JOHN WESLEY YOUNG

WITH AN INTRODUCTION BY
DAVID EUGENE SMITH

HOUGHTON MIFFLIN COMPANY

BOSTON · NEW YORK · CHICAGO · DALLAS
ATLANTA · SAN FRANCISCO

The Riverside Press

CAMBRIDGE · MASSACHUSETTS

PRINTED IN THE U.S.A.

I**8**CTION

In the field of mat[hematics, as in] most other fields of intellectual activity, the [prepar]ing of a teacher necessarily
includes some knowledge of what the world has already done
to bring the subject to its present status. Our offerings in all
branches are manifestly somewhat traditional and are in need
of frequent revision. Even in elementary arithmetic the
topics require constant attention lest they waste time to no
purpose. History tells their story — how they helped some
searcher after truth in times remote, how they served their
purpose, and how they have too often maintained their
status by the mere force of tradition. The same is even more
evident in the case of algebra, since this has been less subject
to scientific criticism; of elementary geometry, the first step
that the pupil takes in real mathematics, because it stands
with the firm support of an unusually long tradition; of
analytic geometry because its propositions, if not its method,
date back like the Euclidean theory two thousand years; and
of the calculus, which so often misses its opportunity simply
because its elements are overloaded with theory and its applied problems have generally not advanced with the increasing demands of the times.

The purpose of a work like this of Dr. Sanford's is clear; it
is to show elementary mathematics — which we may take
as closing with the calculus — as a moving stream instead of
a stagnant pool; a stream which has been constantly fed by
pure springs throughout the centuries of its progress; a
stream which nevertheless has often become so saturated
with sediment as to unfit its waters for human absorption; and
a stream that needs constant filtering if it is to serve this latter
purpose. Instead of the old educational attitude, which demanded that a student should accept the offering or leave it,

modern education like modern hygiene seeks to make its waters both potable and health-giving, and books like this show how it can best be accomplished in the domain of elementary mathematics.

There is no topic in this branch of learning that has not met some human need; to know what this was, and to see why and when it ceased to exist, is to help the teacher recognize present needs and to give him the courage to substitute for the obsolete such material as the present day demands. For example, the Rule of Three has disappeared, better methods of solution having been found. Only yesterday the subject of cube root was taught in all the schools; to-day it has happily gone. But we still give work in numerical fractions and in algebraic factoring that no longer serves any immediately useful purpose, and an excessive number of geometric propositions that seem to the pupil merely to prove the self-evident. "Whence came they? What needs did they meet? What substitutes have we that should take their place?" — such are the questions which the world has constantly been obliged to answer. The story of the past suggests to us the method of answering them to-day, and it is in books like this that the teacher finds the inspiration and courage and knowledge to make the changes that our present civilization demands.

Dr. Sanford has brought to her work a wealth of scholarship that is unusual, and she has presented her subject in that attractive manner in which mathematics itself can and should be taught. Fortunate the teacher who, inspired by this story of "the science venerable," can himself inspire those intrusted to his care, doing this through a knowledge of what mathematics has meant to the world in the past, what it may mean in the present, and what it should mean in the future.

DAVID EUGENE SMITH

PREFACE

UPWARDS of a century ago, Augustus De Morgan presented a brief for the study of textbooks in arithmetic in these terms: "A most sufficient recommendation of the study of old works to the teacher, is shewing that the difficulties which it is now (I speak to the *teacher* not the *rule-driller*) his business to make smooth to the youngest learners, are precisely those which formerly stood in the way of the greatest minds, and sometimes effectually stopped their progress." It was not necessary to limit this to teachers nor to the study of textbooks in a particular branch of mathematics, for the struggle of mankind to formulate mathematical concepts, to evolve a useful symbolism, and to solve quantitative questions arising from his environment are of interest to teachers, students, and bystanders as well.

With these groups in mind, certain chronological details important to the teacher have been summarized in tables, maps have been inserted, and footnote references suggest further work along particular lines.

Many of the illustrations are drawn from Professor D. E. Smith's library, from his collection of portraits of mathematicians, or from his collection of mathematical instruments now in the Museums of the Peaceful Arts in New York City, through whose courtesy they are reproduced here. Others were made available by the kind permission of Mr. George A. Plimpton, Mr. G. H. Hill, Professor Karl Pearson, Dr. Matteo della Corte, the Open Court Publishing Company, the Museum of the University of Pennsylvania, the British Museum, the Science Museum at South Kensington, London, and the Archives Photographiques d'Art et d'Histoire.

It is impossible to list in small compass the individuals to whom the author is indebted for assistance in the preparation of this volume, but particular acknowledgment should be given to Reverend Edgar Lewis Sanford, D.D., who read the manuscript from the mathematical layman's point of view; to Eva Matthews Sanford, of Western Reserve University, who provided many of the classical details; to Professor J. W. Young for his encouragement and his many suggestions, and to Professor David Eugene Smith, not only as adviser and critic in the planning of this work and in its execution, but also as the scholar and teacher to whom the author, in company with many others, owes her first interest in the history of mathematics.

CONTENTS

ILLUSTRATIONS, MAPS, AND TABLES

x   ILLUSTRATIONS, MAPS, AND TABLES

A SHORT HISTORY
OF MATHEMATICS

. .

CHAPTER I

MEN WHO MADE MATHEMATICS

Mathematics when Records Began — Great Mathematicians of
the Ancient World — Hindu Mathematicians — Mathematicians
of the Mohammedan World — The Dark Ages in Europe — The
Period of Transmission — The Period from 1200 to 1500 — Textbooks and Textbook Writers — Sixteenth-Century Algebraists —
The Seventeenth Century — Mathematicians of the Eighteenth
Century — Summary.

MATHEMATICS WHEN RECORDS BEGAN

Two Aspects of Mathematics.   The nature of mathematics
is twofold.   On the one side it deals with quantitative relationships between material objects and thus it becomes a tool
in the world of business, economics, or science.   On the other
side it deduces theorems from arbitrarily chosen postulates
and seeks to carry these theorems to their logical conclusions,
giving but little heed to their use in the world of practical
affairs.   From this point of view mathematics belongs to
philosophy.

It is probable that the first of these aspects of mathematics
had its origin in the counting, weighing, and measuring
needed in primitive barter.   To-day, applied mathematics is
the mainspring of our civilization, for we are becoming increasingly conscious that "to measure is to know."

The speculative side of mathematics has held man's attention almost as long as has the practical one.   It was closely
associated with magic at first, but gradually interest in the
strange properties of numbers shifted from curiosity and awe
to the serious investigation of underlying principles, and the

development of theoretical mathematics began. It later appeared that parts of this subject matter were useful in applied work, but the names "negative," "irrational," and "imaginary" are reminders of the time when the numbers so named were considered only as abstractions which were thoroughly impractical. To-day, however, negatives and irrationals are commonplaces and imaginaries have real application in many fields.

It is fortunate for the world that mathematics has had this theoretical side, for otherwise the progress of science would have been subject to delay whenever new problems arose. As it is, the demands that science makes upon mathematics are frequently met by the use of material that was originally developed without regard for its possible applications. It is interesting to note that both the practical and the speculative aspects of mathematics appeared in the Ahmes Papyrus (*c.* 1650 B.C.), the oldest handbook in the subject now extant, for this includes certain problems that are utilitarian and others that are recreational.

Mathematics in the Ancient World. Our knowledge of the mathematics of Babylonia is based on actual business documents. In that country, records were inscribed on clay tablets that were baked to insure their permanence. Many of these tablets have been deciphered, and in some cases they give what is probably the complete correspondence of certain great mercantile families. Other collections of tablets belonged to temple libraries and to temple schools.

The mathematics of Babylonia was largely commercial and astrological. It is unnecessary to distinguish between the work of the various peoples who successively occupied Mesopotamia, but it is important to note that the Chaldeans who ruled Babylonia from 606 B.C. to 539 B.C. were students of science, especially of astronomy, and that they taught the Greeks to divide the zodiac into twelve parts and the celestial equator into 360 degrees.*

* For Babylonian mathematics, see H. V. Hilprecht, *Mathematical,*

Records from Egypt are found in papyrus manuscripts and
n the inscriptions on stone monuments. Papyrus was made
by cutting thin lengthwise sections of the stem of the reed-like
papyrus plant. These sections were placed side by side. A
second layer was added, the strips being at right angles to the
irst. When dried under a weight, the sap of the plant glued
the sections together, and the finished papyrus resembled a
rough brownish paper. The writing was done with a reed pen.

The best known of the mathematical manuscripts was
copied by the scribe Ahmes from an older work, probably
about 1650 B.C. This is variously called the "Ahmes
Papyrus" after the copyist, and the "Rhind Papyrus" after
A. Henry Rhind, an Egyptologist, who brought the manuscript to England in the middle of the nineteenth century.
The papyrus is now in the British Museum in London. Another papyrus which seems to be a part of this same work is
n the Morgan Library in New York, and a few small fragments from the roll are in the library of the New York
Historical Society.*

In Egypt, arithmetic and geometry were developed to such
a point that the everyday needs of the people were thoroughly
met. The Egyptians could add and subtract whole numbers
and fractions; they multiplied by a clumsy method of doubling
and redoubling, and they divided in a similarly indirect manner. Although this work was slow and laborious, it sufficed
or all ordinary problems of business arithmetic. The
Egyptian knowledge of geometry was such that temples could
be oriented to the proper point of the compass and that the
Nile Valley could be surveyed for the purposes of taxation
after each year's flood. The area formulas that were used
were inaccurate. So, too, were the volume formulas. For
example, the area of a triangle is given as half the product of

Metrological, and Chronological Tablets from the Temple Library of Nippur,
Philadelphia, 1906.

* For facsimiles and translations of the Ahmes Papyrus, see Arnold Buffum
Chace, The Rhind Mathematical Papyrus, 2 vols., Chicago, 1927, 1929; and T.
Eric Peet, The Rhind Mathematical Papyrus, Liverpool, 1923.

its base and its side, no stipulation being made as to the size of the included angle.

The Egyptians developed a rudimentary trigonometry for use in building the pyramids, but this contribution was so slight that it can scarcely be called the beginning of the subject.

At this point, mathematics stagnated. It needed either the external stimulus of new conditions that required new theory, or else it needed the internal momentum of the desire to study the subject for its own sake. Yet Egypt produced neither the new conditions nor the new point of view. Had things continued in this way, mathematics would have developed slowly, keeping pace with scientific discoveries, but, like scientific knowledge, requiring the constant revision of its theorems and hypotheses.

In China, things were somewhat different. The earlier development of civilization and the different character of the race provided the leisure for philosophic speculation and the desire to undertake it. Accordingly, the mysteries of the magic square * and certain permutations and combinations were investigated long before these ideas were evolved in the Occident, but the effect of this work seems to have been confined to China.

Thus, at the beginning of the period when we first know the names of mathematicians, mathematics itself included the commercial arithmetic of Babylonia, the practical geometry of Egypt, and the theoretical, speculative work of the East.

GREAT MATHEMATICIANS OF THE ANCIENT WORLD

In Babylonia and Egypt. The mathematics of Babylonia seems to have been the joint product of the merchants who

---

* The magic square is an arrangement of numbers in the form of a square, such that the sum of the rows, the sum of the columns and the sum of the diagonals shall be the same. For a discussion of magic squares, see page 73. For the history of the mathematics of China and Japan, see Yoshio Mikami, *The Development of Mathematics in China and Japan*, Leipzig, 1913, and David Eugene Smith, and Yoshio Mikami, *History of Japanese Mathematics*, Chicago, 1914.

Rome

Elea

Crotona

Syracuse

Elis

Chios

Athens Samos

Miletus Perga

Rhodes

Gerasa

Alexandria

Syene

THE EASTERN MEDITERRANEAN
IN CLASSIC TIMES

needed arithmetic for their business calculations and the priests who needed it in their astronomy or astrology, but the large quantity of material which shows the application of mathematics to these two fields gives no hint as to the individuals whose work made these uses of mathematics possible. A comparable situation existed in Egypt, where the theoretical work was in the hands of the priests while practical surveying belonged to a group of men known as the "rope-stretchers," the names of no individuals being preserved. Ahmes himself was merely a scribe copying the work of a scholar whose name he does not mention, if, indeed, he knew it himself.

The Ionian Greeks. The earliest Greeks who showed interest in mathematics and philosophy lived in the sheltered islands of the Ægean Sea and in the Greek cities of Asia Minor. To this group belonged Thales of Miletus and Pythagoras of Samos. The Ionian Greeks possessed a lively curiosity. They were in touch with Egypt and Babylonia through their commercial interests, and they traveled widely and observingly. It was under these scholars that geometry became a logical science, that the first map of the world was made, and that the idea of a flat earth covered by a hemispherical dome was replaced by the concept of a spherical earth hung in a spherical heaven.*

Thales. Thales (*c.* 640 to *c.* 546 B.C.) was a merchant of the city of Miletus in Asia Minor. Having made a fortune in his business enterprises, he then devoted himself to the study of mathematics, astronomy, and philosophy, traveling to Egypt and perhaps to Babylonia. He has been characterized as being the first human being who could rightly be called a man of science. His search for an explanation of the universe led him to think of the earth as a flat disk floating on water, and

---

* For a brief treatment of this period see David Eugene Smith, *Mathematics*, Boston, 1923, a volume in the series *Our Debt to Greece and Rome*. For greater detail, see Sir Thomas Little Heath, *A History of Greek Mathematics*, 2 vols., Oxford, 1921. Hereafter referred to as Heath, *Greek Mathematics*.

his philosophy held that water was the first principle from which all things are derived. Like other scholars of his time, Thales took part in the affairs of his city, showing himself to be a clever counselor, perhaps preventing the city from making a disastrous alliance just before the invasion of the Persians, and earning for himself the distinction of being named among the "Seven Wise Men."

Various stories are told of Thales as a merchant. In his day, olive oil was of great importance. It served in place of soap, it provided fuel for lamps, and it was used instead of animal fats for cooking. It is said that one year when olives were particularly plentiful, Thales, fearing a small return for his crop, quietly bought all of the olive presses and was then able to control a profitable market. It is also reported that he had a pack-mule that had discovered that rolling over in the stream which it crossed lightened its usual burden of salt. Thales determined to break the mule of this bad habit, so he ordered a load of sponges to be substituted for the salt. Apparently the cure was effective. Besides being shrewd in dealings of this type, Thales seems to have had a scholar's absorption in his studies, for tradition has it that he fell into a well while gazing at the stars, and that he was taunted with being so eager to know what was occurring in the heavens that he did not know what lay at his own feet.

In the field of practical geometry, Thales showed how the height of a pyramid might be measured by shadow reckoning, that is, by observing that the length of the shadow of a post is to the height of the post as the length of the shadow of a pyramid is to the height of the pyramid. He studied the Chaldean astronomy and is said to have successfully predicted a solar eclipse. His most notable contribution, however, was in beginning the study of demonstrative geometry.

The value of his work cannot be measured by the theorems, five or six in number, that have been attributed to him. Its worth rests on the supposition that he based these on logical reasoning rather than on intuition or experiment, and on the fact that he made geometry abstract by dealing with the relations of lines instead of restricting himself to practical applications as the Egyptians had done in their work which was definitely associated with formulas for areas and volumes. Without the idea of a proof based on logical reasoning, the development of geometry would have been slow and faltering: with it, progress was rapid and direct.

Pythagoras. The most noted of the men who are said to have been pupils of Thales was Pythagoras (*c.* 572 to *c.* 501 B.C.), who probably came from the island of Samos near the mainland city of Miletus where Thales lived. It is reported that after studying under Thales, Pythagoras traveled to Egypt and possibly he may even have gone to India. He eventually settled in Crotona, a Greek city in Italy, where he gathered a group of wealthy men about him and founded the brotherhood of the Pythagoreans. This seems to have been a secret society with an inner group of men admitted to full membership and an outer circle of people who knew only part of the mysteries. Their badge was a five-pointed star and their studies were arithmetic, music, geometry, and astronomy. Their philosophy placed great importance on the idea of the infinite and taught the doctrine of transmigration of souls. Their astronomy had advanced to the point of considering that the earth was a sphere. The difficulty of telling just what work was due to Pythagoras himself is increased by the fact that his followers tended to attribute their own discoveries to their master. It is evident, however, that Pythagoras had great interest in the properties of numbers, and that he devoted considerable attention to the study of areas, volumes, proportions, and the five regular solids. He proved the sum of the angles of any triangle to be two right angles, and tradition has it that he sacrificed an ox on discovering the proof of the theorem that bears his name. His greatest service to mathematics was his inclusion of geometry as one of the liberal sciences essential to a man's education. The influence of the school of Pythagoras was so great that the group was dispersed for political reasons. Pythagoras died in exile, but his followers preserved his teaching and simplified his doctrines.

The Eleans. Another group of philosophers revolted from the Pythagoreans and made its home at Elea which, like Crotona, was a Greek city in Italy. Chief among this group was Zeno (born about 496 B.C.), who is remembered for his paradoxes — four questions framed to challenge certain of his contemporaries who believed that quantities could be divided into an infinite number of particles or atoms. The representatives of the Eleatic school were interested in the famous problems of the squaring of a circle, the trisecting of an angle, and the constructing of a cube whose volume should be twice that of a given cube. These problems will be discussed in Chapter VII, but it should be noted at this point that their consideration led to the study of conics and higher plane curves and also to an approach to the integral calculus.

Thus the period from Pythagoras (c. 540 B.C.) to Plato (c. 380 B.C.) was characterized by activity in many directions, although certain lines of investigation were temporarily blocked. The use of proportions, for example, was checked by the discovery of incommensurable ratios, which necessitated a new definition of a proportion, for the former definition applied only to numbers which were commensurable. In a similar way, the use of infinitesimals was hindered by the enunciation of Zeno's paradoxes.

The Athenians. When Athens became the leading city of Greece in the fifth century B.C., the important mathematicians of the Ægean Islands and of Asia Minor emigrated to that center. Among these men were Anaxagoras (c. 499 to c. 427 B.C.), Hippocrates (c. 460 B.C.), and Democritus (c. 460 to c. 357 B.C.). Anaxagoras, a friend of Pericles and of Euripides, attempted to square the circle. Hippocrates, working on the same problem, discovered an equality between the area bounded by certain arcs and that of an isosceles right triangle. Democritus, a contemporary of Socrates, showed the relation between the volume of a cone and that of its circumscribed cylinder and between a pyramid and its circumscribed prism, thus approaching the methods of the integral calculus.

Plato. The philosopher Plato (*c.* 430 to *c.* 349 B.C.) although not primarily a mathematician, did as great service for mathematics as did any of his contemporaries. He was convinced that mathematics was of great value in disciplining the mind to logical thinking and it is said that the entrance to his Academy bore the inscription, "Let no one ignorant of geometry enter here."

Plato had studied under the Pythagoreans and perhaps under Egyptian scholars also. He seems to have contributed little to the subject matter of mathematics, but he accomplished much by placing its theory on a rigorous footing. Plato considered mathematics an integral part of a liberal education, esteeming arithmetic important for its practical use in military affairs and for its philosophic value in compelling the mind to reason about abstract numbers. He objected to the use of mechanical devices in geometry and, according to tradition, he restricted the subject to the study of those figures which could be drawn by means of compasses and an unmarked straightedge. Such a restriction would be in keeping with his interest in mathematical logic, for the instruments which he discarded had been invented to help in the solution of applied problems which were of no importance in connection with his main objective.

Aristotle. Like Plato, Aristotle (384–322 B.C.) was important for his attitude toward mathematics rather than for his contributions to the subject itself. In fact, it is quite likely that his many interests prevented his actually following the more advanced topics in a rapidly developing body of subject matter. Like his teacher Plato, Aristotle assumed a mastery of elementary mathematics on the part of the students at his school, the Lyceum. He framed his system of logic on models taken from mathematics and he stimulated his students to undertake research in the historical development of the subject. The influence of Aristotle is one of the most interesting commentaries on human thought. As tutor to Alexander the Great, Aristotle was in a position to collect great quantities of scientific information relating to the countries which Alexander conquered. His summaries of this information coupled with his own philosophy were in the main so authoritative that they became the great reference works of the Middle Ages. Unfortunately, medieval scholars tended to accept Aristotle's conclusions without question and it is very likely that their adherence to his doctrines resulted in the retarding of scientific inquiry.

Alexandrian Scholars. After the death of Alexander (323 B.C.), the recently founded city of Alexandria replaced Athens as the center of scientific thought. This was a natural phenomenon, for the new rulers of Egypt, the successors of Alexander's general, Ptolemy, were the interested patrons of science and mathematics and the library of Alexandria was exceedingly fine. The cheapness of Egyptian papyrus as compared with parchment made Alexandria the center of the book-copying industry of the Mediterranean world. Furthermore, the new government not only provided the funds for research, but it also freed the citizens from duties to the state such as had made heavy demands on Thales and on his successors when Greece was a democracy.

It was at Alexandria that Euclid compiled his *Elements*, that Archimedes studied, and that Eratosthenes measured the earth. The influence of Alexandria declined in the second and first centuries B.C. and it received a serious blow with the destruction of its library.

Euclid. Euclid (*c.* 300 B.C.) has the distinction of being the only man to summarize all the mathematical knowledge of his times, for, contrary to popular impressions, the *Elements* were not concerned with geometry alone.* Beyond the fact

* Detailed accounts of the subject matter of the thirteen books of the *Elements* will be found on pages 270–275. See also Sir Thomas L. Heath, *The Thirteen Books of Euclid's Elements*, 3 vols., Cambridge, England, 1926; first edition, 1908. Hereafter referred to as Heath's *Euclid*.

that he taught at Alexandria, we know nothing with certainty about Euclid himself. It is possible that he may have been an Egyptian and not a Greek. Who he was is of small importance, however, compared with what he accomplished in systematizing Greek mathematics as it then existed.

At this point, it would be well to list a group of scholars who summarized various sections of Greek mathematics: Apollonius (c. 225 B.C.) who wrote on conics; Hipparchus (c. 140 B.C.) on trigonometry; Nicomachus (A.D. c. 100) on the theory of numbers; Ptolemy (c. 150) on astronomy; and Diophantus (c. 275) on algebra. As each of these writers was concerned with a particular field rather than with the development of mathematics in general, no further mention will be made of them at this point, but the contribution of each will be discussed in connection with the topics which he treated.

Eratosthenes. Eratosthenes (c. 274 to c. 194 B.C.) was librarian of the university at Alexandria. He was interested in the study of prime numbers, invented an instrument for duplicating the cube, measured the circumference of the earth, and calculated the distance from the earth to the sun and to the moon. It is said that he was a victim of one of the diseases of the eye that are common in the valley of the Nile, and that when he became unable to read, he committed suicide. Although Eratosthenes was noted for his achievements in many different lines, he failed to surpass his contemporaries in any one of them. This has led some to interpret his nickname "Beta" (the second letter of the alphabet) as an estimate of his qualities, but another interpretation is equally probable. This is that the classrooms in the university were marked with letters, and it is thought that Eratosthenes was called by the name of the room in which he taught.

Archimedes. Although Archimedes (278–212 B.C.)* was associated with the city of Syracuse in Sicily, he belonged to

---

* For the life and work of Archimedes, see Sir Thomas Little Heath, *Archimedes*, Cambridge, England, 1897; also a shorter account by the same author and with the same title in the *Pioneers of Progress Series*, London, 1920.

the Alexandrian group of philosophers and mathematicians. He was interested in mathematics that was practical as well as that which was theoretical, and he seems to have reduced mathematical problems to questions of mechanics, as is witnessed by his approach to the calculus (see pages 311–14), yet there is evidence to show that he considered his mechanical inventions as being merely the "diversions of geometry at play."

One of the best-known stories about Archimedes relates how he was called into consultation by Hiero, the King of Syracuse. Hiero had had a crown made as a votive offering to the gods, but he suspected that the craftsman who made it had substituted baser metal for part of the gold. Accordingly, he asked Archimedes to investigate the matter. It is but seldom in the history of mathematics that records are extant of the circumstances which led to discoveries, or of the sensations of the discoverers. In this case, according to legend, Archimedes suddenly realized that the volume of water displaced by an object might be connected with his problem. This idea occurred to him while he was at the public baths of the city. He rushed home, shouting "Eureka," which meant "I have found it," and solved the problem by the comparison of the loss of weight of the crown when placed in water, and the loss of weight of an equal amount of pure gold. The circumstance should be noted as providing material for one of the first of the genuine scientific problems to be included in textbooks.

According to legend, Archimedes was noted among his contemporaries for the system of pulleys by which he drew a ship up onto the shore single-handed, for the burning glasses by which he set fire to enemy vessels in the harbor, for the engines of war by which he terrified even the Romans, and for his boast that, given a place to stand, he could move the earth Among mathematicians, Archimedes is known for his work in mechanics, for his studies in the theory of numbers, and for the investigations which foreshadowed the calculus.

Various accounts are given of his death, which occurred when the Roman general Marcellus captured the city of Syracuse in 212 B.C. According to one story, he was killed by a soldier who tried to persuade him to leave the problem he was studying to go before the victorious general. Some say that Archimedes was at work on the seashore with his diagrams drawn on the sand and that the soldier inconsiderately walked across his work. Archimedes protested and the soldier retaliated by drawing his sword. Another legend has it that he was slain by plunderers who supposed his polished astronomical instruments to be made of gold.

Many years later, Cicero discovered the tomb of Archimedes, which had long been forgotten. He said that it bore the figures of a cylinder and a sphere, symbols of Archimedes's investigations, and he lamented the fate that led the people of Syracuse to neglect the monument to their most celebrated genius.

The Romans. The Romans were in general uninterested in the speculative side of the Greek mathematics. In fact, Cicero spoke disparagingly of the Greek interest in geometry, congratulating his countrymen because they were concerned only with the mathematics that is needed in measuring and in reckoning. It is true that the Romans used a certain amount of mathematics in building their aqueducts, but they added nothing to the theory of mathematics and they were obliged to employ specialists from Alexandria when Agrippa (63–12 B.C.) carried out Julius Cæsar's design of making a survey of the Empire.

Boethius. The knowledge of Greek mathematics which the Romans transmitted to the Middle Ages was meager, most of it being embodied in the writings of Boethius (c. 475–524) who lived in the period immediately after the fall of Rome when interest in Greek philosophy was particularly strong in Italy. He was at one time a favorite of the Ostrogoth king, Theodoric, but later he was imprisoned and executed for political reasons. The Church, however, declared him to be a martyr and consequently his writings were supposed to be highly authoritative. During his imprisonment, Boethius had written a work *On the Consolations of Philosophy* (*De consolatione philosophiae*). This and his *Arithmetic* (*Boetii de institutione arithmetica libri duo*) were taught in the monastic schools of the Middle Ages and excerpts from them appear frequently in the anthologies of philosophy, theology, and literature whose contents are an index of the literary interests of that period.

HINDU MATHEMATICIANS

Anonymous Contributions. It is highly probable that Hindu mathematicians were influenced by the Greeks at an early period, and by the Chinese at a later one, but they also accomplished a large amount of original work. This seems to have included the invention of the numerals that developed into the Hindu-Arabic system and the zero which made the place-value idea possible. It is probable that neither the numerals nor the zero was rated as being of particular importance at the time when they were first introduced. Other systems of numerals were in use and these were apparently quite as valuable as the ones from which our familiar symbols are derived. The invention of a symbol for zero came some time after the idea of a zero was common property. Thus, although the man who first devised the numerals and the man who first devised a symbol for zero did great service to mathematics, they were less great than was the thinker who saw that the two might be combined in a place-value system which would require only ten different characters to write any number, however large. We do not know the names of these men, nor even with certainty when they lived, for it was not until the numerals had been in use for centuries that the history of mathematics in India reached the stage in which the names of important contributors were preserved.

Four Great Hindu Mathematicians. The four important Hindu mathematicians whose names we know are Āryabhata,

Brahmagupta, Mahāvīra, and Bhāskara.   The work of these men is characterized by a strange mixture of things that are of little account with those that are of extraordinary brilliance.

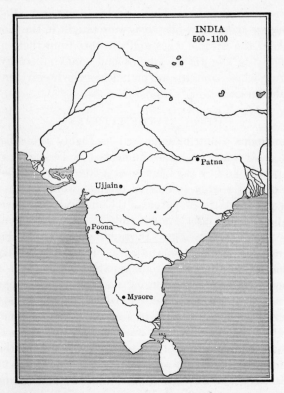

Men who were both scientists and necromancers could scarcely be expected to maintain a high standard in all of their work.   The association of true and pseudo-science, however, was not confined to India.   It has appeared in many instances, a later one being the case of John Napier, the inventor of logarithms, who was popularly supposed to deal in black magic.

Āryabhata.   The first of the great Hindu mathematicians,

Āryabhata (*c.* 475 to *c.* 550), lived in or near the present city of Patna on the Ganges, to the east of Benares.   One of the works of this writer contains the following introduction which is here quoted from Professor Smith's *History*:*

Having paid homage to Brahma, to Earth, to the Moon, to Mercury, to Venus, to the Sun, to Mars, to Jupiter, to Saturn, and to the constellations, Āryabhata, in the City of Flowers, sets forth the science venerable.

Āryabhata wrote on arithmetic, including under this topic arithmetic and geometric progressions, quadratic equations, and indeterminate equations.   He also computed astronomical tables which contained a table of sines.   His work in mensuration was crude and in this respect it somewhat resembled that of the Egyptians.   For example, he gave the area of a triangle by ·a scheme that applies only to the case of an isosceles triangle.

Brahmagupta.   The second of the important Hindu mathematicians, Brahmagupta † (*c.* 628), lived at Ujjain, the site of a great astronomical observatory.   His work is much more detailed than that of Āryabhata.   Like his predecessor, Brahmagupta gave area formulas that were faulty.   He assumed, for example, that the area of an isosceles triangle was half the product of the base and one of the equal sides.   He applied his arithmetic with success to problems in barter, interest, progressions, and shadow reckoning.   He gave the rules for negative numbers in his algebra, solved quadratics, and paid considerable attention to indeterminate equations.

Mahāvīra.   The third of the Hindu mathematicians lived at Mysore about two centuries later than Brahmagupta.

* See David Eugene Smith, *History of Mathematics*, 2 vols., Boston, 1923–1925, I, 155.   Hereafter referred to as Smith, *History*.   Quoted by permission of the author.

† See H. T. Colebrooke, *Algebra with Arithmetic and Mensuration from the Sanscrit of Brahmegupta and Bhāscara*, London, 1817.   Hereafter referred to as Colebrooke, *Brahmagupta* or *Bhāskara*, according to the author cited. The differences in the transliteration of the proper names now and a century ago should be noted.

Mahāvīra's * work (*c*. 850) was more complete than that of
either of the men mentioned above.   It includes a discussion
of operations with zero, treating division by zero as having no
effect on the dividend.   The verbal problems of Mahāvīra's

HINDU CELESTIAL SPHERE (*c*. 1590)
From the collection of Professor David Eugene Smith.   Courtesy of the
Museums of the Peaceful Arts, New York City.

work were fanciful, as may be judged from the following
example:

A powerful unvanquished excellent black snake which is 32 hastas
in length, enters into a hole [at the rate of] $7\frac{1}{2}$ angulas in $\frac{5}{14}$ of a day;
and in the course of $\frac{1}{4}$ of a day, its tail grows by $2\frac{3}{4}$ of an angula.
O ornament of arithmeticians, tell me by what time this serpent
enters fully into the hole?

* See M. Rangacarya, The *Ganita-Sāra-Sangraha of Mahāvīracārya*,
Madras, 1912.

Bhāskara. The last of the Hindu mathematicians lived in Ujjain, the city in which Brahmagupta had worked four hundred years previously. Bhāskara (1114 to c. 1185) was notable for his treatment of negative numbers, which he considered as debts or as losses, and also for his treatise on arithmetic and measurement which he had named for his daughter Lilāvati to console her for the accident which had prevented her marriage. Bhāskara, who was an astrologer as well as a mathematician, had discovered the propitious day and hour for this event. Any other time was prophesied as being sure to bring misfortune. While the bride was watching the hour cup whose sinking would mark the proper moment, a pearl dropped from her headdress and stopped the hole in the cup. The lucky moment passed unnoticed, and in compensation Bhāskara promised his daughter that he would give her name to a book which should last until the "latest times."

Characteristics of Hindu Mathematics. The chief contributions of the Hindus were their system of numerals, the zero, the rules for operations with zero, the study of progressions, and work with quadratics, all of which were borrowed by Western writers. Their work in simultaneous linear equations, however, seems to have been neglected by later mathematicians.

An important and significant feature of the work of these Hindu writers was its poetic quality. This was shown, not only in the introductions to their books, as in the case quoted above, but also in the fanciful and imaginative details of their verbal problems which will be discussed in Chapter V.

MATHEMATICIANS OF THE MOHAMMEDAN WORLD

Arab Conquests. Within a century after the death of Mohammed (632), his followers conquered Egypt, Northern Africa, and a part of Spain. Shortly after, they were in possession of the island of Sicily. They maintained their foothold in Europe until the fifteenth century, although Sicily was lost after an occupation of about a hundred years. In the East, Arab conquests reached to India. The Arabs were equally rapid in their assimilation of Greek and Hindu science and mathematics. Their religious beliefs and practices made necessary the precise fixing of their great feast days by the phases of the moon and even entailed the accurate determination of the hours of the day. It was no accident, therefore, that the majority of the Arab mathematicians began their careers as astronomers.

Arab Mathematicians. About 770, a Hindu astronomer was summoned to Bagdad to translate certain trigonometric tables into Arabic. This translation, so it was said, was the means of bringing the Hindu numerals into Arab mathematics. The works of Euclid and Ptolemy were translated into Arabic for Harun al-Rashid (786–808), the caliph for whom the Arabian Nights were written. Harun al-Rashid's successor, al-Mâmûn, himself an astronomer, measured the earth by finding the length of a degree on a meridian. The story illustrates the arbitrary nature of the standardization of measures, for the caliph directed that the arm length of his favorite slave be used as the official unit in making this measure. Al-Mâmûn should be remembered also for the translations made at his orders from the manuscripts sent him by the emperor of the Byzantine Empire. These translations were made by Christian scholars summoned from Syria to Bagdad. Thus it happened that the works of both Greek and Hindu writers were made available for Moslem students.

Al-Khowârizmî. Among the Arab scholars was Mohammed ibn Mûsâ al-Khowârizmî, whose name means Mohammed, the son of Moses of Khwarezm. This author's great achievement was in writing a book (*c.* 825) * in which the Hindu numerals were used in the solution of equations. The work had great influence in Europe, both in translation and

* See Louis Charles Karpinski, *Robert of Chester's Latin Translation of the Algebra of Al-Khowarizmi*, New York, 1915. Hereafter referred to as Karpinski, *Al-Khowarizmi*.

through the writings of men who commented upon it, and the name of the author, corrupted into "algorismi" and "algorithmi," became the "algorism" and "augrim," that for many years meant reckoning with Hindu-Arabic numerals. The title of this treatise, *'ilm al-jabr wa'l muqabalah*, later furnished the name for the subject "algebra."

THE DARK AGES IN EUROPE

The Venerable Bede. The period immediately following the disintegration of the Roman Empire was one in which all scholarship was at a low point. This was no less true in mathematics than in science and philosophy. A small amount of arithmetic was used in calculating the church calendar, for this depended on the date of Easter which, in turn, depended on the date of the full moon following the spring equinox. Handbooks called *computi*, giving the rules for the calculation of Easter, were the chief mathematical works of the time.* An idea of their content and method may be had from their modern survival, the "Rules for Moveable Feasts" in the *Book of Common Prayer*.

The first European scholar to write on mathematics after the close of the Roman period was the Englishman who is commonly called the Venerable Bede (*c.* 673–735). Bede was a monk who lived at Jarrow in Northumberland. Although he was greatly esteemed as a scholar by his contemporaries, his title was given him long after his death, when his tomb in Durham Cathedral was marked with the couplet

"Hâc sunt in fossâ
Bedae venerabilis ossâ."

Bede maintained that "his constant pleasure lay in learning, or in teaching, or in writing." As would be expected, his work was largely in the field of theology, but we owe to him treatises on finger notation, the calendar, and the theory of numbers.

* See David Eugene Smith, *Le Comput Manuel de Magister Anianus*, Paris, 1928.

Alcuin. The English scholar, Alcuin of York (735–804), was called to France to establish a school at the court of Charlemagne and he later became abbot of the monastery of Saint Martin at Tours. Tradition ascribes to him a series of puzzles in arithmetic called the *Propositiones ad acuendos juvenes*. Alcuin's connection with this work is highly doubtful, but the problems form an interesting illustration of the type of question enjoyed by thinking people in the Dark Ages. There is no attempt to make the problems seem reasonable: A snail spends years in getting to a banquet, and a king raises an incredibly large army by drafting men from thirty villages, the numbers taken from each increasing in geometric ratio.*

THE PERIOD OF TRANSMISSION

The Channels of Transmission. The Greek classics found their way into Europe by several different routes: through the Norman kingdom ·of Sicily, through direct contact with the Arab civilization in northern Africa, and through the Moorish universities in Spain. Of these, the work of the Arabs is of particular interest although the other contacts were of great importance also.†

Beginning with the early part of the tenth century, Christian students traveled to Spain to study Greek classics in their Arabic versions and to translate them into Latin. Their work was unorganized and the Arabic manuscripts which they used were full of inaccuracies. Nevertheless, much that was of value was accomplished.

Gerbert. One of the first Christians to study in the Moorish universities was Gerbert (*c.* 950–1003), who later became Pope Sylvester II. As a result of his work in Spain, Gerbert brought the Hindu-Arabic numerals into Europe, but he apparently did not know the symbol for zero. He wrote on

---

* Other problems from this collection are given on pages 212, 213, 218, 219. The entire collection appears in *Alcuini Opera Omnia*, II, 101, edited by J. P. Migne, *Patrologiae cursus completus*, Paris, 1863.

† For this period, see C. H. Haskins, *Studies in the History of Mediæval Science*, Cambridge, Massachusetts, 1924.

arithmetic and on astrology, drawing his material from Arabic sources. His geometry, however, was based on manuscripts describing the methods of the Roman surveyors which he found in a monastery in Italy.

The University of Toledo. When the Christians succeeded in reëstablishing themselves in a part of Spain, the city of Toledo became the meeting ground for Moors and Christians. There Gherardo of Cremona translated Ptolemy's great work on astronomy, completing his translation in 1175, and there the English scholar, Robert of Chester (c. 1140), made a Latin version of the *Algebra* of al-Khowârizmî.

Jewish Scholars in Spain. The Moors in Spain had been especially hospitable to the Jews, and as a result Spain was not merely a convenient place for Christian scholars to find manuscripts of the Greek classics but it was also a center of research in mathematics and medicine. Among the best known of the Jewish mathematicians was Rabbi ben Ezra (c. 1140), who wrote on the calendar, on astronomy, and on the theory of numbers. He was interested also in number magic and number mysticism and he studied the subject of permutations and combinations because of its application to the conjunctions of the planets, a thing which was very useful in astrology. His work offers further testimony to Professor Haskins's statement that "In the medieval mind, the science of magic lay close to the magic of science."

The Norman Kingdom of Sicily. Standing at the crossroads of the Mediterranean, Sicily was a natural meeting-ground for several civilizations. It had been a Greek colony. Later it formed a part of the Roman Empire. After the fall of Rome it owed allegiance to Constantinople. The Arabs held it for fifty years during the ninth century, but it was recaptured by the Greeks. Subsequently it was taken by a group of Normans who had come to the aid of a rebel faction of the Greeks and who remained to enjoy the booty. Under the rule of the Normans, three languages, Greek, Arabic, and Latin, were used side by side. Occasional embassies were dispatched to Constantinople and to Bagdad. Interest in science and mathematics led to the interchange of manuscripts and to translations made from Greek directly to Latin. These were superior in many respects to those made from Arabic versions in Spain.

The most important of the rulers of Sicily were Frederick II (1198–1250) and his son Manfred (reigning 1258–1266).

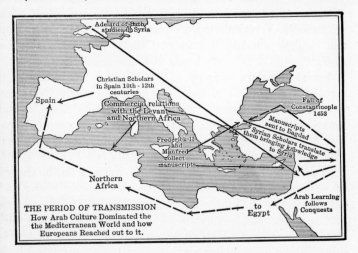

Adelard of Bath studies in Syria

Christian Scholars in Spain 10th - 12th centuries

Spain

Commercial relations with the Levant and Northern Africa

Frederick II and Manfred collect manuscripts

Fall of Constantinople 1453

Manuscripts sent to Bagdad

Syrian Scholars translate them bringing knowledge to Syria

Northern Africa

to Egypt

Arab Learning follows Conquests

THE PERIOD OF TRANSMISSION
How Arab Culture Dominated the the Mediterranean World and how Europeans Reached out to it.

Frederick II was the patron of the Scotchman, Michael Scot (*c.* 1175 to *c.* 1234), a man who had studied in Toledo and who enjoyed an enviable reputation for his knowledge of astrology. Manfred assembled a considerable library of Greek classics. Under each of these rulers, intellectual activity centered in the king's court rather than in the universities, and mathematics and science rather than philosophy and theology were the subjects of study.

The Byzantine Empire. The Eastern part of the Roman Empire survived until the capture of Constantinople by the Turks in 1453, but it produced no mathematicians of importance. It should be noted, however, that the emperors at Constantinople were in occasional communication with the caliphs at Bagdad and with the Norman kings of Sicily and that gifts of Greek manuscripts were made to both rulers. Furthermore, during the twelfth century, merchants from Venice and Pisa had representatives on the Bosphorus and through them a limited knowledge of Greek came into Europe. It is significant that the Byzantine gold coins, the besant and the solidus, were the international coinage of the entire Levant, a fact that accounts for the prominent part which these coins play in the problems given in Fibonacci's *Liber Abaci* which was written in 1202 (see below).

Syria. Besides studying in Spain, twelfth-century scholars sometimes traveled to Syria. Commercial relations with this region had been a coveted prize during the Crusades and at Antioch, as in Constantinople, the Italian cities had residence quarters for their representatives.

Notable among those who went to Syria was the Englishman Adelard of Bath (*c.* 1120). He wrote on the abacus and made Latin translations of Euclid's *Elements* and of al-Khowârizmî's astronomical tables. On his return, he complained bitterly about the state of things in England, saying that "princes were violent, prelates wine-bibbers, judges mercenary, patrons inconstant, common men flatterers, promise-makers false, friends envious, and every one in general ambitious." This being the case, he philosophically decided to ignore it, as this was the one way to treat insurmountable ills.

Fibonacci. The commercial agents sent to the cities in Northern Africa were naturally in close contact with the Hindu-Arabic numerals, and if they were of scholarly bent, they were in an excellent position to study Arab mathematics. It is not surprising, then, that the outstanding work in mathematics of this period was done by Fibonacci (*c.* 1170 to *c.* 1250) * who came in contact with Arabic culture while his

---

* For Fibonacci's works, see *Scritti di Leonardo Pisano*, Boncompagni edition, Rome, 1857–1862; and *Tre scritti inediti di Leonardo Pisano*, Florence, 1854.

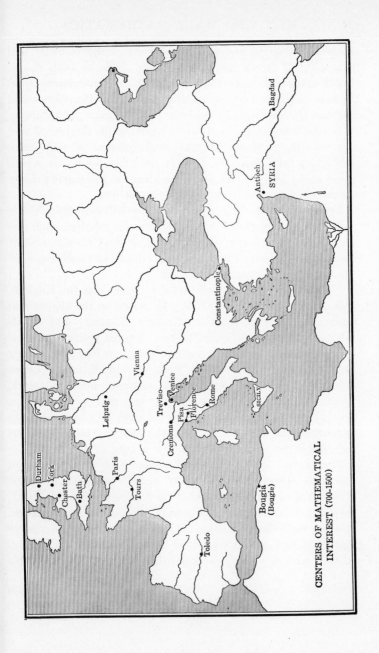

CENTERS OF MATHEMATICAL
INTEREST (700-1500)

father was agent for Pisa in its trade with the city of Bougia in northern Africa.

Fibonacci, or, as he is sometims called, Leonardo Pisano, also studied in Constantinople and in Syria. His fame as a scholar was so great that he was summoned to the court of the Emperor Frederick II to engage in a mathematical contest with the court scholar John of Palermo. The three problems proposed for solution in this contest are given on page 145. Fibonacci's *Liber Abaci* (1202) contains a detailed treatment of the Hindu-Arabic numerals and their uses and it gives an extensive discussion of the Rule of False and the Rule of Three, both of which methods for the solution of problems were destined to retain their popularity for centuries. Fibonacci's work is characterized by a lack of general methods, each problem being considered separately. Furthermore, he was not content with solving a problem as it might conceivably occur, but considered all the variants of the question regardless of their plausibility. For example, he asks how long it will take a given number of men to set out a given number of trees if they work at a specified rate; how many men will be needed to set out the trees in a given time; and how many trees could be planted by a given number of men in a given time.

Fibonacci's *Practica geometriae* (1220) systematized the subject matter of practical geometry, treating square and cube roots, proportion, mensuration of areas and volumes, and the use of a surveying instrument called the *quadrans* (see page 239). Besides these works, Fibonacci also wrote the *Liber quadratorum* (1225) and the *Flos*, whose fanciful title indicated that algebra was to be considered the flower of mathematics.

THE PERIOD FROM 1200 TO 1500

The Thirteenth Century. The thirteenth century witnessed the founding of many universities and it was marked by the work of such men as Campanus (*c.* 1260), who translated Euclid, the German writer Jordanus Nemorarius (*c.* 1225), whose algebra *De Numeris Datis* contained problems of the "Find a number" type, and the Englishmen Sacrobosco (*c.* 1250) and Roger Bacon (*c.* 1250), who was a critic of mathematics rather than a mathematician. It should be noted, however, that Roger Bacon's work shows a knowledge of the writings of Euclid, Apollonius, Archimedes, and Ptolemy. The amount of mathematics taught in the universities was very meager in comparison with this, while the amount known by the merchant class even in Italy, then far in advance of the rest of the world, was limited to casting accounts by means of counters and other simple operations.

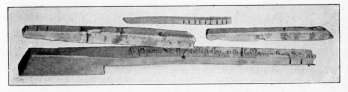

TALLY STICKS OF THE THIRTEENTH CENTURY
From the collection of Professor David Eugene Smith. Courtesy of the
Museums of the Peaceful Arts, New York City.

In the northern countries, the counting board (page 88) was even more popular than in Italy, and bookkeeping was managed by the primitive method of the tally stick. Tallies were flat pieces of wood in which sums of money were indicated by notches, whose length indicated the amounts. The tally was then cut through these notches, the debtor keeping one part and the creditor the other. The use of wooden tallies by the Court of the Exchequer in England continued until the early part of the nineteenth century, the practice being terminated by an Act of Parliament which went into effect in 1826. Examples of tallies of 1812 and of 1822 are to be seen in the Science Museum at South Kensington, London. Much older tallies are shown in the British Museum, and in the Museums of the Peaceful Arts in New York. The tally sticks shown in the accompanying illustration bear the date 1296. These were found in the Chapel of the Pyx in Westminster Abbey where they had lain undisturbed for upwards of six hundred years. The specimens show the notation along the edge of the *stock* or larger piece, which was retained by the lender, and also the slender piece or *foil*, which was given to the borrower. The expression "to hold stock in a company" comes from the practice of the Bank of England in its early days of issuing receipts in the form of tallies, so that the man who loaned the money became a "stock holder." The tally stick itself has left its trace in the expression "to make accounts tally," which is taken from the way in which the two parts of the tally were checked against each other.

Oresme. The activity of the thirteenth century, as seen in the work of Campanus, Jordanus Nemorarius, and a group of English scholars, bore little fruit in the next generations, for the Hundred Years War and the plague that swept through Europe in the middle of the fourteenth century combined to check the development of the universities. The greatest French writer of this period was Nicole Oresme (*c.* 1323–1382), a Norman ecclesiastic whose work was far in advance of his time. He used fractional exponents in his algebra and he foreshadowed the idea of analytic geometry, but brilliant as this was, it seems to have had no influence on Oresme's contemporaries.

Peurbach. Among the scholars who studied Greek for the sake of being able to read the Greek classics in mathematics was the Austrian Georg von Peurbach (1423–1461), who studied in Italy, taught at Ferrara, Bologna, and Padua, and finally settled in Vienna where he lectured on mathematics and on the Latin poets. He began a translation of Ptolemy's *Almagest* but died before its completion, leaving the conclusion of this work to his pupil Regiomontanus.

Regiomontanus. Following a popular custom, Johann Müller (1436–1476) changed his name to that of his birthplace, using the Latin Regiomontanus in preference to the German Königsberg. Regiomontanus was a student at Leipzig at the

age of twelve. He later went to Vienna to work under Peurbach, lecturing there when still too young to be granted a degree. He completed the tables of sines and the translation of
the *Almagest* which had been begun by Peurbach and he was
instrumental in earning for trigonometry a place as a separate branch of mathematics through his treatise *De triangulis
omnimodis*, published about 1464. Shortly after the death of
Peurbach, Regiomontanus traveled to Italy, where he studied
Greek with the purpose of reading the works of Greek mathematicians. The King of Hungary invited him to make a
critical study of certain manuscripts, but war claimed the
King's interest, and Regiomontanus left his royal patron
and devoted his attention to persuading a wealthy citizen of
Nürnberg to build an astronomical observatory, the first in
Europe. In 1475, the Pope invited him to assist in the reformation of the calendar and Regiomontanus again went to
Rome to engage in this work. A year later he died, perhaps
during a pestilence, perhaps poisoned by the son of a man
whose translation of the *Almagest* had been severely criticized
by the German writer a decade before.

Chuquet. The most prominent of the French mathematicians of the fifteenth century was Nicolas Chuquet, whose
Triparty en la Science des Nombres (1484) dealt with rational
and irrational numbers and with the theory of equations.
Like Oresme, Chuquet was too far in advance of his contemporaries to exert any great influence over them.

TEXTBOOKS AND TEXTBOOK WRITERS

Algorisms. On the more popular side, the fourteenth
century was characterized by the production of "algorisms,"
works devoted to the exposition of the uses of Hindu-Arabic
numerals. The name, as has been noted above, is a corruption of al-Khowârizmî, but the books had no other connection
with his work. The algorisms are an interesting commentary
on the slow progress of Europeans in adopting the new numerals. This was due in part to inertia, but an important

factor was the unfortunate association of these numerals with soothsaying through their use by astrologers.

Besides containing a discussion of the new numerals, the algorisms frequently included problems showing the application of mathematics to business; and, as if to show that mathematics was not a purely utilitarian subject, puzzles and recreations were given with their full solutions. An anonymous algorism of the fourteenth century now in the Library of Columbia University, for example, contains the problem of measuring out a single unit of a liquid by means of jugs whose capacities are 8, 5, and 3. The same manuscript also gives the puzzle of the wolf, the goat, and the cabbage that must be ferried across a stream in a boat that will hold but one beside the boatman, the problem lying in the fact that, left alone, the goat would eat the cabbage and the wolf would devour the goat.*

Textbooks in Arithmetic. Prior to 1600, no less than three hundred textbooks in arithmetic had been printed in Europe. This productivity was due to two main causes: interest in education as a result of the Renaissance and increased commercial activity. The first of these led to the establishing of schools variously called *gymnasia* (Germany), *grammar schools* (England), and *Schools of the Teaching Orders* (France and Italy). Instruction in these schools was in Latin and accordingly other subjects had a minor part in the curriculum. Classical tradition led to the retention of such subjects as the classifications of numbers which were once a part of the Greek arithmetic. The classical writers on whose works these texts were based had presented their subjects for adults. Accordingly, the writers of Latin texts in the Renaissance period emphasized the logic of their prototypes and gave careful definitions at the beginning of a topic, reduced processes to rules, and used few practical applications.

The growing commercial activity of Europe, beginning in

* For a description of this algorism, see Elizabeth B. Cowley, "An Italian Mathematical Manuscript," *Vassar Mediæval Studies*, New Haven, 1923.

the thirteenth century, gave rise to another type of text, and the spread of commercial interests from Italy to the Hansa League of Germany, to England and France in the middle of the sixteenth century, and to the Netherlands slightly later, resulted in the production of textbooks in the vernaculars. In contrast to the scholarly writers of the Latin texts, the writers of the works on practical arithmetic were actually teachers of the subject and frequently acted as surveyors, notaries, or gaugers (men who measured or estimated the contents of casks of wine for the excise duties of the towns). Their books are filled with applied problems. Rules for operations are often given in verse to be the more easily remembered and the books contain supplementary material of great value to the merchant: tables of weights, measures, money, lists of important fairs, tables of the time needed for a draft to reach certain cities, etc. These writers tended to approach new theory by means of real problems and their books have surprisingly modern features in their transition from simple to complex operations and from concrete illustrations to abstract cases.

The Treviso Arithmetic. The first books to be printed in Italy were published in a monastery at Subiaco near Rome in 1465. Thirteen years later (1478), an anonymous arithmetic was issued from the press at Treviso, a town lying on the trade route from Venice to the North. It was quite natural, then, that the Treviso Arithmetic should be largely concerned with commercial mathematics. The book contains sections on the writing of numbers, on computation, and on the solution of problems. The problems deal with the uses of the Rule of Three, partnership, barter, and the determining of the proper proportion of metals in coinage. Following this the writer gives certain recreational questions which he calls "accomplishments." These include the problem of the couriers, the problem of the hare and the hound, and several work problems.*

* For the early printed arithmetics, see David Eugene Smith, *Rara Arith-*

TITLE-PAGE OF CALANDRI'S ARITHMETIC (1491)
Showing a fanciful representation of Pythagoras.

Borghi and Calandri. More important than the Treviso
Arithmetic in its influence was Borghi's work, published in
Venice in 1484. This was a commercial arithmetic whose use-
fulness was so great that at least seventeen editions were

metica, Boston, 1908; also "The First Printed Arithmetic (Treviso, 1478),"
Isis, VI (1924), 311–331, and "The First Great Commercial Arithmetic,"
Isis, VIII (1926), 41–50, the latter being an account of Borghi's work of 1484.
A translation of portions of the Treviso Arithmetic also appears in A Source
Book in Mathematics, edited by David Eugene Smith, New York, 1929.
Hereafter referred to as Smith, Source Book in Mathematics.

published during the next century, the last of these appearing in 1577.

Calandri's Arithmetic (1491) was less important than that of Borghi, but it should be mentioned here for two reasons: it was the first printed arithmetic to show our method of long division, and it was the first Italian textbook to use woodcuts to illustrate its problems.

Pacioli. Of the Italian writers of the fifteenth century, the most important was Pacioli (*c.* 1445 to *c.* 1509), a monk who was also known as Fra Luca di Borgo. He seems to have traveled extensively and he spent much of his time in teaching, writing several treatises for the use of his pupils. His greatest work was his *Sūma de Arithmetica Geometria Proportioni et Proportionalita*. This was published in Venice in 1494. As its title indicates, the *Sūma* (abbreviated from *Summa*, a summation) contains a summary of the mathematical knowledge of his time in arithmetic, algebra, and geometry. Very little is original, but the sources of the work are seldom indicated. The book gives valuable information regarding business customs and the like, and its treatment of double entry bookkeeping is especially important.

Widman. Johann Widman's arithmetic (1489) filled a place in Germany that was similar to that of Borghi's work in Italy. Widman taught arithmetic in the university of Leipzig and in 1486 he supplemented these lectures by others on algebra. Widman was the first to use the signs + and − in print, and a study by J. W. L. Glaisher * suggests that these were signs which Widman had found useful in his work in algebra.

Köbel. The mathematics teacher or *Rechenmeister* had an important position in the German schools, whose purpose was the training of future merchants. Among these teachers was Jacob Köbel (1470–1533), a native of Heidelberg, who was a

* "On the Early History of the Signs + and − and on the Early German Arithmeticians." *Messenger of Mathematics*, LI, 1921–1922. This work is summarized on pages 149–151.

FIRST PAGE OF PACIOLI'S "SŪMA" (edition of 1523)

fellow student with Copernicus at Cracow. Köbel's arithmetics were very popular, as is evidenced by the fact that his *Rechenbiechlin* (1514) passed through at least twenty-two editions. It is evident, however, that Köbel was writing primarily for a local group, for many of his problems are located in Oppenheim, where he taught. Köbel's arithmetics gave detailed expositions of counter reckoning, a mechanical means of computation in which flat counters were laid on the lines and spaces of a counting board (see page 88). This method of computation retained its popularity in the northern countries long after it had been discarded in Italy. Köbel also attempted to combine Roman numerals with the Hindu-Arabic method of writing fractions, but the resulting notation never became popular.

Adam Riese.　The most influential of the commercial arithmetics written in Germany, however, were the work of

ADAM RIESE
From the title-page of his *Rechnung nach der lenge auff den Linihen vnd Feder*, Leipzig, 1550.

Adam Riese (*c.* 1489–1559) whose *Rechnung auff der Linien vnd Federn* appeared in 1522. As its title indicates, this treated both counter reckoning and computation with a pen — i.e., with Hindu-Arabic numerals, but the greater emphasis was placed on work with the new numerals. Riese's arithmetics were so popular that even to-day in Germany correct calculations are said to be "nach Adam Riese."

Tonstall. The first work dealing exclusively with mathematics to be printed in England was an arithmetic written in Latin by Cuthbert Tonstall (1474–1559), called *De Arte Svppvtandi* (1522). Tonstall's life was an eventful one. He studied as a young man at Oxford, Cambridge, and Padua, where he became acquainted with the work of Regiomontanus and Pacioli. He held various ecclesiastical and diplomatic appointments under Henry VIII and, like other important clerics of those times, was imprisoned in the Tower by Edward VI, restored to his bishopric by Queen Mary, and deprived of it by Elizabeth. These events would lead one to suppose that Tonstall was not in sympathy with the Reformation, an impression that is strengthened by the story that he objected to having Tyndale's translation of the Bible in common circulation, so he bought up all the copies he could secure and destroyed them. It might be remarked, parenthetically, that Tyndale had once applied to Tonstall for assistance, hoping to become attached to the bishop's house as a protégé of that great man. Tonstall, however, perhaps because doubtful of Tyndale's ability, or perhaps because he was already overburdened with impecunious scholars, decided against it. The *Dictionary of National Biography* says that Tonstall purchased Tyndale's Bible from the conviction that if Bibles in English were not generally accessible, he would have fewer heresy trials. This act had an unexpected result, for Tyndale used the receipts to bring out a revised and better edition.

Tonstall's position among the scholars of Europe may be judged by the facts that the first printed edition of Euclid in Greek (1533) was dedicated to him and that Sir Thomas More paid him many compliments in the introduction to *Utopia*.

Tonstall became interested in arithmetic in order to check his accounts with certain goldsmiths who, as was the custom in those days, acted also as bankers. Later, when he was made Bishop of London, he wrote his textbook as a "farewell to the sciences." Tonstall's arithmetic was founded on Pacioli's work, but it contained several comments of the type one would expect from a learned man writing an elementary text. It was unfortunate that this book was in Latin, for the day had come when elementary texts had greater influence when written in the vernacular.

Robert Recorde. The most important textbook in arithmetic written in England in the sixteenth century was Robert Recorde's *Grovnd of Artes*, published 1540–1542, the date being uncertain. Recorde (*c.* 1510–1558) studied at Oxford and at Cambridge, lived for a time in London, and then became "Comptroller of the Mines and Monies" in Ireland.

Recorde's mathematical works were written in the form of a dialogue between master and student, a style which he chose "because I judge that to be the easiest way of instruction when the Scholar may ask every doubt orderly, and the Master may answer his questions plainly." This style makes Recorde appear to be one of the most human of the writers of the period, and it shows him as a teacher with a modern point of view. He drew on subject matter that was close at hand, as when he illustrated the need for addition by casting up the scholar's accounts. He introduced new topics by proposing problems which required them. Sometimes the scholar suggested pertinent questions himself, and sometimes the master encouraged him when he lost heart at his slow learning.

Recorde's mathematical works were an arithmetic, *The Grovnd of Artes* (*c.* 1542), of which at least twenty-nine editions were printed; *The Castle of Knowledge* (1551), an astronomy discussing the theories of Copernicus; *The pathewaie to knowledge* (1551), which was a geometry; and *The whetstone of witte* (1557), an algebra in which the equality sign was used for the first time. This book closes with the lines:

Master. But harke, what meaneth that hastie knockyng at the doore?

Scholar. It is a messenger.

Master. What is the message; tel me in mine eare. Yea Sir is that the matter.   Then is there noe remedie, but that I must neglect all studies and teaching, for to withstande those daungers. My fortune is not so good, to haue quiete tyme to teache.... I mighte haue been quietly permitted, to rest but a little lõger.

ROBERT RECORDE
From the collection of Professor David Eugene Smith.

The sequel is that Recorde died in the King's Bench Prison in 1558.   For many years, people have supposed that he was imprisoned for personal debt.   This is evidently incorrect,

although no statement of the exact charge has been discovered.   There is reason to suppose, however, that the causes
were complaints lodged against him during his career as
Comptroller of the Mines in Ireland in 1551–1553.*

SIXTEENTH-CENTURY ALGEBRAISTS

The Development of Symbolism.   The sixteenth century
was a period in which algebra made noteworthy progress, due
in part to the development of algebraic symbolism.   Many
symbols were proposed, tried, and discarded.   The process
was far from complete by the close of the century, but the
advance can be judged only by comparing treatises written
at the beginning and at the end of this period.   In Pacioli's
Sūma, for example, the only symbols are abbreviations or
initial letters, and equations are printed in the text with no
attempt to separate them from the general discussion.   During the next hundred years, however, the mechanics of printing improved greatly and work in algebra assumed what is
essentially its modern form.

The Italian algebraists were slow in adopting the new
symbols, using abbreviations and initial letters instead.   The
German writers, on the other hand, were pioneers in the
movement.

The French algebraist François Viète, better known as
Vieta (1540–1603), should be mentioned in this connection.
Vieta was a lawyer who later became a privy counsellor,
studying mathematics as a recreation.   His works on mathematics, which were published privately for distribution among
his friends, show the first use of letters to represent numbers.
As a general thing, Vieta used consonants for known quantities and vowels for unknown quantities.   He was also an
expert in deciphering codes and during a war between France
and Spain he found the key to a Spanish code of several
hundred characters.   The Spanish thought it was by magic,

* Frances Marguerite Clarke. "New Light on Robert Recorde," *Isis*, VIII
(1926), 50–70.

but we might well question whether it may not have been by mathematics.

FRANÇOIS VIETA
From the collection of Professor David Eugene Smith.

Stifel. Chief among the German algebraists were Stifel, Rudolff, and Scheubel.   Michael Stifel (1487–1567) was one of the most erratic figures of the German Reformation.   Educated as a monk, he was converted to the views of Martin Luther, proved, to his own satisfaction at least, that the "Number of the Beast" in the *Book of Revelation* meant the Pope (see page 75), prophesied that the world would come to an end in 1533, and wrote several works on mathematics.   His *Arithmetica Integra* (1544) contained a comparison of geometric and arithmetric progressions which foreshadowed Napier's invention of logarithms nearly a century later.

Stifel's algebra *Die Coss* (1553–1554), so-called from the Italian word *cosa* (a "thing") which was widely used to indicate an unknown quantity, was a revision of a work written by Christoff Rudolff (born about 1500), published in 1525. Little is known of Rudolff's life, but his book as revised by Stifel was very influential in Germany.

Scheubel. Johann Scheubel (1494–1570) was professor of mathematics at Tübingen, where he edited certain books of Euclid's *Elements* and wrote on both algebra and arithmetic, but his work has been criticized as being too heavy for the layman and too elementary for the student.*

Cardan and Tartaglia. The Italian algebraists of the sixteenth century were particularly interested in the solution of the cubic equation, the principal figures in this work being Cardan and Tartaglia. Each claimed priority in the discovery of a solution for the cubic, Tartaglia saying that Cardan had published a formula given him under the pledge of secrecy, and Cardan asserting that Tartaglia's work as given him was worthless. Neither man could be trusted in his statements. The details of this controversy are given in Chapter IV.

Cardan (1501–1576) was professor of medicine at Milan; Tartaglia (*c.* 1506–1557) was a tutor of mathematics at Venice. Cardan studied astrology and science with equal zest and wrote an arithmetic (1539) and an algebra, the *Ars Magna*, Nürnberg, 1545. Tartaglia was hampered by a stammering voice, the result of a saber cut received in his childhood at the taking of Brescia where he then lived. He overcame many obstacles, but being self-taught he was constantly jealous of his prerogatives and either through ignorance or intent claimed the original discovery of the product of other men's minds. An instance of this is in the case of the so-called Pascal triangle (see page 177) which Tartaglia said

* See also Mary S. Day, *Scheubel as an Algebraist*, New York, 1926.

as his own invention, although it had appeared in print in
ιe work of Apianus in 1527.   This and other similar inci-
∋nts may be attributed to ignorance of the literature of the
ιbject.   Tartaglia's works were *Nuova scienza* (1537), on
·tillery science; *Qvesiti ed invenzioni diverse* (1546), which
∩ntained notes on many subjects — algebra, fortification,
ιe making of gun-powder, among others; and *General Trat-
.to di nvmeri, et misvre* (1556–1560).   This last work was an

CHRISTOPHER CLAVIUS
From the collection of Professor David Eugene Smith.

arithmetic containing a complete account of the busine
mathematics of the Venetian merchants.   It also gave tabl
telling the number of days to be allowed in drawing on firn
in other cities, the precursor of the nineteenth-century "da
of grace."

Other Writers of the Sixteenth Century.   Other algebrais
of this period were Rafael Bombelli who wrote on the cub
and the biquadratic equations, his *Algebra* appearing in 157
Simon Stevin (*c.* 1547 to 1620), the author of the first treati
on decimal fractions (1585); and Christopher Clavius (1537
1612), a German Jesuit who wrote both on arithmetic and o
algebra and who was instrumental in introducing Germa
symbolism into Italian mathematics.

Progress Made in the Sixteenth Century.   During th
sixteenth century, algebraic symbolism had made grea
strides, computation with Hindu-Arabic numerals had be
come standardized, and the decimal fraction had been de
veloped.   On the side of theory, algebra had at last passe
beyond the point reached by Diophantus over a millenniu
before, the cubic equation had been solved, exponents ha
been studied, and men were gradually becoming reconcile
to the idea of a negative number.   It is not surprising tha
rapid progress was made in the next hundred years.

THE SEVENTEENTH CENTURY

Galileo and Cavalieri.   The influence of Italy was less pr
nounced in the seventeenth century than it had previous
been.   Two of the Italian mathematicians of this period we
Galileo (1564–1642), whose principal work was in physics b
who made contributions to mathematics also, and Cavalie
(1598–1647), whose work was a precursor of the integr
calculus.   Galileo Galilei was the son of a Florentine nobl
man who was interested in music and in mathematics, b
who intended that his son should become a merchant ar
restore the family fortune.   Instead Galileo studied med
cine.   While at the University of Pisa in 1581, he formulate

the laws of the pendulum, basing his first hypotheses on the vibration of one of the hanging lamps in the cathedral and using the beat of his pulse to note the time of vibration. He gave up the study of medicine for that of mathematics and science and later taught mathematics at Pisa and then at Padua. His construction of a telescope led him to discard the old theories of the solar system, and he finally was tried for heresy on the charge that he had said that the earth moved around the sun. He recanted to save his life, but a tradition of much later date tells that he modified his recantation by murmuring, "It moves just the same."

Less is known of the life of Galileo's pupil, Cavalieri. He was a Jesuit and taught at Bologna. His principal contributions were on the theory of indivisibles which will be discussed in Chapter X.

Descartes. René Descartes (1596–1650) was a French philosopher, physicist, and mathematician, whose life was varied and interesting. He was educated partly in the provinces and partly in Paris. His father was a man of property and he was expected to live the life of a French gentleman. It was during his service in the army of Maurice of Nassau, the son of William the Silent, and the patron of Stevin, that Descartes first had the idea of coördinate geometry. According to one story, he dreamt about it. According to another, his first idea came by watching a fly crawling along the ceiling of his room near the corner and his first problem was that of expressing the motion of the fly in terms of its distance from the walls. A third account states that he developed the subject while lazily lying abed on a cold day during the protracted siege of a town. Descartes left the army in 1621 and spent several years in travel. He then lived in Paris for a time but later went to Holland where he spent twenty years in an unsocial life, studying philosophy and mathematics. He prudently abandoned the publication of a work dealing with the physical theory of the universe, feeling that it would rouse the antagonism of the Church, but in

1637 he published a treatise on universal science called the *Discours de la Methode*. His *Géométrie*, which was concerned both with analytic geometry and the theory of equations, was an appendix to this work.* Descartes was summoned to Sweden in the winter of 1649–50 to the court of Queen Christina. He had never been strong, and the rigors of a northern winter coupled with the demands of a patroness who compelled him to discuss philosophical matters before daybreak combined to cause his death a few months after his reaching Stockholm.

Fermat.   Pierre de Fermat (*c.* 1608–1665) was an obscure Frenchman holding a seat in the provincial parliament at Toulouse. He evidently had had no particular mathematical training and he showed no interest in the subject until he was over thirty. Then, stimulated by a recently published translation of the work of Diophantus, he undertook various lines of investigation, publishing nothing, writing his discoveries to men like Pascal and Descartes, and jotting the proofs of his theorems on the margins of his books or more frequently merely noting the theorems without substantiating them. Although this work has long held the interest of students of the theory of numbers, certain of Fermat's theorems have never been proved.

Mersenne.   The friendship between the Minimite friar, Mersenne (1588–1648), and René Descartes began when the future mathematicians met as schoolboys, and it lasted throughout their lives. Mersenne was interested principally in the theory of numbers, and his connection with the development of analytic geometry is chiefly due to the informal meetings of mathematicians, scientists, and musicians which he sponsored. At these meetings, the discussion often centered on the subject of conic sections; and when any of the group had theorems to present, he would have them printed on loose sheets of paper which would be distributed to the mem-

---

* See David Eugene Smith and Marcia Latham, *La Géométrie by René Descartes*, Chicago, 1925. Hereafter referred to as Smith-Latham, *Descartes.* See also pages 304–306.

ers.   Among the habitués of these meetings were the two
Pascals — the father, Étienne, an able mathematician, his
son, Blaise, a precocious genius.

BLAISE PASCAL
From the collection of Professor David Eugene Smith.

Pascal.   When only sixteen years of age, Blaise Pascal
(1623–1662), presented an essay on conics at one of Mer-
enne's conferences.   The performance was an amazing one
even in view of Pascal's training and opportunities.   Étienne
Pascal, himself a mathematician, gave up a political appoint-

ment in one of the provinces to take his son to Paris.   Prio
to this time, the boy's training had been largely in the clas
sics, but the younger Pascal had made considerable progres
in the study of geometry without the aid of a teacher.   Th
Essay Pour les Coniques (1639) was so comprehensive tha
Descartes at once supposed it to be the work of the father
Three years later, when the elder Pascal was engaged in ad
ministrative work in Rouen which required the compiling o
a quantity of statistical material, his son invented the firs
adding machine to assist in this project.   Later, he mad
investigations in the theory of probability, and on th
cycloid.   His work in physics was no less important.

Throughout his life, he showed a keen interest in philosoph
and in religion, and from the age of twenty-five he spent muc
of his time in the Jansenist monastery at Port-Royal.   Pasca
seems to have been very superstitious, though perhaps n
more so than other people of his day.   In 1654, the fortunate
breaking of the traces of a runaway horse saved his life an
Pascal interpreted this apparent miracle to mean that h
should devote his energies to the contemplation of religion
which he did except for a few brief lapses until the end o
his life.

Other French mathematicians of this period will be men
tioned in connection with the work with which they ar
principally associated.

English Mathematicians.   The English writers of the first
part of the seventeenth century were specialists in the main,
each being associated with a relatively small sector of mathematics.   For that reason, biographical notes relating to
them will appear in connection with their major contributions,
but to show the activity of English writers prior to Newton's
time, mention should be made of Harriot (1560–1621), who
worked in algebra, Briggs (1560–1630), who is connected with
logarithms, and Oughtred (1574–1660), who invented the
slide rule.   Napier, the inventor of logarithms (1550–1617)
although a Scotchman, was in close touch with Briggs and
should be classed with this group despite his nationality.

It should also be noticed in this connection that the seventeenth century was marked by the establishing of important
professorships in mathematics. At Oxford, the Savilian professorships in geometry and astronomy were founded by Sir
Henry Savile in 1619. At Cambridge the Lucasian professorship was founded by Henry Lucas in 1663. In each case, the
donor had given important service to his university at an
earlier date — Savile as Warden of Merton and Lucas as the
representative of the University of Cambridge in Parliament.
The first incumbent of the Savilian professorship in geometry
was Briggs. The first Lucasian Professor was Barrow.

Another important element in the work in mathematics in
England at this point was the Royal Society, an organization
founded in 1660 and granted a charter by Charles II in 1662.
The Royal Society seems to have acted as a clearing house
for information regarding current research, as is seen in the
correspondence between the secretary, Oldenburg, and Newton on the one hand, and between Oldenburg and Leibniz on
the other (see page 180). Other societies of this type were
founded in various parts of Europe at about the same time,
and their activities and publications were of tremendous
importance in providing a means of communication between
mathematicians and scientists. The letters F.R.S. (Fellow of
the Royal Society) written after a man's name indicate
membership in this organization.

Newton's Contemporaries in England. Newton once
observed that if he had seen farther than most men it was because he had stood on the shoulders of the giants. The phrase
was a happy one. Few mathematicians have been really independent of others for the stimulus that prompts a particular line of work, and Newton was greatly indebted to his
predecessors and contemporaries. This must not be interpreted as a disparagement of Newton's work, however, for
his investigations went far beyond the work of his fellows.
Among the "giants" of Newton's comment were John Wallis
and Isaac Barrow.

Wallis. Like Pascal, John Wallis (1616–1703) studied n
mathematics in his childhood.   His training in Cambridg
was in theology, but he was chiefly interested in physics an
mathematics.   During the Civil War in England he earne

JOHN WALLIS
From Wallis's *Algebra* (1685).

an enviable reputation by decoding enemy messages, as Vie
had done in France at an earlier date.   At the beginning
the Commonwealth (1649) he became Savilian Professor
Oxford. His principal works were the *Arithmetica Infinitoru*
sive Nova Methodus Inquirendi in Curvilineorum Quadratura

ıliaque difficiliora Matheseos Problemata ("Arithmetic of
Infinites or a New Method of Studying the Quadrature
(area under) Curves, and other difficult Mathematical Prob-
ems") (1655) and *De Algebra Tractatus; Historicus & Prac-*

ISAAC BARROW
From the collection of Professor David Eugene Smith.

icus (1685).   The first of these was notable for its generaliza-
ion of exponents to include those that were negative and
ractional, but its principal interest in the history of mathe-
natics lies in the fact that the discussion of the area under a
curve given here stimulated Newton to undertake the in-

vestigations that later developed the Binomial Theorem.
Wallis's *Algebra* contained an attempt, falling just short of
success, at representing complex numbers graphically. As
its title indicates, it also dealt with the history of mathematics, and showed the results of wide reading and careful
scholarship.

Barrow. Isaac Barrow (1630–1677) was Newton's teacher
at Cambridge and he had the further distinction of naming
Newton as his successor in the Lucasian professorship in that
University when he resigned to devote himself to theology.
Barrow was born in London and was educated at Charterhouse.* His early career may be judged from his father's
comment that if it pleased the good Lord to take any of his
children, he could best spare Isaac. He was an excellent
scholar in Greek, theology, physics, and astronomy, and did a
considerable amount of writing, especially in editing editions
of various Greek mathematicians. His work in mathematics
is especially interesting for his use of a "differential triangle"
which seems a close approach to the differential calculus.†

Newton. Among the legends connected with the life of Sir
Isaac Newton (1642–1727), there is the story of the apple
whose fall was the occasion of his study of the law of gravitation. There is the tale of a big hole cut in a door for the cat
and a little hole for the kitten. There is the further account
of a pet dog who upset a lighted candle and so destroyed the
notes of many years' work in Newton's study in Cambridge.
It is reported that Newton looked sadly at him and said, "Ah,
Diamond, Diamond, you little know what damage you have
wrought." But despite the circumstantial evidence of scions
from the apple tree at Woolsthorpe and the credence based on
the knowledge of the dog's name, it must be confessed that

* Charterhouse, a corruption from "Chartreuse," was originally a Car-
thusian monastery, but in the early part of the seventeenth century the building was converted into a combination of an almshouse and a grammar school.
Both are described by Thackeray, a former student, in *The Newcomes*.

† See *The Geometrical Lectures of Isaac Barrow*, translated by J. M. Child,
Chicago, 1916. See also page 318.

Newton disliked pets and had neither a cat nor a dog and that
the question of the law of gravitation was one on which
scientists had been working for many years.

ISAAC NEWTON
From the collection of Professor David Eugene Smith.

These stories are of less interest than are the details of
which we can speak with greater assurance. Isaac Newton
was the posthumous son of a Lincolnshire landowner. He

was born at Woolsthorpe and was sent to school in the neigh boring town of Grantham.   Here he seems to have bee relatively inconspicuous in his work, but a notebook * whicl he kept in these years shows an interest in drawing, especiall in preparing paints; in catching fish; snaring birds; making ink and preparing remedies for various ailments; and it give directions for "certain tricks."   On the death of his step father, Newton, then fourteen years of age, was set to worl on the farm, but he was unsuccessful as a farmer and a length his mother was persuaded to send him to Trinit College, Cambridge, where other members of the family hac gone at an earlier date.   He entered college in 1660.   A that time, his training in mathematics was mediocre.   H had attempted the study of Euclid in order to understand book on astrology which he had picked up at a country fair but the theorems in plane geometry seemed trivial to him anc he discarded the project until Barrow persuaded him to take it up again.

The years 1665, 1666 were memorable for the Great Plagu that swept through England.   The University was closed and Newton went home to Woolsthorpe.   At a later date, Newton referred to this period, saying, "In those days, I was in the prime of my age for invention, and minded Mathematics and Philosophy more than at any time since."   It was in this enforced vacation from college that Newton laid the founda- tion for his work in gravitation, in optics, and in calculus which he called "fluxions."   The Binomial Theorem was developed in connection with the last of these topics.   I should be noted that he was then in his twenty-fourth year In 1669, Barrow resigned from the Lucasian professorshir to devote himself to theology and he named Newton as his successor.   This marked the close of one of the three periods of Newton's life.   These periods were of approximately equa

* This notebook is now in the Morgan Library in New York.   A transcrip- tion, edited by Professor David Eugene Smith, appears in *Isaac Newton 1642–1727*, a memorial volume by W. J. Greenstreet for the Mathematica Association in England, 1927.

ength: at the age of twenty-seven he received his professor-
hip which he held for twenty-six years. He then spent
hirty-two years in London, first as Warden and then as
Comptroller of the Mint.

Newton's duties at Cambridge were not heavy. He lec-
ured once a week for one term each year and spent a small
mount of time in conferences with his students. His topic
vas left to his own choice, and no series of lectures was re-
eated. His first subject was optics, but he later lectured on
lgebra and on gravitation. His reflecting telescope at-
racted the notice of the Royal Society and he was elected to
membership on the basis of this work in 1672. Newton's
cknowledgment of this honor contains the following para-
raph:

I desire that in your next letter you will inform me for what
ime the society continue their weekly meetings; because, if they
ontinue them for any time, I am purposing them to be considered
f and examined on account of a philosophical discovery, which
nduced me to the making of the said telescope, and which I doubt
ot but will prove much more grateful than the communication
f that instrument, being in my judgment the oddest if not the
most considerable detection which hath hitherto been made into
he operations of nature.*

The paper promised in this communication was the explana-
ion of the solar spectrum. This and other investigations in
he nature of light were made prior to 1676, but their publica-
ion was delayed for nearly thirty years after that date.

A year after Newton's election to the Royal Society, he
endered his resignation on the plea that he lived too far from
London to attend the meetings. The secretary of the society,
however, realized that the true reason was Newton's inability
o pay the assessment of a shilling a week. Accordingly, the
ecretary persuaded the members to excuse Newton and sev-
ral others from making this payment.

* Quoted from " Newton and Optics," by Dayton C. Miller, in *Sir Isaac
Newton, 1727–1927*, edited by F. E. Brasch, Baltimore, 1928, by permission
f the publishers, The Williams and Wilkins Company. This volume is re-
erred to as Brasch, *Sir Isaac Newton*.

Newton's career at Cambridge was marked by contact with politics at two points. In 1675, he was permitted to retain the income from a fellowship which he held, in spite of the fact that he had not become a clergyman as would normally have been required. Then in 1687, James II attempted to impose his will on the University in compelling the appointment of a Roman Catholic whose religion barred the appointment Newton was among those who protested against this infringement of the rights of the University and in recognition of his services he was made member of Parliament from Cambridge an office which he held for one year only.

Newton's reason for leaving Cambridge and accepting the appointment as Warden of the Mint may have been the need of the greater financial returns of this office, or it may have been a conviction that his days of creative work in science were over, or again, it may have been a desire to experiment in metallurgy, a subject in which he had previously been greatly interested.* Newton's biographer, Sir David Brewster, takes the first point of view, saying, "At the age of fifty the high priest of science found himself the inmate of a college and, but for the generous patronage of a friend, he would have died within its walls." De Morgan added to this, "And where should a high priest of science have lived and died At the Mint?"

At the time when Newton entered upon his work at the Mint, the English coinage was in a serious condition. Coins were imperfect and of unequal weight, and unscrupulous people had debased them by clipping their edges. The degraded pieces kept the new ones from circulation and the situation was further complicated by the fact that England had recently commenced the coinage of a gold guinea † whose value was arbitrarily put at twenty shillings. The abundance and cheapness of silver brought from America, however, made

* See "Newton in the Mint" by George E. Roberts, in Brasch, *Sir Isaac Newton*, 277–98.

† So called because it was made from gold imported from the coast of Guinea.

he gold in a guinea worth actually more than twenty shillings n silver, and as the silver coins deteriorated in value, the ullion value of the gold coins increased. Accordingly, silver oins were exported to countries where their value in gold oins was higher, and in consequence, efforts to keep them in irculation in England were without effect. Newton at once undertook the improvement of the machines that made the oins, and, in the space of three years, accomplished the withdrawal of the coins that were below the standard weight. He ttempted also to equalize the ratio of the gold to the silver y putting the value of the guinea at twenty-one shillings.

Newton's work in science brought him the presidency of he Royal Society in 1703, and also further recognition when Queen Anne knighted him two years later.

Newton's career has been summarized by his recent biographer, Brodetsky,* as follows:

From 1665 to 1696 Newton was essentially a scientific researcher, nd laboured to unravel the laws of nature. For an equal period, 696 to 1727, Newton was the servant of his nation and the foremost epresentative of British learning. No greater mathematician, hysicist and astronomer, combined in one person, ever existed, o greater Master and Warden of the Mint ever existed, and no nore noble figure could be imagined to act as the presiding genius ver British science. Newton's place was in Cambridge for the irst half of his adult life, his place was in London for the second alf of his adult life, when he had performed his scientific mission o mankind, and had become a figure of national and international enown.

n contrast to this, it is interesting to study Newton's own omment on his career:

I do not know what I may appear to the world; but to myself I eem to have been only like a boy playing on the seashore, and liverting myself in now and then finding a smoother pebble or a rettier shell than ordinary, whilst the great ocean of truth lay all undiscovered before me.

* S. Brodetsky, *Sir Isaac Newton*, London, 1927, p. 133. Quoted with the permission of the publishers, Methuen & Co., Ltd.

Newton's Friends. Before discussing Newton's work in connection with the Law of Gravitation, mention should be made of his friends Halley, Hooke, and Sir Christopher Wren.

Edmund Halley (1656–1742) was particularly interested in astronomy. He traveled to St. Helena in 1676 and there observed a transit of Mercury, a piece of work that brought him membership in the Royal Society. Later work based on Newton's conjectures led Halley to the conviction that the path of the comet of 1682 was a long ellipse rather than a parabola. He calculated the interval between successive appearances of this comet and found that comets had been observed in 1607 and in 1531, dates which agreed with the result of his computations. He predicted the return of this comet in 1758–59 and, in honor of this research, the comet was given his name. The most recent appearance of Halley's Comet was in 1910. Halley's friendship with Newton was memorable for his generosity in financing the publication of Newton's *Principia* and for his equally great generosity in giving up projects of his own to correct the proofs of Newton's work. Halley succeeded Wallis as Savilian Professor at Oxford and he later became astronomer royal. His work in connection with the beginnings of insurance is discussed on pages 139 and 201.

In contrast to Halley, Robert Hooke (1635–1703) was jealous of Newton's discoveries. He himself had formulated the law known by his name, that the amount which a spring stretches is proportional to the stretching force, and he had an intuition in regard to the Law of Gravitation which led him to assert that Newton had appropriated his earlier work. Halley averted the possible quarrel by insisting that Newton acknowledge Hooke's independent work in the preface to the *Principia*.

Sir Christopher Wren (1632–1723) is best known as the architect who designed Saint Paul's in London, and who, after the great fire of 1666, built many churches in that city, as well as the Chelsea Hospital, the Observatory at Greenwich, the

Sheldonian Theater at Oxford, and other important struc-
tures.   Prior to this work, however, he was Savilian Professor
of Astronomy at Oxford, and he served for a time as president
of the Royal Society.

The Law of Gravitation.   The astronomer Kepler, basing
his hypotheses on observations made by his master Tycho
Brahe and by himself, enunciated three laws regarding the
motion of planets.   Two of these, published in 1609, stated
that the path of each planet was an ellipse which had the sun
at one focus, and that the line joining the planet and the sun
swept over equal areas in equal times.   The third law, ten
years later, said that the square of the time required for a
complete circuit of an orbit was proportional to the cube of the
orbit's major axis.   These hypotheses at once challenged
the attention of mathematicians and various theories were
advanced to account for them.

In 1665-66, when the University of Cambridge was closed
on account of the Great Plague, Newton busied himself with
the problem of the attraction between the earth and the
moon, hoping to check his calculations by measurements of
the force acting between the earth and a freely falling body.
The work involved the use of four constants: the time of a
complete revolution of the moon about the earth, the radius
of the earth, the distance of the moon from the earth, and the
distance a body falls in one second.   Basing his work on the
third of Kepler's Laws, Newton arrived at the hypothesis that
the attraction between two bodies varies as the product of
their masses and inversely as the square of the distance between their centers of mass.

Newton's computations in verification of this hypothesis
were found by his account to "answer pretty nearly" to the
observed values, but he was blocked by serious difficulties.
These were supposed by some to be due to the use of too short
a value for the radius of the earth, but this does not appear to
have been the case, and a more probable hypothesis is that
Newton was not certain that the attraction between two

spherical bodies acted as if their mass was concentrated at their centers.* Between 1667 and 1672, Newton made a second calculation, suspecting, toward the close of the period, that the pull of gravity showed slight variations according to the latitude of the observations.

About the same time, the Dutch physicist and mathematician Huygens (1629–1695) studied the relation between two bodies which would be such as to cause the one to move in a circle about the other.

Halley, Hooke, and Wren were greatly interested in the question of the path of a planet if the inverse square law were assumed as being true. In 1684, Halley visited Newton at Cambridge to inquire about the matter, and Newton accordingly sought out his earlier work, used the subject for his lectures in the fall term of that year, and showed the material to Halley who persuaded him to offer it to the Royal Society for publication. In course of this study, Newton determined the attraction of a sphere on an external point and discovered that it was as if the mass of the sphere were concentrated at the center. As a consequence, the formulas for the pull of gravity which Newton had supposed were only approximately true were actually mathematically exact. Newton's work, the *Philosophiae Naturalis Principia Mathematica* (the Mathematical Principles of Natural Philosophy), commonly called the *Principia*, was in three books. The first, finished in 1685, contained the derivation of the inverse square law that every particle of matter in the universe attracts every other particle with a force proportional to the product of their masses and inversely proportional to the square of the distances between their centers of mass. Book II, written in 1686, discussed motion in a resisting medium. Book III gave the application of the law of gravitation to the motion of planets.

The Royal Society authorized the printing of this work and

* See " Newton's Twenty Years' Delay in Announcing the Law of Gravitation," by Florian Cajori, in Brasch, *Sir Isaac Newton*, 127–88.

accordingly the name of the pompous and prosy diarist Samuel Pepys, then president of the Society, appears on the title page officially licensing the publication. Funds were not available, however, and the Society passed the resolution: "That Mr. Halley undertake the business of looking after it, and printing it at his own charge."

At this juncture, Hooke came forward with the claim that the work was really his, and Newton, exasperated at the claim of a man who had not verified his conjectures, wrote to Halley:

Now is not this very fine? Mathematicians that find out, settle, and do all the business, must content themselves with being nothing but dry calculators and drudges; and another that does nothing but pretend and grasp at all things must carry away all the invention, as well as of those that were to follow him, as of those that went before.

But Halley acted as a conciliator and persuaded Newton to state in his preface that the inverse square law had been discovered independently by Halley, Hooke, and Wren.

In commenting on this work in comparison with the modern theories of relativity, Professor G. D. Birkhoff says: *

As a first approximation to the facts of nature, the Newtonian dynamics, with its spacial relativity, is likely to stand permanently. It is the simplest theory which explains the main facts.

Newton's work was accepted in England within a short period of years, although the story that one reader copied the entire work longhand, being unable to obtain a copy for himself, should not be interpreted as an indication of general enthusiasm. The book was too scholarly to have this result.

The *Principia* was published in 1687. It was written in Latin and its form followed the model of the Greek geometry. Each statement was established by a rigorous demonstration by Euclidean methods, but without the use of fluxions. The

* See "Newton's Philosophy of Gravitation with Special Reference to Modern Relativity Ideas," Brasch, *Sir Isaac Newton*, 51–64.

reasons for this seem to have been that Newton wished to make his work available to a larger audience than that familiar with the concept of fluxions, and that Newton also considered that work based on a time-honored method would carry greater authority than a discussion based on an innovation.

Newton's theory was criticized by Leibniz on the ground that the law of gravitation could not act instantaneously on distant bodies; but Laplace showed that if the gravitational force traveled with a finite velocity, this would be at least ten times that of light.

In the *Principia*, Descartes's hypothesis as to the constitution of the universe was proved to be false; but as this hypothesis was generally accepted in France, Newton's work was neglected in that country until Voltaire took up its defense.

Leibniz.   Among the contemporaries of Newton on the continent were the elder members of the Bernoulli family (see page 62) and the German philosopher Gottfried Wilhelm von Leibniz.   Leibniz (1646–1716) traveled extensively on the continent in the diplomatic service of the Elector of Maintz, and he paid at least one visit to England where he made the acquaintance of Oldenburg, then secretary of the Royal Society, through whom he corresponded with Newton.   Leibniz was later made librarian to the Elector of Hanover, a position which gave him the leisure for work in philosophy and in mathematics.   His work in connection with the symbolism of algebra and his controversy with Newton in regard to the calculus will be discussed in Chapters IV and X.   It is sufficient to say at this point that his controversy with Newton had the salutary effect of compelling English mathematicians of the next century to lay a rigorous basis for this subject. It is interesting to speculate on the possible outcome had the Elector of Hanover taken his distinguished librarian with him when he succeeded to the English throne as George I in 1714. Newton was at that time the dean of English scientists and the influential Comptroller of the Mint.   His controversy with Leibniz was far from being ended.   What would have been the result?

GOTTFRIED WILHELM VON LEIBNIZ
From the collection of Professor David Eugene Smith.

MATHEMATICIANS OF THE EIGHTEENTH CENTURY

English Mathematicians. By the year 1700, the mathematics now ordinarily taught in the elementary and secondary schools had taken form, and relatively little has been added to this body of subject matter in the last two centuries. Certain tendencies are important, however, and no discussion of the history of mathematics can omit mention of the mathematicians of the eighteenth century in France and in Germany. The English mathematicians of this period were less prom-

inent, being overshadowed by the giant of the preceding era
but, nevertheless, their investigations left a lasting mark on
later work.

Following the death of Newton, the principal concern of
mathematicians in England was the disproving of the claims
of Leibniz as inventor of the calculus and the creation of a
rigorous basis for the subject. Both of these will be discussed
in a later chapter. One aspect of this work, however, should
be mentioned here. The publicity given to the controversy
roused much popular interest in mathematics. It was not
unlike the situation of a few years ago when laymen read
popular works which purported to explain the Einstein
Theory. Skilled mathematicians and untrained amateurs
discussed the subject. Newton's theories were printed in
a popular version entitled *Newton for the Ladies!* first written
in Italian and immediately translated into English. Departments devoted to the solution of mathematical problems appeared in the magazines of the period, notably in the *Ladies'
Diary,* and more than one mathematician earned his living
by tutoring ambitious novices, and by solving the problems
which they proposed.*

The Bernoullis. Jacques Bernoulli (1654–1705) belonged
to a family of mathematicians and for four generations his
collateral relatives made important contributions to the subject. The Bernoulli family was of Belgian stock, but religious persecutions under the Duke of Alva had driven them
to Switzerland. The Bernoullis then became associated with
the university at Basle, but they occupied important positions
in Germany and in Russia as well.

Jacques Bernoulli was intended by his family for the minis-
try, but he preferred the study of mathematics and its allied
sciences to that of theology, and kept to his resolution despite
his father's wishes. He traveled widely in Europe, meeting
Leibniz and other mathematicians and forming the friend-
ships that were later perpetuated in a voluminous correspond-

---

* For a detailed discussion of this period, see Frances Marguerite Clarke
Thomas Simpson, Mathematician and Educator, New York, 1929.

ence.   He was one of the first to make the study of the calculus popular on the continent.   He wrote *mémoires* on a wide
variety of topics, studying the catenary, the cycloid, and the

JACQ. BERNOULLI
Professeur de Mathematique à Basle,
de la Société Royale de Londres et des Académies
des Sciences de Paris et de Berlin.

JACQUES BERNOULLI
From the collection of Professor David Eugene Smith.

logarithmic spiral.   His work on probability, the *Ars conjectandi* (published in 1713) was the classic treatise on that
subject.

It was planned that Jean Bernoulli (1667–1748), a younger
brother, was to become a merchant; but, instead, he devoted
himself first to medicine and then to mathematics.   Jean

Bernoulli was interested in the calculus, constructing an integral calculus and using the term "integral." It might at first be supposed that the two brothers would have been very congenial, but this was not the case. Their disagreements may have been due to differences in age or to similarity of interest, but it must be confessed that Jacques was arrogant

JEAN BERNOULLI
From the collection of Professor David Eugene Smith.

in his dealings with Jean and that Jean was naturally very resentful.

From the time of Jacques Bernoulli until the middle of the nineteenth century, representatives of the Bernoulli family were to be found in the European universities teaching mathematics and making contributions to that subject and to physics.

De Moivre.   Another mathematician whose name is associated with the study of probability is Abraham de Moivre (1667–1754) whose work, *The Doctrine of Chances* (1718), was dedicated to Sir Isaac Newton, then president of the Royal Society.   De Moivré was a French mathematician who had been compelled to leave France at the time of the revocation of the Edict of Nantes.   He settled in London where he earned a precarious living by private teaching and by solving problems and puzzles of mathematical nature for the habitués of the coffee houses.   It is quite probable that his interest in the mathematical treatment of games of chance was the outgrowth of the problems proposed to him by these gentle, men.

Euler.   The earlier part of Léonard Euler's (1707–1783) work was closely connected with the Bernoullis, for Euler's father had studied under Jacques Bernoulli while he himself worked under Jean.   He was an extraordinarily able scholar, well read in theology, medicine, and astronomy.   He taught mathematics and physics at St. Petersburg, and wrote extensively in these fields.   The major portion of his contributions belong to higher mathematics, and it should be noted that the formula connecting the edges, vertices, and faces of a convex polygon, which is often called by his name, had been used by Descartes a century earlier.

The anecdote told by De Morgan * shows Euler as a human being in a way that the recital of his accomplishments fails to do.   De Morgan says that the Czarina of Russia persuaded

* *Budget of Paradoxes*, edited by David Eugene Smith, ii, 4.   Chicago, 1915.   Quoted by permission of the Open Court Publishing Company.

Euler to join her in suppressing the irreligious views which the writer Diderot had been advancing.

LÉONARD EULER
From the collection of Professor David Eugene Smith.

Diderot was informed that a learned mathematician was in possession of an algebraical demonstration of the existence of God, and would like to give it to him before all the Court, if he desired to hear it. Diderot gladly consented: though the name of the mathematician was not given it was Euler. He advanced toward Diderot, and said gravely, and in a tone of perfect conviction:

"Monsieur, $\dfrac{a + b^n}{n} = x$, donc Dieu existe; répondez."*

* "Sir, $\dfrac{a + b^n}{n} = x$, therefore, God exists. Can you answer that?"

Diderot, to whom algebra was Hebrew, was embarrassed and disconcerted: while peals of laughter rose on all sides. He asked permission to return to France at once, which was granted.

Lagrange. When Frederick the Great wrote to Joseph Louis Lagrange that "the greatest king in Europe" wanted "the greatest mathematician in Europe" at his court, he did not exaggerate the reputation of either himself or of the mathematician. Lagrange (1736–1813) was then only thirty years old but he had already won the favorable attention of Euler by his work in the calculus of variations, and he was engaged at that time in the solution of one of Fermat's problems.

On the death of Frederick the Great, Lagrange went to Paris by invitation of Louis XVI. There he was made president of the commission entrusted with the working out of the metric system. When the French Revolution began, Lagrange, being a foreigner, was anxious to leave France, but he was persuaded to stay first by an appointment to teach in the newly organized École Normale and later by a similar appointment in the École Polytechnique. In each institution, he developed a standard of scholarship in mathematics that has remained a distinguishing feature of that school to the present day.

Laplace. Pierre-Simon Laplace (1749–1827) was also associated with the organization of the École Normale and the École Polytechnique. He was a poor boy, educated by men who recognized his ability, but he later found it convenient to forget his humble origin. Throughout the political changes in France, Laplace successfully ingratiated himself with the various parties as they came into power in turn. He was given a title by Napoleon and served as minister of the interior for a time in 1799, but he was dismissed on the ground that he carried the spirit of the infinitesimal into his administrative work. After the fall of Napoleon, Louis XVIII gave him a title, and Laplace was as usual in favor with the Government.

His great works were on celestial mechanics (*Traité de mécanique céleste*, 1799–1825) and on probability (*Théorie analytique des probabilités*, Paris, 1812), but the difficulty of these can be judged from the remark of the American astronomer Nathaniel Bowditch, who said, "I never come across

PIERRE-SIMON DE LA PLACE
From the collection of Professor David Eugene Smith.

one of Laplace's 'Thus it plainly appears' without feeling sure that I have hours of hard work before me to fill up the chasm and find out and show how it plainly appears."

Legendre. Adrien-Marie Legendre (1752–1833) is connected with elementary mathematics through his *Éléments de géométrie* (1794), which presented a sequence of theorems different from that of Euclid, and which was in many respects more valuable as a textbook. This work met with a very favorable reception in America and it molded the form of geometry textbooks in this country. His work in higher mathematics was largely in the fields of the theory of numbers and in elliptic functions.

Unlike Lagrange and Laplace, Legendre failed to keep on good terms with the Government; and owing to a stand which he took when the Government attempted to dictate to the Académie, he was deprived of his pension and died in poverty.

Gauss.   Although the work of the German mathematician Carl Friedrich Gauss (1777–1855) belongs properly to the nineteenth century, he may well be considered as bridging the

CARL FRIEDRICH GAUSS
From the collection of Professor David Eugene Smith.

gap between the work of the eighteenth century and the mathematical rigor of the nineteenth.   Prior to his day, for example, scholars sought to *prove* Euclid's parallel postulate.   Gauss, with his rare insight, anticipated the discovery of a geometry that should not accept this postulate by writing in 1817, "I am becoming more and more convinced that the necessity of our geometry cannot be proved."

Like Laplace, Gauss came from a poor family and owed his school training to patrons who were impressed by his ability. During his years as a student at Göttingen, he worked with the subject of least squares and showed how a regular polygon of seventeen sides could be inscribed in a circle by means of the Euclidean instruments — the compasses and straightedge. His later researches included subject matter from so many fields of mathematics that it is almost impossible to find a topic that is not closely connected with his work.

From the beginning of the nineteenth century, the number of specialists in mathematics increased rapidly; while with the growing complexity of the subject, the number interested in or contributing to many fields suffered a corresponding decrease.   Accordingly, biographical notes on these men will be given in connection with the places where their work touches the elementary branches of mathematics which are our primary consideration.   It will be sufficient to say at this point, that the work of the nineteenth century exhibits a tremendous activity not confined to any one type of work or to any isolated locality.   And, with the rapid growth of exact science and of the applications of statistical methods, no one can foretell the future course of this work, but one may safely prophesy that it will exceed anything we now imagine both in its practical and in its theoretical development.

SUMMARY

Many other names might well be included in this list of the makers of mathematics.   In the case of those whose contribution was restricted as was Napier's to a relatively small field, biographical notes are given in connection with the man's major contribution.   For other scholars, the reader is referred to the larger general histories or to works which deal with special periods.

What has been given thus far is a picture of the development of mathematics, setting forth the type of people interested in the subject in different countries and at different periods: the priests of ancient Egypt, the merchants and astrologers of Babylonia, the philosophers of Greece, the practical Romans, the scholar-monks of the Dark Ages and of medieval times, the poet-minded writers of India, and the Arabs who were as quick to assimilate the knowledge of other nations as they were quick to conquer their territory. Following these, were the writers of practical textbooks in the century immediately after the invention of printing, and, side by side with them, the speculative scholars who were frequently instructors in the universities and who were interested in the theoretical aspects of the subject. In the seventeenth century, there is a group of notable figures, with Descartes, Pascal, Leibniz, and Newton as the most prominent. It is only by contrast with these exceptional figures that the men of the eighteenth century seem less important than their predecessors.

The chapters which follow will be devoted to the history of various topics in elementary mathematics, showing the practical work of the Egyptians and Babylonians, the deductive science of the Greeks, the algebra of the Hindus, the number mysticism of the Middle Ages, the commercial applications of mathematics in Europe during the Renaissance, and the development of algebra which this made possible. Later chapters will also show the linking of algebra and geometry in analytics and the study of infinitely small quantities in the calculus, the strengthening and developing of these theories in the eighteenth century, and, in briefer fashion, the interlocked but highly specialized topics of more recent times.

CHAPTER II

ARITHMETIC

The Name "Arithmetic" — Number Magic — Number Systems —
Computation with Ancient Systems of Numerals — The Abacus —
Hindu-Arabic Numerals — Computation with Hindu-Arabic Nu-
merals — Fractions — Summary.

THE NAME "ARITHMETIC"

Meaning of "Arithmetic" in Classic Times. The origin
of mathematics was probably utilitarian, but from a very
early period men seem to have been interested in the abstract
relationships between numbers. As a result scholars developed number theory, and even amateurs were concerned
with number magic.

In Babylonia and in Egypt, the study of mathematics was
in the hands of the priests and it is possible that no distinction
was made between the utilitarian and the theoretical aspects
of the subject. In Greece, as one would expect, number
mysticism was closely associated with the theoretical side and
eventually merged into it. The two main divisions of the
work were treated separately and under different names. The
practical computation of the merchant was called logistic:
the theoretical work of the scholar was called arithmetic.
This classification persisted through the Middle Ages. Toward the close of the fifteenth century, however, books were
published whose content combined the practical and the
theoretical, and the name arithmetic was sometimes applied
to the whole subject.

Meaning of "Arithmetic" To-day. In continental Europe,
the word *arithmetic* has its ancient significance, as contrasted
with the German "Rechnung" and the French "calcul,"
both meaning computation. In England and in America, its
popular meaning is synonymous with that of the Greek logistic, although in higher mathematics it is applied to abstract
work of whose existence the ordinary man is not aware.

Among the names given to computation at various times, several are derived from the word abacus; others come from the word practice in such forms as "pratiche" and "prattica." Works showing the use of Hindu-Arabic numerals were frequently called "algorisms." Computation was also called the "minor art" (*l'arte minore*) to distinguish it from the theoretical "major art" (*l'arte maggiore* or *ars magna*).

NUMBER MAGIC

Universal Interest in Number Magic. It is characteristic of human beings that ignorant men accept strange and unusual things as marvels that cannot be explained, while trained thinkers view them as phenomena that are worthy of careful consideration. It is for this reason that the same properties of numbers have been the assets of the necromancer and the object of study of the mathematician.

Magic Squares. An example of this number magic is a

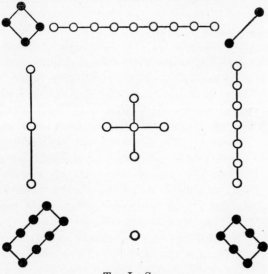

THE LO-SHU
From the Chinese classic the *I-King*.

square array of numbers that appears in the decorations of fortune-telling bowls and amulets in China, Thibet, and India. This magic square, the lo-shu, is said to have been discovered by the Emperor Yu (c. 2200 B.C.), who found it on the back of a tortoise near the Yellow River. The magic in the square lies in the fact that the sums of the numbers in the rows, columns, and diagonals of the square are equal.

The problem of finding rules for the construction of magic squares interested Seki Kōwa, the greatest Japanese mathematician of the seventeenth century. The same scholar also gave considerable attention to the making of magic circles. Here n concentric circles were cut by n diameters, and numbers were placed at the points of intersection. The sum of the numbers on any diameter or along any circle was to be a constant. Magic squares were known in Europe also, coming perhaps through the Arabs. Several mathematicians of note studied them, and of the various treatments that of the sixteenth-century Italian, Cardan, was one of the most elaborate.

Amicable Numbers. An Arab superstition maintained that two talismans engraved with the numbers 220 and 284 would establish friendship between their wearers, since each of these numbers is the sum of the aliquot parts of the other. In this computation, 1 is counted as a factor. Thus the factors of 220 are 110, 55, 44, 22, 20, 11, 10, 5, 4, 2, 1 and the factors of 284 are 142, 71, 4, 2, 1. In Europe these were known as *amicable numbers*. The problem of finding other pairs of amicable numbers was attempted by many people; but although the first pair was known to the Pythagoreans, the second and third pairs were not found until the seventeenth century. Euler (1750) discovered fifty-nine of them, and Dickson (1922) added others to the list.

Perfect Numbers. Another subject of veneration and interest was the *perfect number*, a number which is equal to the sum of its aliquot parts. The first two of these are 6 and 28, for $6 = 3 + 2 + 1$ and $28 = 14 + 7 + 4 + 2 + 1$. The deermination of perfect numbers attracted much attention. Pythagoras studied them. Euclid gave a formula for them. In the sixteenth century, Robert Recorde could give but eight of them, and of his eight three were wrong.

The scientific study of the properties of numbers is beyond the pale of elementary arithmetic. Accordingly the discussion of this topic will be postponed until a later chapter (see page 329).

Arithmology. A different type of number mysticism was concerned with associating a number with each letter of the alphabet, a scheme that may perhaps be traced to the actual use of letters as numbers by the Hebrews and other Eastern nations. This gave rise to the practice of giving names cryptically by citing the sum of the numbers in the letters of the name. Thus the author of the *Book of Revelation* says: "Let him that hath understanding count the number of the beast: for it is the number of a man; and his number is six hundred threescore and six." It has recently been shown that this number spells Nero when given in the letter symbols of the Aramaic language in which the book was originally written, an interpretation which is reasonable, since a cryptogram was certainly necessary in writing about this emperor. It has been the fashion for Christian writers of every period to interpret this number to mean the arch-enemy of their own thinking. Towards the close of the sixteenth century, Napier, the inventor of logarithms, said that this clearly meant the Pope of Rome. A Jesuit contemporary, Father Bongus,* declared it to be "that most impious man, Martin Luther." During the World War, the old theory was used to show that the number 666 could mean no one other than the German Kaiser. An extreme example of the type of reasoning used in this science is the reasoning of the German algebraist Stifel (see page 39). His object was to prove that the number

---

* Bongus is noteworthy for a work published in 1583–84 entitled *Mysticae Nvmerorvm significationis liber in dvas divisvs partes*. He applies number mysticism to theology in general and to the study of the Bible in particular.

applied to Leo X who was then Pope. From Leo Decimus, h
retained LDCIMU, then adding X because it was Leo Tent
and omitting the M which stood for Mystery, the letters be
came DCLXVI.

NUMBER SYSTEMS

Anonymous Invention. The names of many people are as
sociated with the history of the theoretical side of mathematics
but the majority of the contributions to its utilitarian develop
ment have been made anonymously. For instance, no on
knows who invented the numerals of any country or who firs
devised methods of working with them. In fact, the difficult
of deciding which of several men first thought of the decima
fraction gives rise to the conjecture that all these topics wer
the result of slow development, no one person being wholl
responsible for any one of them. Thus the history of practica
arithmetic must begin with a survey of the number system
and methods of computation as these existed at the time of th
earliest records now known, and it must include the gradua
development of these to the present, the record being one o
tendencies and slow growth rather than a clear-cut sequence o
definite contributions made in this year or that decade, and b
this or that individual.

Finger Notation. The simplest way of representing a num
ber is on the fingers, and in all probability this is a far olde
method than either number symbols or number names. I
fact, the early written symbols for 1, 2, 3, and 4 were univer
sally the repetition of a vertical or horizontal stroke as if the
were the representation of the proper number of fingers. Th
name "digit" (i.e., *finger*) for the numbers 1 to 9 can undoubt
edly be traced to this source.

From primitive beginnings, the representation of numbers o
the fingers was extended to include the largest numbers use
in commercial transactions. The system became an interna
tional one, and in the Middle Ages it formed the necessar
equipment of merchants who dealt with foreigners. Th

nglish scholar Bede (*c.* 710) described the finger notation as
existed in the eighth century and a similar system appears

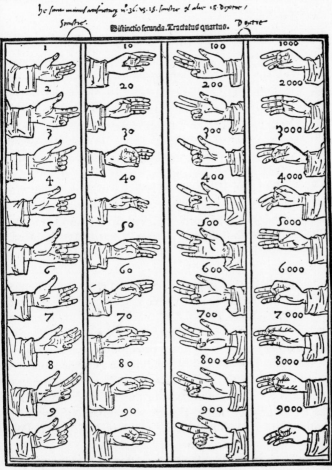

FINGER NOTATION FROM PACIOLI'S "SŪMA" (1494)

n Pacioli's work of 1494.   The significance of Bede's description is best appreciated when one realizes that he, like many

other scholars of the Middle Ages, was interested in mathe matics that was theoretical rather than practical. An exam ple of this form of notation is given in a ninth-century riddl that is sometimes attributed to Alcuin (*c.* 775).

I saw a man holding eight in his hand, and from the eight h took seven, and six remained.*

The dialogue in which this appears does not explain that th eight was made by bending over the ring finger and the littl one; the seven, by bending the little finger only; and the six b bending the ring finger. These facts were assumed to be com mon property, for the person of whom the riddle was aske retorted, "Even school boys know that," perhaps showing th solution on his fingers.

The Base of Our Number System. The widespread use o 10 as the base of number systems is certainly due to represent ing the first ten numbers on the fingers, yet English numbe names show recognition of the usefulness of a system based o 12 in the fact that we count the numbers after 12 as being "i the teens." Our expression "threescore years and ten" sug gests a system based on 20, as does the French "quatre-vingt" (four twenties, i.e., 80). It might be stated that the numbe system based on 10 is the natural one to use, while a system based on 12 is the logical one because of its convenience ir having 2, 3, 4, and 6 for factors. In this case, however, the use fulness of the fingers in number representation fastened the base 10 on the human race even in spite of the convenience of 12 as it is found in the 12-inch foot, in the 12 pence in a shilling, and in the 12 ounces that at one time made a pound the change to a 16-ounce pound being of a relatively recent date.

Number Systems of the Ancient World. The connection between methods of computation and number systems neces-

* "Vidi hominem octo in manu tenentem et de octonis rapuit septem, et remanserunt sex." Beeson, *Primer of Medieval Latin*, 172. See also Eva M. Sanford, "De Loquela Digitorum," *Classical Journal*, XXIII (May, 1928) 588.

tates a discussion of the latter before we can appreciate the
ormer. The number systems of the ancient world with which
e shall be particularly concerned are the Babylonian, Egyp-
ian, Greek, and Roman, for these were the nations whose con-

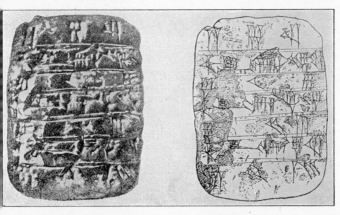

A BABYLONIAN TABLET (*c.* 2400 B.C.)

From H. V. Hilprecht, *Mathematical, Metrological and Chronological Tablets from the
emple Library of Nippur.* Reproduced by the courtesy of the Museum of the Uni-
ersity of Pennsylvania. The top line of this tablet shows the numbers 2·60, 5·60, and
2·60.

ributions to mathematics were the greatest. In studying
hese systems of numerals, it will be well to bear in mind that
ne important qualification of a system of numbers is that it
e easy to master, and often the smaller the numbers of sym-
ols, the easier their comprehension.

Babylonian Numerals. Babylonian numerals * combined
he bases of 10 and 60, for they included symbols for 1, 10, and
00, while the symbol for 1 might stand for any of the powers
f 60. The addition principle was used in writing a number.
'or example, 42 would be represented by the symbol for 10
ritten four times and the symbol for 1 written twice. Simi-

* *C.* 2400 B.C. For detailed discussion of these and other numerals, see
lorian Cajori, *A History of Mathematical Notations,* i, Chicago, 1928. Here-
'ter referred to as Cajori, *Notations.* See also, Smith, *History,* ii, Boston,
)25. For Babylonian business mathematics, see page 117.

larly, 142 would be written as 1 written twice (i.e., 2×60,
10 written twice (2×10), and 1 written twice.   A sign for
subtraction sometimes occurred, its use permitting the writing
of numbers such as 79 as $60 + 20 - 1$.   Addition was indicated
by writing the numbers side by side.

The use of a single symbol to represent 1, 60, 60^2, and even
60^{-1}, etc., necessitated the use of a symbol to show when a

	1	2	3	5	10	20	21	50	100	500	1000	10000
Babylonian	↑	↑↑	↑↑↑	↑↑↑↑	<	<<	<<↑	<<<<	↑⊷			
	)	))	)))	))))	•	• •	• •)	••••				
Egyptian Hieroglyphic	ı	ıı	ııı	ıııı	∩	∩∩	ı∩∩	∩∩∩∩∩	ꝯ	ꝯꝯꝯ	⚱	⌓
Egyptian Hieratic	/	//	///	⅂	⌃	⅄		⅀	⌐	⸛	♭	
Greek Herodianic	I	II	III	Γ	Δ	ΔΔ	ΔΔI	Γᴬ	H	Γᴴ	X	M
Roman	I	II	III	V Λ	X	XX	XXI	L↓	Θ,ℂ	D,ꓷ	⊂ꓑꓶ M ⋈	⊂⊂|))

NUMBER SYSTEMS OF THE ANCIENT WORLD BASED ON THE
REPETITION OF CHARACTERS

power of 60 was missing, as would be the case in such numbers
as 3602 ($60^2 + 0 \times 60 + 2$).   The great disadvantage of the
system, however, was that there was no way to tell whether
the lowest place in a number was a unit, a multiple of 60 or of
60^2, or even a multiple of $\frac{1}{60}$.   The place value idea had not
been extended to include the use of a zero to locate the unit
in the number.   Furthermore, although a symbol took the
place of an intermediate multiple of 60 if one was lacking in
the number, this symbol does not seem to have been used
as a zero in computation.

The writing instruments of the Babylonians were a stylus
and a clay tablet.   Accordingly, their writing shows wedge-
shaped or cuneiform characters made with the squared end of
the stylus, combined with circular imprints made with the

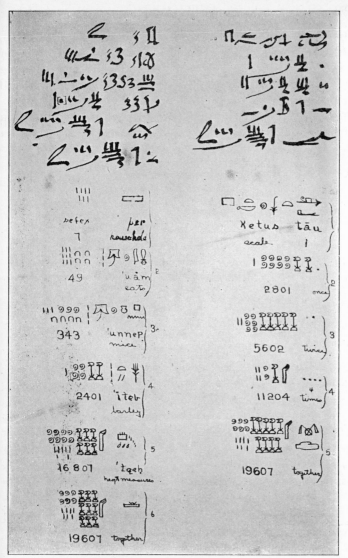

A PROBLEM IN HIERATIC FROM THE AHMES PAPYRUS AND ITS
EQUIVALENT HIEROGLYPHIC FORM

From A. B. Chace, *The Rhind Mathematical Papyrus*. Reproduced by the courtesy of the Open Court Publishing Company. The problem, involving a geometrical progression, is given on p. 210.

rounded end. There were two systems of numerals, the wedge-shaped and the circular ones (see page 80). The sign for subtraction belongs to the wedge-shaped group of symbols, but it was used with both the wedge-shaped and the circular numerals.

It should be noted that there were many variants in the form of the larger numerals whose use was less frequent than the smaller ones and which, because of this fact, were less well standardized. It should also be realized that this was the only number system in the ancient world to make use of the place value idea; but since the use of the base 60 made the representation of a number very difficult, it is not surprising that the device was not copied by other nations.

Egyptian Numerals. The Egyptian hieroglyphic numerals dating from about 3300 B.C. were based on symbols for 1, 10, 100, 1000, and 10000. These were the numerals used in inscriptions and, like the hieroglyphics that stood for words, the form of the numerals was somewhat governed by the fact that they were designed to be cut into the stone monuments on which the Egyptians carved the deeds of their kings. Another form of writing was the hieratic, a cursive style developed from the hieroglyphic, but freer in that it was used by scribes writing on papyrus with a reed pen. A third form, the demotic, developed at a later date.

The hieroglyphic symbols have been interpreted as standing for concrete objects: — the 1 for a vertical staff; 1000, a lotus plant; 10 000, a pointing finger; and 1 000 000, a man holding up his hands as if in great astonishment. The symbols were repeated as often as was necessary and the order of the symbols was immaterial.* Numbers were commonly written from right to left, but they were sometimes written from left to right, and sometimes vertically.*

Greek Numerals. There were three important number

* For matters connected with Egyptian numerals see Arnold Buffum Chace, *The Rhind Mathematical Papyrus*; and T. Eric Peet, *The Rhind Mathematical Papyrus*. For computation with these numerals, see page 86. For work with fractions, see page 102.

systems in Greece. The oldest of these was obtained by assigning number values to the twenty-four letters of the Greek alphabet. Thus A was 1; B, 2; Γ, 3; etc. Such a system was almost useless for practical work, but it has survived in the numbering of the books of the Iliad and the Odyssey.

1 A	10 I	100 P	1000 /A
2 B	20 K	200 Σ	2000 /B
3 Γ	30 Λ	300 T	3000 /Γ
4 Δ	40 M	400 Y	4000 /Δ
5 E.	50 N	500 ϕ	5000 /E
6 F	60 Ξ	600 X	6000 /F
7 Z	70 O	700 Ψ	7000 /Z
8 H	80 Π	800 Ω	8000 /H
9 Θ	90 ۹	900 ⋗	9000 /Θ

IONIC NUMERALS

Both of the other systems were alphabetic also, but they were far more useful than the one that has just been described. In the Ionic system, the alphabet was augmented by the addition of three symbols, one being an obsolete form and the other two being borrowed from the Phœnicians. Of these twenty-seven letters, the first nine represented the first nine numbers; the second nine letters were multiples of ten; and the third nine were multiples of one hundred. Multiples of one thousand were represented by the first nine letters written with a stroke to show their new value. Thus A meant 1, but /A meant 1000.

The third system of Greek numerals has been given the name "Herodianic" after the writer who described them in the second century, but they were in use long before his time. In this system, an upright bar stands for unity, the letter, Γ, an old form of Π, for five; Δ for ten; H for one hundred; X for one thousand; and M for ten thousand. These were initial letters of the names of the numbers they represented.* These

* The number names were Πέντε, Δέκα, Ἡέκατον, or later Ἕκατον, Χίλιοι, and Μύριοι.

symbols were combined to represent multiples of five.   Thus
⌐ᐃ stood for 50, ⌐ᴴ for 500, ⌐ˣ for 5000, and ⌐ᴹ for 50000.
This system continued in use in Athens until about 95 B.C.
During the supremacy of that city, it was adopted by other
Greek states, but it was eventually replaced by the Ionic
numerals.   Instances have been noted in which both systems
are used together in much the same way as that in which
we refer to a volume of the Encyclopedia by a Roman numeral
and to a page reference in the volume by a Hindu-Arabic
one.

Roman Numerals.   Roman numerals resembled the Herodianic system in having symbols for multiples of five as well as
for powers of ten.   The subtractive principle, of which we
hear so much in modern textbooks in arithmetic, was used in
the case of numbers of two or more digits which ended in
nine, but seldom for those ending in four, or for four or nine
standing alone.   These were written as IIII and VIIII.   The
number 19 was represented as XIX or as IXX.   The variants
of the symbols for 500 and 1000 as given in the table on
page 80 should be noted, and one should remember that the
Roman numerals given on a clock face are closer to the common usage in Rome itself than are the symbols of the ordinary
text in arithmetic.   The use of Roman numerals in giving
the date of a printed book exhibits interesting variants.   This
perpetuates the Roman idea of writing ↺ or D for 500, and
C or ↄ for 100 according to the appearance of the page.   In
the seventeenth century and later, periods or commas were
sometimes used to separate parts of a number just as commas
are used to point off the thousands, millions, etc., in numbers
written in Hindu-Arabic numerals.   Thus the second edition
of Bachet's collection of puzzle problems bears the date
M.DC.XXIIII.   A similar instance in America is in a book
from the press of Benjamin Franklin, which has the date
M,DCC,LIV.

In the Middle Ages, numerals were frequently written in
a form that suggests the columns of the abacus (see page 87).

A document of the year 1291, now in the collection of Professor David Eugene Smith is headed

"lan de grce mil ii^{c} iiij^{xx} & xi"

(year of grace one thousand, two hundred, four score and eleven).

The Maya Numerals. Quite independently of these systems, the Maya Indians of Yucatan developed a system of

1	•	10		
2	• •	15		
3	• • •	20		
4	• • • •	37		$\begin{pmatrix} 1 \times 20 \\ 2 \times 1 \\ 15 \times 1 \end{pmatrix}$
5	——	300		$\begin{pmatrix} 15 \times 20 \\ 0 \times 1 \end{pmatrix}$
6	—•—	360		$\begin{pmatrix} 1 \times 360 \\ 0 \times 20 \\ 0 \times 1 \end{pmatrix}$
7	—••—	7202		$\begin{pmatrix} 1 \times 7200 \\ 0 \times 360 \\ 0 \times 20 \\ 2 \times 1 \end{pmatrix}$
8	—•••—			
9	—••••—			

MAYA NUMERALS

the scale of 20, using symbols for 1, 5, and 20. In writing a number, the symbols in the lowest line were units, those in the line above multiples of twenty, those in the next line multiples of three hundred sixty, and in the next multiples of seven thousand two hundred. This scheme made possible the representation of the very large numbers needed in astronomical work in which the Mayas excelled, and which survives to-day in their calendar stones and other inscriptions, relics of a civilization that was nearly extinct when the Spanish discovered Central America.

Summary. The diversity among these examples is an indication of the fact that each nation of the ancient world invented its own number system, some of these being based on the alphabet and others being based on the repetition of symbolic devices.   It must be remembered that, in each of these cases, one should make allowances for the changes in usage over a long term of years and in sometimes widely separated districts.   The study of the different written forms of Hindu-Arabic numerals now in use in the various European countries would present certain significant differences, while if the study were carried over a period of several hundred years, the differences would be very striking.   It seems inconceivable, however, that so much could have been discovered in mathematics before the invention of a symbol for zero.   A probable explanation is that the more important number systems of the ancient world depended for simplicity on the repetition of characters whose values were to be added. An exception exists in one of the Greek systems, but here the lack of a zero necessitated the use of twenty-seven characters and thus masked the value of the first nine of these.   Furthermore, men who might have improved the system of notation were concerned with number theory and not with computation.

COMPUTATION WITH ANCIENT SYSTEMS OF NUMERALS

Introduction.   It is hard to judge the difficulty of computation with number systems other than our own, for we are apt to forget that the actual work is done mentally and that the figures are merely used to record the results.   Thus lack of familiarity with the symbols hinders the rapid reading and writing of the numbers that are involved, and accordingly the numerals are branded as being too clumsy for use.

Addition and Subtraction.   Practice in adding or subtracting Babylonian, Egyptian, Herodianic, or Roman numerals shows that they call for little knowledge of number combinations.   They require only the ability to count the number of symbols of each kind and to change these to the next higher unit.   In the case of the Ionic numerals, it is necessary to know the addition combinations, for the fact that B added to Δ gives ϝ cannot be found by the study of the symbols themselves any more than can the fact that 2 added to 4 gives 6. This group of numerals, then, requires more skill in its operation than does any of the others.

Multiplication and Division. The Egyptians avoided the difficulties of multiplication and division by an ingenious system of doubling. They recognized the fact that any number may be expressed as the sum of terms selected from the series 1, 2, 4, 8, ... 2^n. Accordingly, if two numbers such as 213 and 37 were to be multiplied, the task would be accomplished by finding first that 37 is the sum of 32, 4, and 1 and then computing these multiples of 213 by doubling and redoubling. The work, in modern numerals, would appear as follows:

/1	213
2	426
/4	852
8	1704
16	3408
/32	6816

A check by any number would indicate that this number was needed to make the multiplier while the number at the right would be needed to make up the product. In this case, then, the product would be $213 + 852 + 6816$ or 7881. Division was accomplished in a similar manner. Thus to divide 580 by 32, the divisor would be doubled and redoubled:

1	32
/2	64
4	128
8	256
/16	512

Then since $580 = 512 + 64 + 4$ or $16 \cdot 32 + 2 \cdot 32 + 4$, the quotient will be 18 and the remainder 4.

Greek examples of multiplication and division now extant employ the Ionic system and the work is arranged substantially as ours is to-day. At first sight, this work seems unnecessarily complicated, but in actual computation this is not the case. After much practice in the use of these numerals in multiplication, the French mathematician, Paul Tannery, concluded that the twenty-seven Ionic numerals have certain advantages over our ten digits.

For this computation, Tannery chose the Sand Reckoner of Archimedes, an attempt to prove that the number system could be used to express the number of grains of sand needed to fill the universe completely. This was in answer to the objections raised by some that the number required to fill the earth would not be infinite but would yet be too large to be expressed in numbers. In making this computation, Archimedes purposely chose dimensions that erred by excess, and he discussed numbers of the orders that we would denote as multiples of 1, 10^8, 10^{16}, 10^{24}, etc., culminating in $10,000,000 \cdot 10^{56}$ or 10^{63}.

THE ABACUS

Introduction. In all the countries of the ancient world, and indeed in many parts of the modern one also, computation with numerals was paralleled by work with the abacus. This

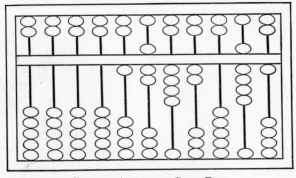

CHINESE ABACUS OR SUAN-PAN

had several forms. The purpose of certain of them was to simplify operations and to make them so concrete that little arithmetic would be required for ordinary calculations. Others were merely substitutes for expensive writing materials and served as slates or as scratch paper.

The importance of the abacus in the world to-day may be judged by the fact that the operation of the Russian abacus, the *s'choty*, forms a regular part of the curriculum beginning in the third school year, in Japan, *soroban* calculation is also a regular branch of school work, while in China, native clerks employed in foreign banks use the *suan-pan* in preference to Western computing machines. Forms of the abacus are also in use in Turkey and Armenia. All of these are of the type in which numbers are represented by beads sliding on wires.

The Sand Board. Unlike the modern forms of the abacus, the wax-covered tablet of the Greeks was merely a sort of slate, and computation was performed by marking the needed figures with a stylus. This tablet was sometimes replaced by a board covered with fine sand on which the computer would mark his numerals, obliterating each figure as it was used. The scheme reminds one of the story of Archimedes drawing his diagram on a sand beach in Sicily.

Other Forms of the Abacus. Other forms of the abacus were mechanical devices for computation. In the simplest type, numbers were represented by loose counters laid on the lines of a counting board.* Counters on the first line represented units, on the second, tens, on the third, hundreds, and so forth. The use of the place value idea as shown in this abacus was so well known that a Greek writer compared the favorites of a tyrant to the pebbles on a reckoning board with the remark that their value is sometimes more and sometimes less. A Frenchman of the seventeenth century made a similar epigram with regard to the court favorites of his own day.

In some cases, as in the modern abacus, the counters were

* For an account of this work, see F. P. Barnard, *The Casting Counter and the Counting Board*, Oxford, 1916.

replaced by beads strung on a wire or by buttons sliding in a groove. In a Roman abacus of this type, each groove is divided into two parts with four buttons in the longer part and one in the smaller. This corresponds to the Roman number system, for each of the four buttons in the units groove stands for I, the single button for V, the four in the longer part of the tens groove are each X, and the single one is L. In the hands of a skillful operator, computation with this instrument must have been as rapid as is the work of a Chinese storekeeper with his *suan-pan*. Gradually, however, this type of abacus was replaced by the counting board. The reason can only be conjectured, but it probably was because the use of counters, though slower, requires less skill.

The number of counters needed was diminished by representing 5, 50, 500, etc., by counters in the spaces between the lines. Gerbert (970) advocated replacing groups of counters by single ones marked with Hindu-Arabic numerals. Thus instead of representing 203 by five counters, two in the hundreds place and three in the units, he would need only two, one marked 2 and one marked 3. This suggestion was due to an interest in the place value idea of the abacus rather than to a desire to reduce the number of counters. It was academic rather than practical.

Operations with the Abacus. The influence of operations with the abacus on later computation with numerals makes it desirable to illustrate this work in some detail.

The loose-counter abacus may be easily reproduced. A piece of paper marked with four or five horizontal lines serves as a counting board. In medieval times this would have been a table with the lines chalked or painted across it, or it might have been a piece of fabric with the lines woven or embroidered in the proper pattern. Coins may be used to represent the counters. In former days these would have been flat disks of copper, silver, or gold, according to the rank of the owner. Counters embossed with symbolic designs were used as souvenirs of important occasions and bags of gold counters were the proper New Year's gifts for princes. In fact, Louis XV regularly had a half-dozen gold plates made from the counters he received each year.

To add two numbers as 282 and 369, the counters are placed as in the accompanying figure, in which the numbers to

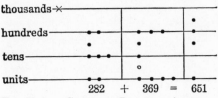

$$282 + 369 = 651$$

THE USE OF COUNTING BOARD IN ADDITION

be added and the sum are both represented although in actual work this would not be the case. Since five counters on the units' line are equivalent to one in the fives' space, five of the unit counters are removed and one is *carried* to the next space, leaving one counter on the units' line in the sum. The two counters now in the fives' space are equal to one counter on the tens' line. Accordingly, the two counters are removed and one counter is carried to the next line. The process is repeated until the sum remains in its simplest form. It is clear that the only skill required is to know how to lay out the counters and to be able to replace five counters on a line by one in the next space or to put one on the next line for every two that appear in a space. In subtraction, the subtrahend is literally *taken away* from the minuend and whenever any line or space in the minuend has an insufficient number of counters, others are *borrowed* from the space or line next above.

The difficulty of telling the place value of the partial products in multiplication was settled by shifting the units' line as the work proceeded. The multiplicand and multiplier were laid out at the left. The top line of the multiplier was then taken as a unit and the multiplicand was laid out on the board as many times as there were counters on this line of the multiplier. These multiplier counters were then removed and the next line was taken as a unit. Parts I, III, and IV illustrate this part of the work. In multiplying by 5 as in II (p. 91), the next higher line is taken as a unit and the multiplicand is divided by 2. At the conclusion of the work, the counters that represent the partial products are added and the sum appears at the right. It should be remembered that in the actual work the multiplier counters are removed when each has been used.

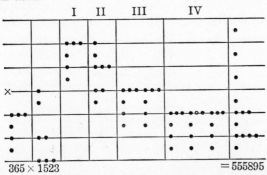

365 × 1523   = 555895

THE USE OF THE COUNTING BOARD IN MULTIPLICATION

Division was accomplished by repeated subtraction, and the computer used his counters to record the number of times the divisor had been subtracted. Here again the units' line was shifted as the work progressed.

Counter reckoning had a disadvantage in that some of the numbers with which the computer is concerned disappear as the work proceeds. Accordingly, the work could not be checked by reviewing the several steps in the process and other methods of checking the work had to be devised. Among these were the check by elevens and " casting out the nines." In applying the check by nines, the digits of each number concerned are added. In each case, the nearest multiple of nine is subtracted from this sum and the resulting number is called the "check number." These check numbers are added, subtracted, multiplied, or divided as the occasion demands, and the excess of the result over the nearest multiple of 9 should equal the check number of the result of the operation with the original numbers. In subtraction, if the check number of the minuend is less than that of the subtrahend, it should be added to the former. In the check by elevens, the sum of the digits in the alternate places in a number beginning with the tens' place, is subtracted from the sum of the digits in the alternate places beginning with the units digit. This difference gives the check number, and the work proceeds as in the case of the check by nines. Neither check is absolutely reliable, for neither detects errors that are multiples of the number that forms its base.

COUNTER RECKONING
From the title-page of Köbel's *Rechenbiechlin* (1514).

The Use of the Counting Board.

Apparently the Italian merchants made less use of the abacus than did the Germans ᵻnd the English, perhaps because they were the first to employ he Hindu-Arabic numerals. Counter reckoning was care-ully described in the German and English arithmetics of the ᵻixteenth century, where it appeared side by side with "com-putation with the pen." It is interesting to note that, al-though the edition of F. le Gendre's *L'Arithmétique en sa per-fection* printed in 1687 does not include this subject, a sup-plement on counter reckoning appears in the edition of 1781 with the comment that although counter reckoning is in gen-ᵻral more needed by women than by men, nevertheless gov-ᵻrnment clerks practice it with success.

HINDU–ARABIC NUMERALS

Origin. The Hindu-Arabic numerals* that eventually re-placed the ancient number systems of Europe originated in India, probably in the third century B.C. There is no founda-tion for the theory that these symbols were so contrived that the number of angles in each was the same as the number of units that it represented. The numerals were probably cabalistic signs invented by Hindu priests, and, prior to the invention of a symbol for zero, these numerals had no ad-vantage over other number systems then in use in India.

The Zero. The date of the invention of the zero is not known. It was at least as early as the ninth century, but recent investigations show references to the symbol that place it much earlier, perhaps even in the second century B.C. The Hindu method of stating a number would in itself aid in the invention of a name and symbol for zero. The Hindus never resorted to such abridged expressions as "nineteen-twenty-eight." They would state each multiple of ten in turn, as if we were to say "one thousand, nine hundreds, two tens, and eight."

When some now unknown priest or scholar invented a symbol to be used whenever one of these places was vacant, it permitted him to write as large a number as he pleased by

* For a discussion of Hindu-Arabic numerals see D. E. Smith and L. C. Karpinski, *The Hindu-Arabic Numerals*, Boston, 1911.

I	ꝣ	ꝫ	ꝗ	Ꝟ	b	ꝷ	8	9			976
T	ꙍ	И	P	Ꝟ	ꝏ	V	3	S		ꝸ -	Ꙁ
ꝭ	ꝺ	ꝫ	ꝗ	ꝗ	ꝉ	ꝛ	ꝸ	2			977
I	ꝺ	ꝫ	ꝗ	Ꝗ	ꝏ	ꝛ	8	ꝥ			Ⅺ
I	ꝺ	ꝫ	ꝗ	ꝗ	ꝏ	ꝛ	8	ꝥ	◦		Ⅺ
I	ꝺ	Ħ	B	ꝗ	ꝏ	Λ	ꝣ	ꝿ	◑		Ⅺ
I	ꝺ	ꝫ	ꝷ	ꝗ	ꝉ	ꝛ	8	9			Ⅺ
ꝭ	ꝺ	ꝫ	ꝷ	ꝗ	ꝉ	Λ	8	ꝥ			Ⅺ ~ Ⅻ
ꝭ	ꝺ	ꝫ	ꝗ	ꝗ	ꝏ	V	8	ꝺ			} ꝉꝗ Ⅻ
ꝭ		ꝫ	ꝗ	ꝗ	P	ꝉ		ꝏ			
ꝭ	ꝺ	ꝫ	ꝗ	ꝗ	ꝉ	ꝛ	8	ꝗ			Ⅻ ?
ꝭ	ꝫ	ꝫ	ꝗ	ꝗ	ꝉ	V	ꝣ	ꝥ			Ⅻ
ꝭ	ꝺ	ꝫ	ꝗ	ꝗ	ꝉ	V	8	ꝷ		x ꝛ	Ⅻ ꝺ ꝛ
I	ꝺ	ꝫ	ꝫ	ꝗ	ꝏ	ꝛ	B	ꝺ			c. 1200
I	ꝣ	ꝫ	ꝫ	ꝗ	ꝏ	Λ	ꝺ	ꝥ			c. 1200
I	ꝺ	ꝫ	ꝏ	ꝗ	ꝏ	ꝷ	8	9			?
	ꝺ	ꝫ	ꝗ	ꝗ	ꝏ	ꝉ	8	ꝛ			?
I	ꝺ	ꝫ	ꝫ	ꝗ	ꝏ	Λ	8	ꝥ			?
ꝭ	ꝺ	ꝫ	ꝫ	ꝗ	P	Λ	ꝭ	ꝛ	•		ⅩⅤ }
ꝭ	ꝫ	ꝫ	ꝫ	ꝗ	ꝉ	Λ	ꝸ	ꝛ			ⅩⅤ
I	ꝺ	ꝫ	ꝫ	ꝗ	ꝉ	Λ	8	9	◦		ꝩⅥ early

HINDU-ARABIC NUMERALS FROM THE TENTH TO THE SIXTEENTH CENTURIES

From G. F. Hill, *The Development of Arabic Numerals in Europe*, Oxford, 1915. Reproduced by the kind permission of the author.

using nine characters and a zero. It is interesting to note that this invention was made in India where the contempla-tion of an absolute void or nothingness characterizes native philosophy.

Introduction into Europe. Knowledge of the incomplete number system was carried to the Mediterranean world, and it is possible that Boethius was acquainted with it. The presence of these numerals in the earliest manuscript of his

Geometry now extant may be a later interpolation, however; even the *Geometry* itself may be wrongly attributed to him.

The completed number system was introduced into Bagdad in the ninth century. The astronomer al-Mâmûn probably made use of it in the tables he translated from Hindu sources, and the mathematician al-Khowârizmî explained its use in an arithmetic written about 820. The numerals reached Europe through traders who learned them in their traffic with Moorish merchants and through scholars who studied in the Spanish universities.

Fibonacci was the first European to write an extensive discussion of these numerals, his work, the *Liber Abaci*, appearing in 1202. The recognition of the value of the symbols was so slow that, nearly a century later, Florentine bankers were forbidden to use them and booksellers were obliged by law to mark their stock "not in ciphers (Hindu-Arabic numerals) but in intelligible letters."

The *algorisms* (see p. 28) of the succeeding centuries explained the use of the new numerals. These works were written in the vernacular, occasionally in verse. They contain directions for the various operations with the new numerals, not infrequently urging the computer to check his work.*

The popularity of Hindu-Arabic numerals in computation varied inversely with the popularity of the abacus. Where counter reckoning was most prevalent, as in Germany, numerals were used only to record the result of an operation and the Roman system served this purpose as well as any other. In Italy, where the abacus was less popular, Hindu-Arabic numerals were in common use at least a century earlier than in France and Germany. It is of interest to note that

---

* See Suzan R. Benedict, *A Comparative Study of the Early Treatises Introducing into Europe the Hindu Art of Reckoning*, Concord, 1914; Robert Steele, *The Earliest Arithmetics in English*, London, 1922; Elizabeth Cowley, "An Italian Mathematical Manuscript," *Vassar Mediæval Studies*, New Haven, 1923; and E. S. R. Waters, "A Thirteenth Century Algorism in French Verse," *Isis*, XI, no. 35, 45–84, and "A Fifteenth Century French Algorism from Liège," *ibid.*, XII, no. 38, 194–236.

ARITHMETIC

96

LATE USE OF ROMAN NUMERALS IN COMMERCIAL ACCOUNTS IN
ENGLAND

From an account book of 1602 (44th year of Elizabeth) now in the collection of
Professor David Eugene Smith.

the transition from Roman to Hindu-Arabic numerals was
incomplete in England even in the reign of Elizabeth, and that
records of the year of the Spanish Armada (1588) show such
entries as "v *li.* ix *s.* 4 *d.*" for £.5 9 *s.* 4 *d.* In France, it has
been stated that Roman
numerals appeared in the
government accounts as late
as 1734.

| 1 | 2 | 3 | 4 | 5 | 6 | 7 | 8 | 9 | 0 |

MODERN ARABIC NUMERALS

Summary. Our number
system, then, had an origin independent of that of the systems it replaced in Europe. Its name Hindu-Arabic is
significant of the race that invented it and of the one through
whom it was transmitted to Europe. It should be noted,
however, that number forms have changed until now there is
little resemblance between modern European numerals and
those in use by the Arabs to-day, and that in India itself
various local systems are still in use.

COMPUTATION WITH HINDU-ARABIC NUMERALS

Addition. The operation of *addition* has been called by various names. Among these are composition, collection, and summation. The result has been called the sum, the product, and the collected number (*numerus collectus*). The use of the word "carry" may be traced to the actual carrying in counter reckoning, but it is less expressive than are the sixteenth-century phrases "keepe in minde" and "keeping reposed in memorie."

The process of adding two or more numbers has apparently never changed. Gemma Frisius (*c.* 1540) tried to simplify it by adding each column separately and then combining the several sums, but this method was not adopted by other writers. Tonstall (*c.* 1522) showed a modern idea in advocating learning the elementary sums (i.e., the addition combinations), saying that this would take only an hour's time.

Subtraction. The variety of names for *subtraction* in current use is paralleled by its names in the past. The word "subtraction" literally means to draw from under. The operation was also called extraction (to draw out), detraction (to draw from), and subduction (to lead from under). The word became *substraction* in French. In this form it spread to England and then to America where it was widely used in colonial times.

Methods of subtraction are interesting for the way in which they meet the question of subtracting a large digit from a smaller one. Such problems are of frequent occurrence and the difficulties of explaining them led to the early evolution of the methods we use to-day. Unfortunately we do not know how the Greeks presented the subject, but a brief survey of the schemes used by European writers in the Middle Ages and during the Renaissance is interesting both for the variety of methods and for their bearing on our present devices.

The *Crafte of Nombryng* (*c.* 1300), which is the earliest work on arithmetic in English, directs the reader to "borro" when he has to subtract 1134 from 2122. The Columbia Algorism of about the same period avoids the issue by beginning the work at the left. Oddly enough, although this method of subtraction had wide application in the scratch method in division (see page 101), it does not seem to have been used as a method in subtraction when considered by itself except in rare instances. The problem as given in the Columbia Algorism is to subtract 5982 from 7678. The work is as follows:

Thus 5 from 7 leaves 2, 9 from 26 leaves 17, 8 from 77 leaves 69, and 2 from 8 leaves 6. The remainder is 1696. In each step the figure in the subtrahend and the corresponding figure in the minuend are crossed out as soon as they are used.

STEPS IN SUBTRACTING 5982 FROM 7678

The Treviso Arithmetic (1478) * gives three cases in subtraction: when the subtrahend is equal to the minuend, the result is zero; when it is less, the result is the difference of the numbers; when it is greater, the result is found by adding the complement of the subtrahend to the minuend and also adding 1 to the next figure of the subtrahend. In other words, instead of subtracting n, 10 is added to the subtrahend and $10-n$ is added to the minuend. An

452
348
———
104

EXAMPLE ILLUSTRATING SUBTRACTION FROM THE TREVISO ARITHMETIC

example given in the text illustrates all three cases. The correctness of the answer was established through a check by nines.

The "borrow and pay back" method was used by Fibonacci (1202) and it also appears in Borghi's commercial arithmetic of 1484. According to this scheme, when 24 is subtracted from 52, 4 is taken from 12 and the 1 that was *borrowed* from the 5 is *paid back* to the 2 and then 3 is subtracted from the 5. "Additive subtraction" was used by Buteo, a French writer of the sixteenth century. Three hundred years later German

* See page 30.

educators observed this method in use in the schools in Austria, and since that time it has been frequently called the "Austrian method."

Multiplication. A person using the counter abacus had no need for multiplication tables, but a man who reckoned with numerals needed them constantly. Accordingly, as counters lost favor, textbook writers urged their students to learn their tables and they provided memoriter devices for folk who failed to do so. Tartaglia, for example, advised the use of the complements of a number (i.e., the difference between the number and ten). He showed that 8 times 6 was 10 times 6 minus 6 times the complement of 8 or, as we would put it, $8 \times 6 = 10 \times 6 - 6 \times 2$. The tables given in the texts terminate with 9 times 9 except for cases needed for denominate numbers. Tartaglia gives tables of twelves, twenties and twenty-fours, calling them tables "per Venetia" since Venetian measures were based on them. In this connection, it should be noted that the sixteens table is memorized in India to-day because of the fact that the Indian currency includes a rupee equivalent to 16 annas.

Various devices were designed to save trouble in placing the partial products. Pacioli gives eight different methods and Tartaglia, seven. Fibonacci begins his work by advising the reader to keep his partial products in his hand (*in manu*). He then says that this "chess board" arrangement (shown at the right in the accompanying illustration) does away with the difficulty of the first scheme. The product is found by adding the numbers diagonally, beginning with the upper right-hand corner. The multiplier is written at the right with the units' digit in the top line, the tens' digit just below, etc.

"Gelosia" multiplication appears in the Treviso Arithmetic (1478) also. Here the units' digit of the multiplier is placed in the lowest line of the work, and the presence of the diagonals makes it possible to record each partial product without doing any addition whatever. In this respect, this scheme is simpler than is the one given above. The name *gelosia* was applied to this device because of its resemblance to a window grating called by that name. Two examples of this method are given in the accompanying illustration.

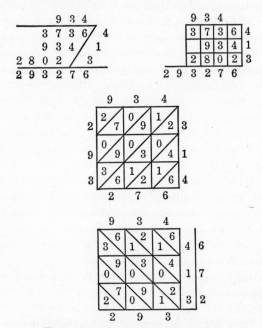

FOUR METHODS OF MULTIPLICATION

Adapted from the Treviso Arithmetic (1478), and used by the kind permission of Mr. George A. Plimpton. Note that modern numerals have been used instead of those in the original.

Another device from the Treviso Arithmetic is interesting for its scheme of shifting the partial products automatically. The fact that these two methods occur in the same text, and that a short one, indicates the way in which writers sought to adapt their work to people of differing ability.

Division. Fibonacci treats several cases in division. The first is division by a one-figure number. He uses 10000 divided by 8 as an example, writing the quotient below the

dividend and the remainders above it. Fibonacci advises
the reader to divide by the factors of a number whenever
possible; and when the divisor is greater
than 10, he suggests using the nearest
multiple of 10 as a trial divisor.

These schemes were largely replaced
by the "galley" or "scratch" method,
also given by Fibonacci, and probably
obtained by him from the Arabs. It
simplified the subtraction incidental to long division, and
it was particularly well adapted to the use of the sand
abacus. In dividing 65284 by 594, for example, the first
figure of the quotient is seen to be 1. This is written at

24

10000

8

1250

DIVISION BY A ONE-
FIGURE NUMBER FROM
FIBONACCI

the right and the first figure of the
divisor is subtracted from the first
figure of the dividend. The remainder is written above the first figure
of the dividend, and both figures that
have been used are crossed out. Then,
9 is subtracted from 15 leaving 6, and
4 is taken from 62. The divisor is
then rewritten with the digits moved

15
533
10878
65284(109
59444
599
5

THE SCRATCH METHOD
OF DIVISION

one place to the right, and since it is evident that 594 is
greater than 588, a zero is added to the quotient and the
divisor is again moved one place to the right. It is interesting to try this method in a problem and then to compare the number of figures used in this method and in our
ordinary long division. The arrangement of the work as we
know it was introduced in the fifteenth century, but the galley method continued in use for upwards of three hundred
years after that date.

FRACTIONS

The Name "Fraction." In the Greek arithmetic, fractions
were considered as the ratio of two numbers. In Egyptian
mathematics, on the other hand, a fraction was simply a part

of a number.   This concept became the popular one in elementary work, as is shown by the names used by various authors.   Several of these names, like our word *fraction*, are derived from the Latin verb *frangere* (to break).   Among these are Chaucer's *fraccion* and Pacioli's *fracti* and *fractioni*. These should be compared with Adam Riese's *gebrochene zal* and with the idea as stated by Robert Recorde's Scholar: "Marie sir, I thinke a Fraction (as I haue heard it often named) to be a broken number that is to say to be no number but a part of a number."

Three Ways of Simplifying Work with Fractions.   The difficulties of working with fractions were avoided in three ways: by restricting the numerators to unity; by computing with submultiples of a unit weight, measure, or coin; and by restricting the denominators to powers of a single number. Decimal fractions are the latest and the most important of the developments in this direction.   The Egyptians made extensive use of fractions that had unit numerators, the Romans confined most of their work to submultiples, while the Greeks used both common fractions and sexagesimals — fractions whose denominators were powers of 60.   The unit fraction is the least convenient of these devices, but the submultiples, with their inevitable inaccuracies, are nearly as bad.   Common fractions, although far better than the unit fractions and submultiples, are less useful than are sexagesimals and decimals.   So, although this will violate a strictly logical sequence, the history of fractions will be discussed in the following order: unit fractions, submultiples, common fractions, sexagesimals, and decimals.

Unit Fractions.   In the Egyptian number system, all fractions except $\frac{2}{3}$ had the numerator 1.   Any other fraction was represented as the sum of unit fractions, thus $\frac{2}{5}$ would be written as $\frac{1}{4} + \frac{1}{10} + \frac{1}{20}$.   The notation was simple.   In hieroglyphics, the symbol $\bigcirc$ above a number meant 1 divided by the number.   This served for all possible unit fractions and the symbol $\oplus$ stood for $\frac{2}{3}$.   It is interesting

o speculate whether the symbolism prevented the use of
ractions with other numerators or whether the exclusive
ıse of unit numerators was the reason for the symbol-
sm.   The occasional use of $\frac{1}{2} + \frac{1}{4}$ or of $\frac{1}{8} + \frac{1}{16}$ for $\frac{3}{4}$ and
$\frac{3}{6}$ by people untrained in arithmetic seems to indicate that
ınit fractions are easier to comprehend and to manipu-
ate than are common fractions.   This, however, is not the
·ase.   Where computation involved denominators larger
han 4, tables were necessary to give the value in unit frac-
ions of such sums as $\frac{1}{5} + \frac{1}{5}$.   The Ahmes Papyrus has a table
ıf such values extending to $\frac{1}{101} + \frac{1}{101}$.   The addition and
iubtraction of unit fractions were comparatively simple, but
ınultiplication and division were complicated by the fact that
.ll work was restricted to doubling and halving.   This may be
llustrated by finding the product of $1\frac{1}{2} + \frac{1}{7}$ and $2\frac{1}{4}$.   The
vork would be as follows:

1	$1\frac{1}{2} + \frac{1}{7}$
2	$3 + \frac{1}{4} + \frac{1}{28}$
$\frac{1}{2}$	$\frac{1}{2} + \frac{1}{4} + \frac{1}{14}$
$\frac{1}{4}$	$\frac{1}{4} + \frac{1}{8} + \frac{1}{28}$
$2\frac{1}{4}$	$3 + \frac{1}{4} + \frac{1}{4} + \frac{1}{8} + \frac{1}{28} + \frac{1}{28}$ or $3\frac{1}{2} + \frac{1}{8} + \frac{1}{14}$

This should be compared with the Egyptian multiplication as
ţiven on page 86.   Division by a fraction or by a mixed
ıumber was accomplished in a way similar to division by an
nteger, the divisor being repeatedly doubled or halved.

Secondary Units.   An important way to avoid the diffi-
:ulties of computation with fractions is by the use of second-
ıry units.   The choice of such a unit is a matter of conven-
·ence.   Division into a few parts means greater ease in compu-
ation.   Division into many parts means greater accuracy, for
ınore fractions may be expressed exactly in terms of these
iubunits.   The Romans met this dilemma by dividing their
ıound, their foot, and even one of their coins into twelfths.
These divisions were all called *unciae* (i.e., twelfths), a word
rom which both *inch* and *ounce* are derived.   In the case of

the coinage, each division of the *as* has its own name and it
own symbol. These were comparable to our *quarter* an
dime (tenth) and their names indicated that they represente
$\frac{1}{12}$, $\frac{1}{6}$, $\frac{1}{4}$, etc. These names and symbols were: *uncia* ($-$
sextans ($=$), *quadrans* ($=-$), *triens* ($==$), *quincunx* ($==-$
semis (S), *septunx* (S$-$), *bes* (S$=$), *dodrans* (S$=-$), *dextan*
(S$==$), *deunx* (S$==-$).

Common Fractions. As already stated, the Greeks had tw
sets of fractions. One of these was for scientific work and th
other for ordinary computation. In the Middle Ages, th
first were called "astronomical" or "physical" fractions, bu
they are known to-day as sexagesimals (from *sexaginta* = 60
their denominators being limited to powers of 60. The frac
tions in everyday use were sometimes called *minutiae vulgare*
or the "usual small divisions." Later, the name became th
English "vulgar fractions" and then, by the substitution o
a synonym, the American "common fractions."

The Ionic system of numerals included symbols for $\frac{1}{2}$ an
$\frac{2}{3}$. Unit fractions were represented by writing the denom
nator followed by an accent ($'$), and other fractions wer
represented by writing the numerator once and the accente
denominator twice. Thus Γ' represented $\frac{1}{3}$, $\Pi\Gamma'$ was $\frac{1}{13}$
and $\mathrm{BI}\Gamma'\Pi\Gamma'$ was $\frac{2}{13}$. An early approach to our moder
notation was in the work of Diophantus (*c.* 275). This write
avoided the ambiguities of the Ionic system by writing th
denominator above the numerator. This is equivalent t
having $\frac{4}{3}$ stand for $\frac{3}{4}$.

The scheme of writing the numerator above the denom
nator was used by Brahmagupta in the seventh century
The Arabs improved this by inserting a bar between the tw
numbers. Fibonacci wrote his fractions in this way, but h
habitually placed the fractional part of a mixed number t
the left of the number itself. Köbel (1514) tried to combin
Roman numerals with the Hindu-Arabic fractional notatio
writing $\frac{1}{4}$ as $\frac{\mathrm{I}}{\mathrm{IIII}}$ and $\frac{6}{8}$ as $\frac{\mathrm{VI}}{\mathrm{VIII}}$, but this suggestion neve
became popular. The difficulties of printing fractions cause

eibniz to advocate the use of a colon between numerator and
denominator, a scheme that is in some ways preferable to the
commonly used /.

Operations with Common Fractions. The familiar scheme
of introducing fractions by cutting an apple appears in Köbel's
work of 1514, and Tonstall (1522) illustrated finding the
product of $\frac{1}{5}$ by $\frac{1}{5}$ by dividing a square into five vertical
strips and five horizontal ones. Thus in many ways the
treatment of fractions in the sixteenth century, and indeed
earlier, is very similar to that given to-day.

Work with fractions generally followed set rules, and many
authors made use of guide lines or of a frame work for the
various processes. Rudolff (1530) added $\frac{2}{3}$ and $\frac{3}{4}$ by one of
these schemes. He placed the common denominator below
the fractions and put their new numerators above them. The
sum was given at the right and the work appeared as follows:

$$\begin{array}{cc} 8 & 9 \\ \hline \frac{2}{3} & \frac{3}{4} \end{array} \text{ makes } \frac{17}{12}$$
$$12$$

Chuquet (1484) and Trenchant (1566) explained the division of fractions by reducing both divisor and dividend to the
same denominator and then dividing the numerators. Widman (1489) used a method of cross multiplication. The
quotient of $\frac{2}{3} \div \frac{3}{4}$ would be found by writing the fractions in
his way: $\frac{2}{3} \times \frac{3}{4}$, multiplying along the guide lines and thus
getting the quotient $\frac{8}{9}$. Although the idea of inverting the
divisor was known to the Hindus and to the Arabs, it did not
come into common use in Europe until the seventeenth
century.

On the whole, the textbook treatment of common fractions
was characterized by the use of devices to make the work
mechanical. The emphasis given to this subject in the sixteenth century is justified by its importance in business, where

ARITHMETIC

the diversity of measures and coins demanded the solution of such problems as the following, which is taken from Cataneo's work of 1546.

I bought saffron in Siena paying at the rate of 18 lire a pound and I took it to Venice, where I found that 10 ounces in Siena weight are equal to 12 Venetian ounces and 10 lire of Siena coinage are equal to 8 lire in Venetian coinage. I sold the saffron for 14 lire a pound. What was my per cent of gain?

In solving problems of this sort, the computer was obliged to use huge and unwieldy denominators, for he had no means of confining his work to a reasonable degree of accuracy. As practical a writer as Adam Riese (1522), for example, reported the result of an example in compound interest as 6 florins, 14 groschen, 9 and $\frac{2125564802804 5}{3938980639167}$ pence.

Integra	Mi.	$\bar{2}$	$\bar{3}$	$\bar{4}$	$\bar{5}$	$\bar{6}$	$\bar{7}$	
29,	31,	50,	7,	30				*Multiplicandus*
13,	10,	35,	1					*Multiplicans*
			29	31	50	7	30	*Producta*
	17	13	34	14	22	30		*Multipli-*
4	55	18	21	15	0			*cationis*
383	53	51	37	30				*sparsa*
389,	6,	24,	2,	31,	12,	37,	30	*Productū*

The Product of Two Sexagesimals

This example is copied from the work of Gemma Frisius (1540). It shows how closely work with sexagesimals resembles work with decimals.

Sexagesimal Fractions. Sexagesimal fractions may have been invented by the Babylonians who made use of 60 as base in their number system. It is certain, at least, that these fractions were used by the Greeks, for they are a prominent feature of Ptolemy's Tables (*c.* 150). During the Middle Ages, the orders of these fractions were called "the first small divisions" (*pars minuta prima*), "the second small divisions" (*pars minuta secunda*), etc. Eventually these names were shortened to the *minutes* and *seconds* of our hours and degrees, but the smaller divisions of thirds, fourths, and the like have disappeared. There was wide variation in the sym

»olism for these fractions.   Among the forms used in the six-
eenth century for units, minutes, and seconds were:

$\bar{g}$.	$\bar{m}$.	$\bar{2}$.	$\bar{3}$.	Gemma Frisius (1540)
ntegra	$\tilde{1}$	$\tilde{2}$	$\tilde{3}$	Peletier (1569)
0	I	II	III	Schöner (1569)
°	′	″	‴	Reinhold (1571) writing signs before the numbers to which they applied.
⊙	①	②	③	Stevin (1585)

)ne writer (Fineus, 1530) used a period to separate his units
ιnd minutes, writing 5.36 instead of $5\frac{36}{60}$ or 5 36′.

Computation with sexagesimals resembles work with dec-
mals, although multiplication and division are complicated
)y the frequent necessity of dividing by 60 in changing from
ractions of one order to the next higher one.

Decimal Fractions.   It seems strange that men waited
ιntil the sixteenth century to complete the Hindu-Arabic
ιotation by extending it backwards to include fractions.   It
should be remembered, however, that the scientific work of
the Arab and European scholars was largely in astronomy
where the time-honored sexagesimal division of the angle was
)erpetuated in trigonometric tables.   Thus the people who
were the most likely to invent decimal fractions were working
with a system that was almost as good for their purposes.
So it happened that the first devices pointing toward the
ινention of such a system appeared in the elementary works
ιnd were used by business men, but the actual invention of
the decimal fraction is due to a scientist who was a practical
mathematician as well.

The Hindus had known that if a number was not a perfect
square, its root might be approximated by finding the root of
the same number with an even number of zeros added and
then dividing the root by 10, 100, 1000, etc., according to
whether the number of zeros added was two, four, eight, and
so on.   Thus Adam Riese gave a table of square roots, assuming that the numbers had been multiplied by 1000000.   The

se: Den ersten Punct setz 1. vnd setze da für drei
nulla / Ziehe dañ Radicem quadratam daruon
so kommen 1000. Dann preponir dem anderen
Puncten/das ist der Ziffern 2. auch sechs 0/vnd
ziehe Radicem quadratā dauon/so komen 414.
Den dritten Punct mach auch also. Setz 3.vñ
darnach sechs 0. Extrahir dann Radicem quadratam dauon/kommen 832. Also thũ mit allen
Puncten/so machstu die Tafel selber. Es ist a-
ber groß mühe vnd verdrossen arbeyt/ Darum
hab ich dir hie ein Tafel außgezogen / die gehet
biß vff 240.Punct der tieffe/ der mañ gnũg has
vff groß oder kleyne vaß.

Tabula Radicum quadratarum.

1	1	1000		17	123		33	747
	2	414		18	242		34	833
	3	732		19	358		35	917
2	4	1000		20	472	6	36	1000
	5	234		21	584		37	82
	6	449		22	692		38	163
	7	645		23	757		39	244
	8	833		24	900		40	324
3	9	1000	5	25	1000		41	403
	10	162		26	98		42	482
	11	316		27	191		43	558
	12	446		28	290		44	634
	13	606		29	384		45	709
	14	742		30	477		46	783
	15	873		31	567		47	858
4	16	1000		32	659		48	930

ADAM RIESE'S TABLE OF SQUARE ROOTS
From *Rechnung auff der Linien vnd Federn*, Erfurt, 1522.

arrangement of his table is shown in the accompanying illustration. It should be noticed that the integral part of the
root appears at the left, the number itself in the second
column, and the fractional part of the root in the third column.
Thus the square root of 2 is $1\frac{414}{1000}$. The 1000 in the first

nd fourth lines is deceptive, but since it appears only in cases
a which the number is a perfect square, it seems reasonable
o suppose that this was to call attention to the fact that the
ntegral part of the root has changed, a scheme that is compa-

RUDOLFF'S COMPOUND INTEREST TABLE

From the *Exempel-Büchlin* (edition of 1540). This shows the amount of
375 florins, compounded annually for ten years at five per cent.

rable to the use of an asterisk under similar conditions in a
table of logarithms.

Forerunners of the Decimal Point. Rudolff (1530) used
an upright bar in an interest table to mark off fractions whose
denominators were powers of 10. Earlier than that, Pellos
(1492) had used a period to cut off one, two, or three places.

FIRST DECIMAL POINT IN PRINT
From the Pellos Arithmetic, 1492.

in the dividend when his divisor was a multiple of 10, 100, or 1000. Thus in dividing 7896573 by 400, he marked off two places in the dividend and then divided by 4. These devices may have been used merely to simplify the printing of tables or to make division easier. In the latter case, the use of the point can be readily explained by reference to division by counters.

One or all of these writers may have appreciated the significance of this work, but it is certain that no one of them generalized it beyond a single case. The idea of the decimal fraction may indeed be traced to these isolated instances, but it is likely that the man who first developed laws for their use in ordinary computation was not influenced by these early and perhaps unwitting applications.

Stevin's Work. The first writer to give a systematic treatment of decimal fractions was Simon Stevin (1548–1620), a native of Bruges. Stevin lived in the Netherlands in the days of the great struggle against Spain, and, according to the historian Motley, he was chosen by William the Silent as tutor for his son Maurice of Nassau. It is certain that he became inspector of the dikes, quartermaster-general of the army, and minister of finance. In the latter capacity he introduced the Italian system of bookkeeping into the accounts of the Netherlands. He also wrote on accounting (following Pacioli), physics, and hydraulics, and established the laws of the equilibrium of a body resting on an inclined plane.

It is evident that Stevin arrived at his discovery of decimal fractions through an effort to combine the essential features of sexagesimal fractions with the place value idea of the Hindu-Arabic numerals. His essay on decimals appeared in 1585. It contained a preliminary statement of the value of the invention, which, by the way, was stated to have had a thorough trial by practical men who found it so useful that they had voluntarily discarded the short cuts of their own invention to adopt this new one. Following this introduction, definitions were given, symbolism was explained, and operations with these new numbers were discussed. The latter part of the essay treated the applications of these numbers to real problems. Throughout the discussion, Stevin held to the point made in his subtitle, that this system of numbers "Teaches how all Computations that are met in Business may be performed by Integers alone without the aid of Fractions." He defines the decimal system as follows:

The decimal system is an arithmetic based on the idea of the progression by tens, making use of the ordinary Arabic numerals in which any number may be written and by which all computations that are met in business may be performed by integers alone without the aid of fractions.

A whole number is called a unit (*Commencement*) and has the symbol ⊙. The tenth part of a unit of an integer is called a Prime and it has the symbol ①, and the tenth part of a unit Prime is called a Second and it has the sign ②. Similarly for the tenths of a unit of each order.

These names and symbols are of course the same as those which Stevin had used in his discussion of sexagesimal fractions in the *Arithmetic* of which the discussion of decimals formed an Appendix. In writing decimals, he used three different schemes according to the exigencies of the case. Thus 3.14 would appear as 314② or as 3⊙ 1① 4②, or as $\overset{\odot}{3} \overset{①}{1} \overset{②}{4}$.

Stevin shows that these numbers may be used in the same fashion as are ordinary integers, and he checks his illustrations of addition, subtraction, etc., by changing his numbers and results to common fractions. His rule for multiplication states that the symbol of the last number of the product is found by adding the symbols of the last figures of multiplicand and multiplier, and that in division the symbol of the last figure of the quotient is found by subtraction.

The author then shows how this invention may be applied to practical work. A surveyor, for example, would find his work less complicated if he would adopt a decimal division of his unit of measure for all computation, changing to the

III. VOORSTEL VANDE
MENICHVVLDIGHINGHE.

Wefende ghegheven Thiendetal te Me-
nichvuldighen, ende Thiendetal Menich-
vulder: haer Vytbreng te vinden.

TGHEGHEVEN. Het fy Thiendetal te Menichvuldighen 32 ⓪ 5 ① 7 ②, ende het
Thiendetal Menichvulder 8 9 ⓪ 4 ① 6 ②. TBE-
GHEERDE. Wy moeten haer Vytbreng vinden.
WERCKING. Men fal
de gegevé getalé in oir-
den ftellen als hier nevé,
Menichvuldigende naer
de gemeene maniere van
Menichvuldighen met
heele ghetalen aldus:
Gheeft Vytbreng (door
het 3°. Prob. onfer Fran.
Arith.) 29137122: Nu
om te weten wat dit fijn,

			⓪	①	②
			3	2	5	7
			8	9	4	6
		1	9	5	4	2
	1	3	0	2	8
	2	9	3	1	3
2	6	0	5	6
2	9	1	3	7	1	2	2
		⓪	①	②	③	④

men fal vergaderen beyde de laetfte gegeven teec-
kenen, welcker een is ②, ende het ander oock ②,
maecken tfamen ④, waeruyt men beſluyten ſal,
dat de laetfte cijffer des Vytbrengs is ④, welcke
bekentwefende foo fijn oock (om haer volghende
oirden) openbaer alle dander, Inder voughen dat
2913⓪7①1②2③2④, fijn het begheerde
Vytbreng. BEWYS, Het ghegheven Thiendetal
te menichvuldighen 32 ⓪ 5 ① 7 ②, doet (als
blijct

MULTIPLICATION FROM THE FIRST BOOK ON DECIMALS

From Stevin's *La Thiende*, Leyden, 1585. Reproduced by
the courtesy of the Société des Bibliophiles Anversois.

customary divisions at the end of the work. Stevin extends the idea to units of area and volume, dividing each unit into tenths and into hundredths, thus sacrificing the simple connection between subunits of length, area, and volume that is such a valuable part of the metric system. The scheme that Stevin had in mind would mean that in all tables of denominate numbers, one unit would equal 10 Primes, one Prime would be 10 Seconds, etc., whereas in the metric system as it was later organized, measures of length are based on the series, 1, 10, 100; those of area on the series 1, 100, 10000; and those of volume on the series 1, 1000, 1000000. Stevin also urged the decimal division of the degree, although he later published trigonometric tables on the old basis. He suggested the application of the idea to coinage and advised the extensive use of this system by individuals wherever possible, pending the time when decimals should be the legal subdivisions of all units. The task that remained was the perfecting of the symbolism and the converting of people to the use of these fractions. It is significant that the substitutes that Stevin proposed for the use of surveyors are among the important compromises in effect to-day: the decimally divided mile on the sign post, the decimally divided foot on the surveyor's tape, and the decimally divided inch on the micrometer in the machine shop.*

Symbolism for Decimal Fractions. The development of symbolism was slow. Had there been a standard symbolism for sexagesimals, this might not have been the case. As it was, many different schemes were used and the matter has not been settled to-day, for the comma is used as a decimal point on the continent and the form $3 \cdot 14$ is the accepted one in England. Among the symbols used in the first century after the invention of decimals were the following: Bürgi (1592) 3.14 and 3,14; Napier (1617) 3,14 and 3,1'4''; Kepler

---

* A facsimile of the original edition of Stevin's work on decimals, together with critical notes and introduction by H. Bosmans, S.J., is given in *La "Thiende" de Simon Stevin*, Antwerp, 1924. A translation is given in Smith, *Source Book in Mathematics*.

(1616) 3,14 and 3(14); Oughtred (1631) 3 $\lfloor$14; van Schooten (1657) 314.

A translation of Stevin's work into English was published by Robert Norton in 1608. Norton was so impressed with the value of decimals that he announced himself ready to go about England giving instruction in the subject free of charge, saying that he proposed doing it for his country's good. The real impetus to the use of decimals, however, was in Wright's translation of Napier's Table of Logarithms (1616).

Oughtred (1574–1660) extended the operations with decimals slightly by introducing abridged multiplication and division, omitting the figures that detract from the accuracy of the results; but the study of the answer book of almost any text in mathematics shows how far we are from appreciating the approximate character of our computation and from making use of work such as that of Oughtred.

SUMMARY

The history of computation gives clear and direct evidence that its fundamental ideas were known at an early period. As will appear later in the discussion of its application to commercial mathematics, the purpose of computation during the Babylonian period was the same as it is to-day. Number systems developed slowly and they were probably devised long after need for them arose. It is possible, for instance, that the idea of a zero was current among Hindu philosophers for centuries before it was represented by a symbol. It is certain, however, that symbols and methods of computation with both integers and fractions were devised long before the time of the earliest mathematical literature now extant.

Progress from alphabetic systems of numerals and those based on the repetition of characters to the use of a place value notation was slow. It must be remembered that the thinkers who were most likely to appreciate such refinements were, in Greece and to some extent in Rome also, not concerned with ordinary business affairs where the defects of the former notations were most clearly evident. The adoption of the Hindu-Arabic numerals was unnecessarily retarded by prejudice, but the world has always been reluctant to alter its time-honored ways of dealing with everyday matters. It is important to note, however, that although operations with the counting board seem to have changed but little from the days of the Romans to the sixteenth century, a comparatively short time sufficed for Europeans to bring computation with the Hindu-Arabic numerals to its present state. Furthermore, it was a relatively short time after Hindu-Arabic numerals came into common use that the system was completed by the invention of the decimal fraction.

CHAPTER III

COMMERCIAL MATHEMATICS

General Survey — Problems Connected with the Great Fairs —
The Question of Interest — Investment Schemes of the Middle
Ages — Modern Business — Summary.

GENERAL SURVEY

The Need for Arithmetic. Of the fields in which mathematics is an important tool, the earliest to develop was that of commerce. Undoubtedly the first need for counting, weighing, and measuring was in connection with barter, and, as civilization developed, mathematics found increasingly important applications.

The connection between computation and commerce makes it desirable to study the history of the two together, but it must be remembered that, although arithmetic processes improved from time to time and although the situations in which they were used varied in their external conditions, the financier of Babylon and the magnate of Wall Street are concerned with things that are substantially the same.

Many of the business practices of to-day are the direct descendants of those of the past, but in some cases external conditions have had a great effect upon the emphasis given to problems. For example, in the sixteenth century, short-time partnerships were a popular method of investment and customs duties were more onerous than now. Accordingly, these topics were given greater importance in the arithmetics of that period than would be warranted in arithmetics to-day.

Our knowledge of the applications of mathematics comes from several sources, the most important being the textbooks that deal with practical uses of computation. These are particularly valuable for the period immediately following the invention of printing. The uses of arithmetic in the commercial life of the ancient world, however, may be conjectured from the customs shown by actual business documents and from the references to commercial usage in other literature.)

Babylonia. (The earliest commercial records now extant are found in the clay tablets of Babylonia. These include the correspondence of great mercantile families as well as the records that concern property belonging to the temples. The commercial development of Babylonia is shown in certain provisions in the laws of the great ruler Hammurabi)(c. 2100 B.C.). These stipulated that an agent was entitled to a share in the profits of his employer; that he was to be exonerated for losses due to the hazards of travel; but that he was to forfeit double the sum entrusted to him if he was found guilty of mismanagement. Property was mortgaged, loans were made, partnerships operated — all with capital of dates, date wine, flour, oil, barley, and sometimes silver. Promissory notes were given by tenant farmers for money to tide them over until the next harvest. These bore interest at high rates ($33\frac{1}{3}$ per cent under Hammurabi) if they were not paid when due, the underlying principle being that if the harvest was good, the owner's share would reimburse him for the use of the capital, while the fear of the forfeit would spur the tenant to greater endeavor. In the records from the city of Nippur, no interest rate is stated, a fact which seems to indicate the existence of a fixed legal rate.

The shekels of silver mentioned in these records were a fixed weight of silver which was originally cast in bars of metal. In the period from 1500–1300 B.C., these were replaced by small flat rings of silver which were naturally more convenient than the bars. Actual coinage was probably not invented until about the seventh century B.C., when coins were struck in the city of Sardis in Asia Minor.

Commercial considerations were responsible in part for the conquest of Babylonia by Assyria (c. 745 B.C.), and it has been suggested that Solomon's many matrimonial alliances were the result of his desire for commercial aggrandizement.

Egypt. The commerce of Egypt was relatively slight until that country fell into the hands of foreign rulers (c. 1600 B.C.); but Egypt was more self-sufficient than was Babylonia, and even after this capture trade was not encouraged for the next millennium. The situation changed at the time that the activity of Greece began, when Thales, Pythagoras, and others traveled to Egypt under the urge both of their business interests and of their desire to study under the Egyptian priests.

Phœnicia. ⟨ The greatest commercial nation of the ancient world has left no records that compare in completeness with those of Babylonia. In the period from 1600–1000 B.C., the Phœnicians carried on an active overland trade by their caravans, and they sent ships to Spain and even to England for silver and tin.⟩ They were the middlemen of the past, but their greatest service so far as the later development of commerce is concerned was the designing of ships, in which they were so skillful that Solomon had Phœnician builders work for him. The ships they constructed were transported piecemeal to the head of the Red Sea, where they were assembled for use in Solomon's sea trade with Arabia.

Greece. ⟨ The Greeks were driven into commerce by their lack of certain products at home. Greek cities grew up on the Black Sea, in Italy, and on the coast of Asia Minor. Of these cities, Miletus, the home of Thales, was the first to become important. During the Persian Wars in the fifth century B.C., Athens gained the commercial leadership of Greece, keeping it until about 300 B.C. when Alexander's conquests shifted the center of commerce. ⟩ The newly founded city of Alexandria in Egypt then became an important commercial center. So too did the sheltered island of Rhodes.⟩

We have no specific records of this extensive Greek commerce. This is due to the fact that the Greeks put utilitarian arithmetic in a different category from the theoretical work, the latter alone being worthy of preservation. References in other literature show that drafts were in use, and it is probable

hat mortgages, promissory notes, and the like were in exist-
nce and that they bore a close relation to those of Babylonia.

The importance of these considerations in the history of
mathematics is due to the fact that commerce with its at-
tendant wealth ultimately produces the conditions under
which the arts and sciences can flourish, and the centers of
learning in Greece followed the centers of trade from the coast
of Asia Minor and from the Italian colonies to Athens, and
from Athens to Alexandria and Rhodes.

Rome. (The Romans were predominantly an agricultural
people at first, but their necessary carrying trade led them into
commerce and they acquired an enviable reputation for
honesty and fair dealing.   Augustus fostered Roman commerce and, as the old aristocracy broke down under the empire,
a new aristocracy that was interested in business grew up.)
In the first century A.D., Roman vessels reached India, and
within the next hundred years, they made the voyage to
China, thus supplementing the already existing overland
trade.   Accordingly silks and spices from the East, hides and
amber from the Baltic, grain from Egypt and from Southern
France, together with many other products, were brought
to Italy in Roman ships, whose cargoes were frequently covered by insurance.

The difficulties of Roman navigators were to persist for
a long period.   At one season of the year, for example, the
prevailing winds accelerated the passage of ships from Rome
to Alexandria: at another season the opposite was true.   Accordingly, a ship trying to go in the contrary direction would
have the alternative of moving at night when the wind
dropped or of taking the longer passage around the coast of
Syria and Asia Minor where local breezes were sometimes
favoring ones.*   A survival of this practice appears in Buteo's
arithmetic of 1559:

Two ships 20000 stadia apart weighed anchor to sail straight

* Martin Percival Charlesworth, *Trade-routes and Commerce of the Roman
Empire*, Cambridge, England, 1924, 23.

toward each other. It happened that the first one set sail at day
break with the North Wind blowing. Toward evening, when i
had gone 1200 stadia, the North Wind fell and the Southwest Win
rose. At this time the other ship set sail and sailed 1400 stadi.
during the night. The first ship, however, was driven back 70
stadia by the contrary wind, but with the morning North Wind i
was driven ahead in the usual manner of outward sailing while th
other went back 600 stadia. Thus alternately night and day
the ships were carried along by a favorable wind and then drivei
back by an unfavorable one. I ask how many stadia the ship
sailed in all and when they met?

Medieval Commerce. After the fall of Rome, communica
tion between different parts of Europe became more and mor
hazardous. The centralized government broke down and ii
its place came the feudal system, under which countries wer
loose alliances of petty rulers, each nominally subject to ar
overlord. These rulers levied taxes on merchants who passec
through their borders, a process which naturally tended to
stifle trade. Such commerce as there was dealt in salt anc
iron, commodities needed by the otherwise self-sufficien
agricultural villages, and in the luxuries of wines and spice:
which were bought by the great feudal princes or by the
monasteries.

About the year 1000, certain towns began to increase ii
size and became the centers of trade. These towns wer
notable for their guilds, some being associations of workers ir
the same craft, others being commercial organizations. The
towns imposed their own duties. For example, in London ir
the eleventh century the toll charges depended on the type o.
ship and the nature of its cargo. A boat loaded with plank:
paid one plank. A man bringing in a basket of hens paid one
hen. If he brought in eggs, he paid five eggs from each basket
Cloth tolls were imposed on certain days of the week only and
cheese-mongers were subject to tax at Christmas time.

The towns regulated trade through their town markets,
which were subject to such rulings as a fixed price for bread
and ale. These regulations survived in textbooks in problems
asking for the just price of a loaf of bread given the present

nd the former prices of wheat and the former price of a loaf
f specified weight.

Commerce was hindered by the wretched condition of the
oads, by the attacks of robbers who often acted under the
rotection of the feudal lords, and by the local customs duties.
Much of the commerce centered about the great fairs which
were held at specified intervals and at which merchants from
all Christendom met to exchange their wares. At Lyons, for
example, in the sixteenth century, the fairs were at All Saints,
Epiphany, Easter, and Whitsun Day. The merchants were
protected by special laws during these affairs and cases against
hem were tried in special courts.

Venice. The city of Venice held important commercial
rights in Constantinople during the eleventh century, but the
Crusades supplied her greatest opportunity. She bartered
coöperation with the crusading armies for coast towns and
islands and soon became a great commercial power in the
Mediterranean. Overland expeditions to Germany increased
her importance, as did the yearly venture of the "Flanders
Galleys" — a fleet of ships freighted by the citizens of Venice
and dispatched to London, Antwerp, and Bruges.

Other Commercial Cities in Italy. Other cities in Italy
reached commercial importance also. Among these were
Pisa, the home of Fibonacci, Florence, the chief city of the
interior, and Genoa. These were pioneers in the development of business methods. Double-entry bookkeeping, for
example, had its origin here with Pacioli as its first exponent.
In fact, the frequent references to "Welsh" (i.e., Italian) business practice in books written in other parts of Europe indicate
that Italy provided a model for the rest of Christendom.

The Hanseatic League. During the fourteenth century,
an association of cities called the Hanseatic League was
formed in Germany. Its purpose was mutual protection in
trade and to this end trading posts or "factories" similar to
those of the Italian cities were established in England, France,
Russia, Scandinavia, and elsewhere. This organization for

protection should be contrasted with the competition of the
Italian cities. For a time, the League held a monopoly of
the trade of Europe with the Baltic, but during the sixteenth
century the power of the League was definitely broken and
the heyday of Dutch and English commerce began.*

PROBLEMS CONNECTED WITH THE GREAT FAIRS

Barter. Much of the trading at the great fairs was done
by barter, that is, goods would be exchanged directly for
other commodities of the same value. At times, three prices

QUENTIN MATSYS' MONEY-LENDER AND HIS WIFE
From the painting in the Louvre by the courtesy of the Archives
Photographiques d'Art et d'Histoire.

* For a more extensive treatment of this topic, see Clive Day, *A History of
Commerce*, New York, 1926; first edition, New York, 1907.

would be quoted on an article, a cash price, a price in barter, and a price to be paid at the end of several months. Cases are on record in which a man purchased wool in England on three months' credit, sold it for cash in Bruges in Flanders at a lower price, traded with this capital for the remainder of his three months, and cleared a profit on the transaction.

The question of deferred payments led to interesting problems, of which the following is a common type. This question appears in Cataneo's work of 1546.

Two men barter cloth for wool. A bolt of cloth is worth 12 lire in cash or 15 lire in barter. At the end of 10 months, a hundred-weight of wool will fetch 20 lire cash or 24 in trade. When should the bargain be made and how much wool should be paid that the exchange may be equal? *

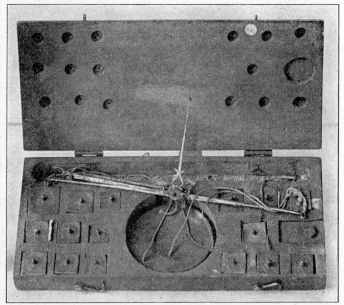

MONEY-CHANGER'S WEIGHTS
From the collection of Professor David Eugene Smith. Courtesy of the
Museums of the Peaceful Arts, New York City.

* For additional problem material, see Smith, *History*, II, 532–599, and also
Vera Sanford, *History and Significance of Certain Standard Problems in
Algebra*, New York, 1927.

Exchange. The diversities of weights, measures, and especially of coinage furnished another group of problems that arose wherever commerce passed beyond a very limited area. With the breaking up of the Roman Empire, local authorities claimed the right to set their own standards of measures and to coin their own money. As a result, most commercial transactions involved changing from one system to another. One of the problems which Tartaglia gives illustrates this situation, showing also a method of answering the question.

If 100 lire of Modon money amounts to 115 lire in Venice, and if 180 lire in Venice comes to 150 in Corfu, and if 240 lire Corfu money is worth as much as 360 lire in Negroponte, what is the value in Modon coinage of 666 lire Negroponte money?

The solution reads:

	54000			6210000		
Negroponte	Corfu	Corfu	Venetia	Venetia	Modon	Negroponte
360	240	150	180	115	100	666
		2877120000		11988000		66600

The answer given is $463\frac{7}{23}$.*

This problem is of particular interest, since in it Tartaglia, writing in Venice, refers to a series of ports over which Venice had gained control in the early years of the thirteenth century. Corfu, Modon in the southern part of Greece, and Negroponte or Eubœa commanded the route to Constantinople while Crete and Rhodes, also controlled by Venice, guarded the way to Asia Minor.

Customs Duties. Duties included export and import taxes, gifts to officials, and many other allowances. In the Dark Ages, all commerce was subject to the demands of the lawless

---

* I.e., $\dfrac{666 \times 100 \times 180 \times 240}{360 \times 150 \times 115}$. It should be noted that lack of symbolism necessitated the learning of rules for placing these quantities and for drawing the guide lines for the computation. It is interesting to note that in Borghi's work (Venice, 1484) the first great commercial arithmetic, this rule is illustrated by a problem based on the same exchange ratio between the same cities.

feudal barons, who charged tolls for the use of roads and
bridges and who frequently confiscated all wares of traders
who passed through their lands.   As these days passed, the
increasing security of the various governments lessened the
risks of complete loss, but it also put many levies of taxes on
a legal basis.   As a result, in the fifteenth century the taxes
imposed as merchandise passed from the seacoast to Paris
were equivalent to the value of the goods.

The close proximity of boundary lines and the duties
charged from city to city made customs duties a more vital
part of commercial mathematics than they are to-day.   The
type of work that resulted is illustrated by a problem from
Clavius's *Arithmetic* (1583):

A merchant bought 50000 pounds of pepper in Portugal for 10000
scudi, paying a tax of 500 scudi.   He carried it to Italy at a cost of
300 scudi and there paid another duty of 200 scudi.   The transportation from the coast to Florence cost 100 scudi and he was obliged
to pay an impost of 100 scudi to that city.   Lastly the government
demanded a tax from each merchant of 1000 scudi.   Now he is
perplexed to know what price to charge per pound so that, after all
these expenses, he may make a profit of 2 giulij a pound.

Profit and Loss.   Diversities of measures, customs duties,
high charges for transportation, and the inevitable spoiling
of part of a shipment en route made the computation of the
per cent of profit on a transaction a difficult matter.   In an
example of this type, Fibonacci (1202) declares that the work
is "impossible" unless the reader will grant that the merchant
may have lost — an early case of a negative number's being
interpreted in this way.*   The detail of the following problem
is not uncommon:

A man bought a number of bales of wool in London, each bale
weighing 200 pounds, English measure, and each bale cost him 24 fl.
He sent the wool to Florence and paid carriage duties, and other
expenses amounting to 10 fl.   He wishes to sell the wool in Florence
at such a price as to make 20 per cent on his investment.   How
much should he charge a hundredweight if 100 London pounds are
equivalent to 133 Florentine pounds?

* See page 182.

The author of the work in which this appears was the Florentine Ghaligai (1521). His book was intended as a practical manual for merchants.

Drafts. Another development of international commerce was the necessity of paying bills at a distance. To transfer coin from one country to another was hazardous and costly. The need for this transfer was so acute, however, that the Lombard bankers in England established a credit system whereby the money due from England to the papal treasury might be drawn on by the Florentine manufacturers to pay for the English wool which they had bought, while the payments made by the men in Florence were credited to the English for the papal chest. This system was extended over Europe and, accordingly, textbooks contained long explanations of the meaning of exchange at a premium and at a discount. Tartaglia even gave a table showing the time that must be allowed to draw on the various cities.

The drafts that were given differed but little from those in use to-day, as is shown by this example from the work of Trenchant (1566).

July 24, 1558

On August 13, next, pay to Cretofle Didier the sum of one thousand écus at 66 sous an écu for value received of the aforesaid Didier, and charge this to the account of Pierre Iulani.

Alexandre Dauid

Summary. These problems illustrate the type of mathematics that was needed to meet the exigencies of foreign trade in the Middle Ages and during the Renaissance. It should be remembered that this work differs from that given later only in the fact that with the unification of the European countries and the blotting out of many customs barriers, the limits of local trade have spread and many cities that were formerly quite separate so far as coinage, duties, and measures are concerned are now united within the same boundaries. A similar situation existed in this country during Colonial times and in the first years of our independence. The Colonies and later the States issued their own coinage and the breaking down of customs lines between the States was one of the important tasks that confronted Congress. For fifty years after the adoption of the Constitution, however, textbooks gave rules for changing money from the currency of one State to that of another.

THE QUESTION OF INTEREST

Early Use of Interest. The practice of paying interest is probably as old as is money itself, for charging interest for the use of money is as inevitable as is charging rent for the use of a house, a farm, or any other property.

The earliest records of transactions that involve interest are in Babylonia and date from at least as early as 2000 B.C. At that time, commodities such as grain, oil, date wine, and cattle served as capital, and interest was sometimes computed in grain and sometimes in silver. Promissory notes given by tenant farmers to the owners of the property stipulated interest at rates as high as 40 per cent, and there is evidence that a legal rate of interest was enforced in certain cities.

Regulation of Interest Rates. Although interest charges were customary in Greece, India, and China, these are of less importance in the history of commercial mathematics than is the regulation of interest rates in Roman times and in the Middle Ages.

The concentration of capital in the hands of a few people inevitably leads to an increase in the rate of interest, and this, by the greater pressure it exerts on the borrower, tends in turn to increase the size of the debtor class and to concentrate capital still further. The process can be checked only by the establishing of a maximum legal rate, but, as is evident to-day, such a process is only a check — it does not prevent many ingenious schemes for collecting a higher rate from the very class of people that the legal regulation is framed to protect.

The first code of the Roman Law (451–449 B.C.) restricted

interest rates to one twelfth of the capital a year.* At a later date, Cicero considered the 48 per cent demanded by Brutus extortionate, and he fixed the interest rate for the province of Cilicia at 12 per cent. At the beginning of the Christian era, 25 per cent was the maximum legal rate. Five hundred years later, the Emperor Justinian allowed nothing higher than one half of one per cent a month, or 6 per cent a year.

The Attitude of the Christian Church. The early leaders of the Christian Church were so aroused by the oppression of the poor by wealthy Roman money-lenders that they declared that the practice of charging interest on loans was sinful.† At the time the Church had no control over the government of the Roman Empire. As time passed, however, it became more influential in civil affairs and thus was in a position to enforce this regulation. This could be done so long as there was no great demand for capital, but conditions changed with the beginning of the Crusades in the eleventh century.

Money was needed to equip armies and to transport them to Palestine. Genoa and Pisa sent ships to Syria selling provisions to the armies, and Venice made commercial treaties with the crusading armies. All this required capital and the demand became permanent; for the Crusaders returned to Europe with a taste for Eastern spices and a love of Eastern luxuries, and thus they created a market for goods from the Levant and caused a permanent revival of commerce.

At first the Jewish bankers were the money-lenders, and the relations between them and their Christian patrons were cordial or the reverse according to whether loans were being solicited or being paid. It is quite possible that the feeling against the Jews was resentment at their monopoly of banking rather than a racial matter. In London, for instance, a century after the expulsion of the Jews the merchants peti-

* This should be compared with the Roman use of 12 in their division of the foot and of the pound. See page 103.

† See the article "Usury," by John Dow, *Encyclopedia of Religion and Ethics*, James Hastings, editor, New York, 1922.

tioned for the expulsion of the Italian bankers who had succeeded the Jewish ones, wishing to have the trade for themselves.

It is significant to note that the first Christians to become
bankers were from Italy.   In the thirteenth century this
country was far in advance of the rest of Europe in everything
that pertained to business, and Italian merchants in England
acted as the Pope's representatives in money matters.   Even
to-day their name survives in Lombard Street in the financial
district of London.

From 1202 onward mathematics books gave problems concerning both simple and compound interest.   The latter was
sometimes called "Jewish usury."   The Dutch mathematician Gemma Frisius (c. 1540) explained that compound interest was so useful that he was obliged to explain its computation "although many Christians consider its very name an
abomination."   It is evident, then, that even the Church
could not stop the practice.   Wealthy men had many ways of
evading the law.   For example, Antonio in *The Merchant of
Venice* loaned money gratis, but he made his capital bring in
large return by investing it in trading fleets or argosies, joining in many adventures for safety rather than risking everything on an individual enterprise.

By 1515 even the Church realized the futility of its position
and permitted the charging of a moderate rate of interest.
This action accomplished the very purpose of the measure
which it repealed.   Interest rates dropped and the evils of
extortionate charges diminished.   From 20 to 28 per cent in
England, interest went to 10 per cent in the reign of Henry
VIII and to 8 per cent less than a century later.

The Name "Per Cent."   The idea of computing interest or
profit and loss on a per cent basis may be the result of the
Roman taxes which were reckoned as $\frac{1}{25}$, $\frac{1}{20}$, $\frac{1}{100}$.   Taxes
and duties on a similar basis were levied in England in the
sixteenth century and later, when we read that Parliament
granted the king an impost of $\frac{1}{10}$ and $\frac{1}{15}$ on goods brought in

through certain ports. During the Middle Ages, it became customary to compute profit and loss as so and so many in a hundred. The words *per cento* were variously abbreviated. They became *p cento, p cēto*, writing the *n* as a dash above the *e, p $\overset{o}{c}$*, and occasionally *p.* 100., and *p cent.* No author felt obliged to limit himself to any one of these.

The symbol (%) seems to have been derived from the fifteenth-century form *per $\overset{o}{c}$* or *p $\overset{o}{c}$* by way of the seventeenth-century *per $\frac{0}{0}$*.

Problems that Involve Interest. The problems that involve interest include theoretical consideration as well as practical applications. Fibonacci (1202) asks the academic question:

A certain man puts one denarius at interest at such a rate that in five years he has two denarii, and in every five years thereafter the money doubles. I ask how many denarii he would gain from this one denarius in 100 years.

Cardan works ingeniously to find the actual rate of interest that is paid when 10 per cent is compounded semiannually. But in the main, problems involving interest fall into two classes: those concerning the computation of the interest given principal, time, and rate, and those that involve rent charges or annuities.

Interest Tables. Until the close of the sixteenth century, great commercial companies computed their own interest tables, preserving them in manuscript and guarding them from theft by copying. One of Stevin's contributions to business mathematics was a printed table (1582) which told how much money would amount to 10,000,000 in a given number of years at specified rates of interest. In other words, it was a "present value" table. The years were from 1 to 30; the interest rates from 1 to 16 per cent, including fractional parts by fourths from $3\frac{3}{4}$ to $5\frac{1}{2}$. The table also gave the amounts that would yield 10,000,000 a year for the required term. Thus it could be used directly in telling the present value of an annuity. It could also be used as a compound-interest table by finding the sum that would amount to 10,000,000 in the given time and then finding the amount of a given sum by the Rule of Three.

Discount.   In its operation, discount is the opposite of interest.   Writers of the sixteenth century who treated this subject were principally concerned with the problem of discounting a note bearing compound interest when the date of maturity was not coincident with the close of an interest period.   Where to-day the amount of the note would be computed to the close of the preceding interest date and simple interest on the remainder added, the method current in the sixteenth century consisted in finding the amount at the next following interest date and discounting that amount.

INVESTMENT SCHEMES OF THE MIDDLE AGES

Rent Charges.   Medieval capitalists were greatly hampered in their investments by the attitude of the Church in regard to interest.   But in spite of this, methods were devised to enable Christians to make a profit from their capital without transgressing the law.   One of these schemes was that of "rent charges."   These were simple in theory but their computation was difficult.   A man who wished to borrow a sum of money would give his creditor a house or other property as security.   The creditor would then retain possession of the house until the rent which it brought should be equivalent to the amount of the loan and its interest. Problems of this sort appear in the *Liber Abaci* (1202) as well as in works of the later centuries through the sixteenth.   Although they were based on real subject matter, some of these problems carried the computation not only to the years and months that the creditor might keep the house, but even to the days and hours.

Partnerships.   Another of the schemes for making money productive without charging interest was the short term partnership.   The work of the citizens of Venice in stocking the Flanders Galleys and the operations of the German merchants in the Hansa League have already been mentioned. Other ventures were made on a smaller scale and the textbooks in elementary arithmetic have many examples based on them. In Fibonacci's work (1202), the capital contributed to a partnership was frequently in commodities such as pepper, sugar, and wool. Profits were generally divided according to the amount of the original investment, but it sometimes happened that one of the partners received a larger share as payment for particular services to the company. When an agent was employed, his salary was often rated as a certain fraction of the profits. Capital might be withdrawn or additional funds invested at different dates, and when this occurred the profits were computed according to the time the money was in the service of the company as well as according to the amount. The following problems from Humphrey Baker's *Well Spring of Sciences* (1568) illustrate questions of frequent occurrence in regard to partnerships.

Three merchantes haue companied together: the first layd in the firste of January 100 li. [pounds] and the firste of Aprill, he hath taken backe againe 20 li.; The seconde hath layde in the first of Marche 60 li. and afterward he did lay in more li. the first of August. The third layd in the first of July 150 li. And the first of October he did take backe agayne 50 li. And at the yeares ende, they founde that they had gayned 160 li. I demaunde how much euery man shall haue of the gayne?

Two marchauntes haue companied together, the first hath layde in the first of Januarie, 640 li. The seconde can lay in nothing vntill the firste of April. I demaund how much he shall lay in, to the end that he may take halfe the gaynes.*

The legend of Dick Whittington and his cat is indicative of these partnerships. A cat was an unusual venture, but many cases are on record in which a master invested the small capital of his servants, believing that his kind offices in giving them a share in his enterprises would result in greater profits from the trip. The study of the problems that concern

* The solution of the second problem shows that the partnership was to last for a single year from the date of the first man's investment.

partnership gives interesting information as to trade routes. Eastern spices, northern amber, English wool, and Florentine fabrics are among the commodities that are listed.

In the course of time these partnerships merged into the great trading companies whose headquarters were at such cities as York and Bristol. The London Company, indeed, was instrumental in equipping the Pilgrims for their expedition to America in 1620, and the Dutch East India Company was largely concerned in the founding of New York. Eventually these organizations became stock companies, and today problems regarding partnerships are being replaced by those relating to the shareholders in the great corporations that have become so significant in the business life of the twentieth century.

MODERN BUSINESS

Stocks and Stock Exchanges. Although isolated instances of the sale of stock are found at an earlier date, the practice became an important factor shortly after the establishment of the Bourse (or exchange) at Antwerp in the sixteenth century. The Bourse was a place where merchants met to exchange their goods without actually showing them, and in a short time credit became the principal commodity sold on the exchange. According to Professor Day: *

When shares of the Dutch East India Company were put on the market in 1602 they were taken up to a considerable extent by capitalists of Antwerp who no longer had use for their money at home; much of the money needed to rebuild London after the fire of 1666, and a large part of the capital of the bank of England, came from the Dutch; shares of the English companies trading with Asia and Africa circulated freely on the Amsterdam exchange; a loan to the German Emperor was floated in London.

In this country, the practice of buying and selling shares in the capital of various enterprises led to the informal organi-

* Clive Day, *A History of Commerce*, 1926 ed., 156, quoted by the permission of Longmans, Green and Company.

zation of the NewYork Stock Exchange in 1792. This began
as a small group of associates meeting under a certain button-
wood tree on Wall Street. These men pledged themselves
to trade with each other in preference to outside parties, while
investors not belonging to the exchange were expected to use
the members as their agents. The volume of their business
can be judged by the fact that less than a score of stocks was
listed in 1809, and it is interesting to note that these were
stock of banks or of insurance companies only.*

Problems Based on the Buying of Stock. Although questions of exchange of credit appeared in the early printed textbooks, the sale of shares of stock does not seem to have been
introduced before the close of the eighteenth century. A
possible explanation of this is the unfortunate association of
the subject with the South Sea Bubble, the Mississippi Bubble, and other investment schemes which brought misery to
thousands who had speculated with their entire capital.
During the eighteenth century, the subject of stocks may
quite probably have had a connotation similar to that of
gambling schemes to-day.

In America, Pike, who usually gives full explanations, devotes a quarter page of his edition of 1808 to "Buying and
Selling Stocks," and he prefaces his two examples with the
statement: "Stock is a general name for the capitals of
trading companies." Dilworth's *Schoolmaster's Assistant* †
which was extensively used in this period, seems to ignore the
subject entirely, but this is probably due to the fact that new
topics are less likely to be introduced into revisions of time-
honored texts than into works that are just being assembled.
The first edition of Pike's book was 1788, that of Dilworth was
about 1743.

---

* The original agreement and the stock list mentioned above may be seen
in the Governors' Room in the New York Stock Exchange.

† By Thomas Dilworth. The first edition was about 1743. The twenty-
second edition appeared in London in 1784. Karpinski (*History of Arithmetic*) notes nineteen editions printed in this country between 1773 and 1800,
and at least two editions (1800 and 1815) came out in the nineteenth century.

In Emerson's *North American Arithmetic** (1832), the topic was explained in terms which show the rapid advance made in industry and transportation in the meantime. Emerson says:

Stock is a property, consisting in shares of some establishment, designed to yield an income. It includes government securities, shares in incorporated banks, insurance offices, factories, canals, railroads, etc.

The Erie Canal was opened in 1825 and the first railroad in this country was begun three years later. In 1832, this road, the Baltimore and Ohio, was operating less than a hundred miles of track, and the first sale of railroad stock on the New York Exchange had been made in 1830. Emerson was certainly quick to utilize new subject matter of paramount interest at the time at which he wrote.

Annuities. There is little difference between the medieval idea of rent charges and the modern idea of an annuity. In the one case a yearly income is purchased for a definite period. In the other case, the income may be bought for a fixed period or else for the lifetime of the beneficiary. This connection between rent charges and annuities suggests a possible origin for the use of the term "annual rent" as applied to the income from an annuity.

Among the instances of annuities in textbook problems, two are worthy of particular notice, the one because of its modern content and the other because of the extreme difficulty of its solution before the invention of logarithms. Both are apparently genuine problems, for in the first case the author substantiates his data by giving a full description of the occasion, and in the second the writer says that the question was actually put to him by gentlemen from Barri who declared that it had really happened:

In 1555, King Henry borrowed money from his bankers at the

* Two years after publication, this work replaced Colburn's *First Lessons in Arithmetic* as being the required text in the "Writing Schools" in Boston. Frederick Emerson, the writer, was "principal in the department of arithmetic" in the Boylston School.

rate of 4 per cent payable at the fairs, this being a better rate for the bankers than 16 per cent compounded annually. (There were four fairs each year.) In the same year, he borrowed 3954641 écus on condition that he should pay 5 per cent of the loan at each fair until he should have made 41 payments at which time the account would be considered as closed. Which of these conditions is the more advantageous for the bankers? *

A merchant gave a university 2814 ducats on the understanding that he was to pay 618 ducats a year for nine years at the end of which the 2814 ducats should be considered as paid. What interest was he getting on his money? †

The difficulty of solving either of these problems by arithmetic makes one appreciate the tremendous value of logarithms and of tables.

Practical problems concerning annuities were to be found in the purchase of freehold estates in England. Here the selling price was held to be equal to the present value of an annuity equivalent to the rent, to be paid forever. Another illustration lay in a scheme used by the Dutch government to raise money for its wars with Spain in the latter part of the sixteenth century. The scheme was the sale of *annuities* payable during the life of the beneficiary, the price being half that of a perpetuity of the same amount.

Marine Insurance. The oldest type of insurance seems to have been designed for the protection of merchant vessels. This was in vogue even in Roman times, and while we have no information as to the basis on which the insurance rates were determined, we know that they fluctuated according to the activities of the Mediterranean pirates and that during the Punic Wars they were prohibitively high.

References to practices in the Italian cities in the late Middle Ages seem to show a scheme of insurance, but the issue was frequently met by a merchant's distributing his capital among several enterprises, trusting that profits in one would compensate for possible losses in another.

* This problem is from Trenchant's work of 1566. For a discussion of Fairs, see page 121.

† This problem occurs in Tartaglia's *General Trattato* (1556). The interest rate is over 19 per cent.

The history of marine insurance in England is largely the history of the organization known as Lloyd's. This began sometime before 1688 as a group of merchants who met for business and gossip at the coffeehouse kept by Edward Lloyd in Tower Street, London. The method of insuring a ship and its cargo consisted in submitting a declaration as to the vessel and its load with a request for such and such an amount of insurance. The statement was then passed about among the merchants, each one underwriting whatever amount he wished until the required total was reached. Thus the insuring of a ship by many underwriters was similar in many ways to the making of a partnership by many investors. In course of time, Lloyd's organization became more formal, but the same procedure of insurance is followed to-day and insurance of all types may be bought there.

The importance of marine insurance in New England in the early days of our independence is illustrated by the following problem from Pike's *Arithmetic* (1797 ed.):

A merchant adventured 480 *l.* 10 *s.* from Newburyport to South-carolina, from thence to Jamaica, and from thence, home, and the premium was 5 percent. from port to port; what sum must he take out a policy for, to cover his adventure, the voyage round, supposing the risks to be equal out and home, and tantamount to the several equal risques?

By the close of the nineteenth century, marine insurance was computed on a more scientific basis than had previously been the case. For example, Pike prefaced his problems by a brief description of insurance policies, stating that

The average loss is 10 per cent; that is, if the insured suffer any damage or loss, not exceeding 10 per cent, he bears it himself, and the insurers are free.

Fire Insurance. The topic of fire insurance appears in text-books of the early nineteenth century as a sort of codicil to marine insurance, a single heading being used for both. Fire insurance as a business practice, however, dates from 1681 in

138 COMMERCIAL MATHEMATICS

London and from 1752 in this country, the first fire insurance company here having been organized in Philadelphia. As one might expect, Benjamin Franklin served on its board of directors. It is interesting to note that these companies reduced their risks by maintaining their own fire departments. Each house covered by a policy bore a metal plate marked with the name of the company. Thus, in case of a fire, there would be no doubt as to the houses which the company was anxious to save. Such plates may be seen on several houses on South Thirteenth Street in Philadelphia to-day.

The Scientific Basis for Life Insurance. The invention of logarithms greatly facilitated the computation of annuities, but it was not until the close of the seventeenth century that studies were made leading to the scientific determination of the price of life annuities.

The attitude of a contemporary writer on such investigations is generally illuminating and interesting. Accordingly, it seems desirable to quote the comments made by John Ward in his *Young Mathematician's Guide*, a book which was published in 1706 and which is mentioned among the texts used at Harvard and at Yale in the eighteenth century. The book included "Arithmetick, Algebra, the Elements of Geometry, Conick Sections, and the Arithmetick of Infinites." The following excerpts (from the edition of 1758) indicate respect for the work of notable mathematicians but skepticism as to its practical value. These remarks are preceded by several problems dealing with annuities, with tables of the amounts of £1 yearly, half yearly, quarterly, and by days and months at 5 per cent. He says:

Thus far concerning Annuities, or Leases, etc. that are *limited* by any assigned Time; and 'tis only such that can be computed by *Theorems* or certain *Rules*. However, it may not perhaps be *unacceptable*, to insert a brief Account of some Estimates that have been reasonably made, by *two* very ingenious *Persons*, about the proportion of Difference of *Mens Lives*, according to their several *Ages*; which may be of good Use in computing the *Values* of *Annuities*, or taking of *Leases* for *Lives*, etc.

Here Ward gives an account of the work of Sir William Petty (1674) on life expectancy. He continues to that of a friend of Sir Isaac Newton:

The *ingenious* and great *Mathematician*, Doctor *Edmund Halley*.*. doth with great *Industry* and *Skill*, draw an *Estimate* of the *Proportion* of *Mens* Lives, from the *Monthly Tables* of the *Births* and *Funerals* in *Breslaw* ..... Whence he proves that it's 80 to 1, a Person of 25 *Years Old* will not die in a Year; that it is 5½ to 1, that a Man of 40 will live 7 *Years*: That a Man of 30 *Years Old* may reasonably expect to live 27 or 28 *Years*, etc.

Now from these and the like *Proportions* (he justly infers) that the *Price* of *Insurance* upon *Lives* ought to be regulated, there being a great Difference between the Life of a Man of 20 and one of 50. For *Example*: 'Tis 100 to 1, that a Man of 20 dies not in a Year, but 38 to 1, for a Man of 50 *Years* of *Age*. And upon these also depends the *Valuation* of *Annuities* for Lives; for it is plain, that the *Purchaser* ought to pay only such Part of the *Value* of any *Annuity*, as he hath *Chances* that he is living.............

The same *ingenious Gentleman* proceeds on, and shews how to estimate or find the *Value* of *Two Lives*, and then of *Three Lives*, which being too long a Discourse to be recited here, I have, for Brevity's sake, omitted it; and shall only add this serious Observation,

Viz. How unjustly we repine at the Shortness of our *Lives*, and think ourselves wrong'd if we attain not to *Old Age*; wheras it appears, that the *One Half* of those, that are Born, *die* in Seventeen Years Time. For by the aforesaid Bills of Mortality at Breslaw, it was found, that 1238 were in that Time reduced to 616. So that, instead of murmuring at what we call a *Short Life*, we ought to account it as a great Blessing that we have *surviv'd*, perhaps by many Years, that *Period* of *Life*, wherat the one Half of the whole Race of Mankind does not arrive.

In spite of Ward's views on the improbability of reducing life insurance or life annuities to formulas, the problem was an especially important one in England, where many estates were liable for a life annuity as the dower rights of the late owner's widow, where property was held during the lifetime of a beneficiary and then reverted to the former owner, and where government rewards often took the form of life annuities. Many problems based on life expectancy were proposed,

* See page 56.

and several people engaged in the compilation of mortality tables. Unfortunately, however, these tables yielded different results when applied to the same problem, and these discrepancies were the cause of several controversies.

De Moivre and other mathematicians of the period were engaged in working out the theory of probability as it applied to these situations, and at least two life insurance companies were formed: the "Laudable and Amicable Societies of Annuitants" and the "Society of Equitable Assurances on Lives."

These insurance companies were more speculative than are companies to-day, and insurance was associated in the minds of many people with wild-cat schemes that, according to Professor Day, were "companies that proposed to insure against loss of servants, against burglars, and against highwaymen." *

Like investments in stocks, life insurance could not be used as the basis of textbook problems until it had become well safeguarded. So it was probably not until the middle of the nineteenth century that problems regarding life insurance were included in elementary texts.

SUMMARY

The history of commercial mathematics reflects the history of commerce at many points, but although external conditions vary from time to time, the major problems continue as they have for centuries. Buying stock in a corporation to-day is more impersonal than was the sharing in a partnership of the fifteenth century, but the underlying idea is the same.

Our methods of computation are superior to those of former times, and we have better mechanical aids through tables, logarithms, and calculating machines, but it must be admitted that commercial problems of a high degree of difficulty were solved without this assistance. It cannot be said, then, that commercial computation has been the direct cause of the investigation of any work in mathematics beyond the most elementary operations with integers and fractions.

* Clive Day, *A History of Commerce*, 1926 ed., 159.

CHAPTER IV

ALGEBRA

GENERAL SURVEY

The Slow Development of Algebra. The development of methods of computation was dependent upon the invention of a convenient system of numerals and the evolution of the place value idea. The process was a long one, as we have seen, but it was simple in comparison with the development of algebra. Here there was the double need for a means of representing unknown quantities and for ways of indicating the various operations as well. It was not sufficient to be able to write an equation involving one unknown quantity; methods had to be devised for showing powers and roots, and for indicating several different unknowns. Furthermore, the desire of the algebraist to make his theorems as general as possible led to the invention of numbers that were called negative, irrational, and imaginary — names that reflect the conflict between traditional ideas and new concepts. These discoveries were cumulative. Symbols suggested new processes: processes required new symbolism. Of the many ways in which a topic might have been studied, the way in which it was actually evolved was not always the simplest nor even the most natural one. Thus the history of algebra is not a tale of the logical development of a body of subject matter. Instead, it deals with the simultaneous development of apparently unrelated branches of the subject and with the later attempts to reduce this body of thought to a logical system.

Algebra in Egypt. Algebra may be said to have begun in Egypt, for the Ahmes Papyrus contains arithmetic and geometric progressions as well as several problems of the following type: "A quantity whose seventh part is added to it becomes 19." It is possible that Egyptian scholars considered this to be merely the inverse of the problem: Find the sum of $16\frac{5}{8}$ and $2\frac{3}{8}$. The solution seems to have followed an arithmetic scheme which will be discussed later under the topic of the Rule of False Position. Other manuscripts show that the Egyptians were able to solve certain quadratic equations, apparently using the Rule of False in this case also.

Algebra in Greece. The treatment of algebra by the Greeks in classic times was geometric, but we know from Plato's writings (c. 380 B.C.) that various verbal problems were popular. The subject matter mentioned by this philosopher is similar to that of certain problems in a collection of epigrams made by Metrodorus (A.D. c. 500).* Thus, although there is no actual proof that this is the case, it seems reasonable to assume that these problems are of ancient origin. No one of them can be called a practical problem, yet several appear in somewhat modified form in our textbooks. Among these is the so-called work problem which Metrodorus gave in the following form:

Brick-maker, I am in a hurry to erect this house. To-day is cloudless, and I do not require many more bricks, but I have all I want but three hundred. Thou alone in one day couldst make as many, but thy son left off working when he had finished two hundred, and thy son-in-law when he had made two hundred and fifty. Working all together, in how many days can you make these?

Diophantus. The algebraic knowledge of the Greeks was brought together by Diophantus of Alexandria (c. 275) in a work called the *Arithmetica*.† Little is known of the life of Diophantus himself, but tradition has it that his career is given in this problem:

Diophantus passed $\frac{1}{6}$ of his life in childhood, $\frac{1}{12}$ in youth, and $\frac{1}{7}$ more as a bachelor, five years after his marriage was born a son who died four years before his father at half his father's age.

* The text and translation of the epigrams may be found in volume 5 of the *Greek Anthology*, edited by W. R. Paton and published in the *Loeb Classical Library*.

† See Sir Thomas L. Heath, *Diophantus of Alexandria*, Cambridge, England, 1910.

It is probable that the questions proposed in the *Arithmetica* were collected from many sources, but Diophantus made outstanding contributions himself as is witnessed by the many unusual features which his work presents: he used symbols for an unknown quantity and its powers; he wrote quantities that were to be added side by side, but used a symbol for subtraction; and he knew the rules of signs for multiplication, but classed the negative, irrational, and imaginary roots of an equation as "impossible." He also found approximate values for the irrational roots of quadratics. The major part of his work was devoted to the study of problems particularly those whose solution is indeterminate. These problems, almost without exception, belong to the "Find a number" class with the following as a typical example: "Find three numbers in arithmetic progression such that the sum of any pair is a perfect square." The difficulty of finding any of the sets of numbers which satisfy these conditions shows the point to which Diophantus had carried his algebra — a point which it did not surpass for over a thousand years.

Commentaries on the work of Diophantus were written by Hypatia * (*c.* 410), the first woman mathematician whose name has come down to us, and by others, including an Arab writer of the tenth century. In the latter part of the fifteenth century, probably in 1464, Regiomontanus discovered a Greek manuscript of the work of Diophantus in Venice. He deplored the fact that no translation had been made of the "very flower of the whole of arithmetic," but apparently did not undertake making it himself. A century later, Xylander † published a translation into Latin, confessing in his preface that he had once taken great pride in his own contributions to

* Hypatia of Alexandria is the heroine of Kingsley's novel of the same name. She appears to have profited by the fact that so few women have made contributions to mathematics and her work is probably much overrated. None of it is now extant.

† Xylander's real name was Wilhelm Holzman. He was professor of Greek at Heidelberg but he was also interested in mathematics, translating Euclid's *Elements* into German, and writing a book (*Opuscula Mathematica*) which contained a treatment of surds.

algebra, but that he now realized that the work of Diophantus completely overshadowed his own efforts.

Algebra in India. The Hindu writers Āryabhata (*c.* 510), Brahmagupta (*c.* 628), Mahāvīra (*c.* 850), and Bhāskara (*c.* 1150) were particularly concerned with series, permutations, and linear and quadratic equations, an interest that is recorded in the so-called "Hindu" method for solving a quadratic. The work of these Hindu writers contained many problems of a fanciful and poetic nature. Examples of these are given in connection with verbal problems in Chapter V.

The Name "Algebra." The greatest Arab writer on algebra was Mohammed ibn Mûsa al-Khowârizmî * (*c.* 825) whose treatise *al-jabr w'al muqâbalah* provided a name for this branch of mathematics. The name "algebra" was variously explained by the writers who adopted it as a title. Some invented a king of India named Algor who was reputed to have been its originator; others referred to Geber, a fictitious Arab philosopher. Apparently the word *al-jabr* means the transposing of a negative quantity, and *al-muqâbalah* means the transposing of a negative quantity and the combining of terms. Recent investigation shows that the word *al-jabr* is closely similar to an Assyrian term meaning "equal in rank." It suggests that this term survived in Asia Minor and that it was adopted by the Arabs together with whatever knowledge of algebra the Syrians had inherited. It is well known that the Arabs were indebted to the Syrians for translations of Greek manuscripts that dealt with mathematics and medicine. A possible explanation of the title, then, is: the Arabs received their first knowledge of Greek mathematics through the Syrian Christians living in Asia Minor. Together with this knowledge, they may have received the ancient name for equality as applied to an equation. Having the

---

* This name means Mohammed, the son of Mûsa (or Moses), from Khwarezm, a locality south of the Black Sea. The Arab custom of giving a man the name of his city appears also in the case of al-Karkhî, whose name is that of one of the sections of Bagdad. For al-Khowârizmî's work see Karpinski, *Al-Khowarizmi.*

subject with a foreign name, they then translated *al-jabr* into Arabic as *al-muqâbalah* and referred to the subject by the two names, each a synonym of the other and each meaning the *science of equations.**

Arab Algebraists. Al-Khowârizmî's solution of quadratic equations will be treated under that subject (see page 167). Among the other Eastern algebraists to whom later reference will be made are Abû Kâmil (*c.* 900), al-Karkhî (*c.* 1020), and the Persian poet Omar Khayyám (*c.* 1100).†

Algebra in Europe. Al-Khowârizmî's work became known in Europe in the twelfth century, but it is likely that Fibonacci's contact with it was through the work of Abû Kâmil. The interest given to Fibonacci's work in algebra may be judged by the fact that he was summoned to the court of the Emperor Frederick II where a certain Master John of Palermo challenged him to a mathematical tournament. One of the problems proposed by John of Palermo was to solve the equation $x^3 + 2x^2 + 10x = 20$. Fibonacci's answer, expressed in sexagesimals, was as follows: $x = 1^0\ 22'\ 7''\ 42'''\ 33^{iv}\ 4^{v}\ 40^{vi}$. Another of the questions was to find a number such that if 5 be added to its square, or if 5 be subtracted from its square, the resulting sum and difference will both be square numbers. The third problem was widely copied by later writers:

Three men agree to share a certain sum of money, their shares to be in the ratios $\frac{1}{2}$, $\frac{1}{3}$, and $\frac{1}{6}$. But while they were making the division, they were surprised by an enemy and each snatched what he could. Later the first man gave up half of what he had, the second gave up one third, and the third one sixth. This money was then divided among them equally and each then had the share to which he was entitled. What was the total sum?

The problem is indeterminate, the smallest sum being **47.** The question is perplexing enough even with modern symbolism and the fact that Fibonacci was able to find an answer is an index of his ability in algebraic analysis.

* This question is discussed by Solomon Gandz in an article entitled "The Origin of the Term *Algebra*," *American Mathematical Monthly*, xxxiii, 437.

† See Daoud Kasir, *The Algebra of Omar Khayyám*, New York, 1931.

Another of the thirteenth-century writers on algebra was Jordanus Nemorarius, a German contemporary of Fibonacci, whose book bore the significant title *De Numeris Datis* (Concerning Given Numbers).

During the next centuries, progress in algebra was relatively small and the writers whose work showed the greatest promise were unappreciated by men of their time. Nicole Oresme (1360), a Norman ecclesiastic, worked with fractional exponents and made other contributions of note, but his work seems to have had little influence. A century later, Nicolas Chuquet (1484) wrote on rational and irrational numbers and on the theory of equations. It is interesting to note that the recently discovered *Arithmetic* of Jehan Adam (1475) resembles Chuquet's *Triparty* in certain important respects. Both writers lived in Paris, they wrote within a decade of each other, each carried numeration to trillions (Jehan Adam writing it as *trimillion*), and each speaks of a Master Bartholomew whose work is as yet unknown except for these references.* The debt of these writers to their contemporary can only be conjectured.

The increased facility of communication that came with the invention of printing was accompanied by great activity in mathematics. The formation of burgher schools for the education of merchants led to the writing of textbooks in the different vernaculars. It also resulted in the partial separation of arithmetic and algebra.

The study of the works on elementary mathematics printed in the sixteenth century shows the progress of algebra from a period in which everything was written in words with only a few abbreviations to a time when the work appears in much the same form as that in which we see it to-day. The force of this assertion will be the more apparent when we have considered the history of the methods and symbols of algebra in greater detail.

* Lynn Thorndike, "The Arithmetic of Jehan Adam, 1475 A.D." *American Mathematical Monthly*, XXXIII, 24–28.

SYMBOLS USED IN ALGEBRA

Importance of Symbols in Algebra. Any one who is perplexed by the apparent slowness of the progress of algebra should consider the tools which the writers of each generation had at their command. For example, try solving the problem that Master John of Palermo set for Fibonacci, remembering that Fibonacci was acquainted with Hindu-Arabic numerals, but that he had no symbols for operations, no equality sign, and no way of representing unknowns except by the word *res*. Such an exercise will be sufficient test of the statement that progress in algebra is largely dependent upon its symbolism.

Diversity of Symbols. It seems at first to be logical and inevitable that mathematicians should adopt a unified symbolism for expressing universally accepted ideas. This, however, is not the case. The lack of uniformity even in commonly used symbols is shown by the fact that England, France, and the United States have three different methods of writing decimal fractions; certain countries including those in Scandinavia, tend to denote subtraction by the sign ÷; and continental Europe uses the sign : for division where we commonly use ÷. Furthermore, the symbolism in vogue in a single country occasionally contains two methods of denoting the same thing, as is the case in our radical and exponential notations.

The causes of this diversity and duplication can be discovered only through a study of the evolution of these symbols and through a survey of the chance nature of the selection that retained some forms and discarded others.

Influence of Chance in the Development of Symbolism. The development of symbols has been haphazard. Each writer has copied what he wished from the work of his predecessors and contemporaries with no basis for selection other than personal preference or the necessity of conforming to the restrictions imposed by his printer. For example, Albert (1541) used $-/-$ for a plus sign, evidently copying Widman's $+$. Stevin (1585) attempted to borrow Bombelli's notation

for the unknown quantity in an equation but substituted ①
for ⨄. Professor Cajori describes the result as "a mosaic of
individual signs of rejected systems." *

The influence of chance in the history of symbolism is
illustrated in the case of the sign ÷ which was used to denote
division by Rahn (1659), a Swiss mathematician, writing in
German. His work was never popular in Germany, and the
persistence of the sign is due to the vogue of an English translation of his book made nearly thirty years later. The use of
the same sign with the meaning of subtraction can be traced
to the popular writer Adam Riese (1525). A comparison of
the influence of the two men would naturally have led one to
predict that the sign would have retained the meaning that
the prominent German gave it rather than the one used by
the obscure Swiss.

Conscious Efforts to Improve Symbolism. Even in cases
in which considerable experimentation with symbols has been
made, it is impossible to foresee the exigencies arising from
new developments in mathematical theory. New concepts
may require the combination of symbols already adopted or
they may necessitate the generalization of old ideas. Nevertheless, the efforts to unify symbolism are interesting.

No one was more active in the attempt to attain a convenient and practical symbolism than was Leibniz (1646–
1716). He experimented for years with different notations
not only for the calculus, but also for multiplication, equality,
and the like. His correspondence with Jean Bernoulli contains many references to the comparative advantages of
various signs and he seems to have been particularly anxious
to develop a symbolism that would be easy to print. For this
reason, he preferred to write fractions in the horizontal form
$a:b$ rather than in the vertical form $\frac{a}{b}$.

Rivals of Present Symbolism. In studying the evolution
of present-day symbolism, it should be remembered that the

* For this and other details see Cajori, *Notations*.

introduction of a sign destined to survive was no signal for its
immediate use by the writer's contemporaries, nor did it
mean that no other symbols were to be suggested.   For example, Descartes (1596–1650) used the sign ∞ for equality.
His Dutch followers adopted it, and if Recorde's = had not
been used by Newton and Leibniz, it is possible that Descartes's symbol would have superseded the more expressive
one of the English writer.

Plus and Minus Signs.   In the Ahmes Papyrus (*c.* 1650
B.C.), addition is indicated by the sign ⟋⟋ and subtraction
by ⟍. Diophantus (*c.* 275) wrote quantities that were to
be added side by side and he indicated subtraction by the
sign ⋀ .   Sir Thomas Heath is of the opinion that this symbol for subtraction is composed of the two initial letters of
the Greek word meaning "wanting."   The peculiar form of
this symbol is due to the fact that the two letters written
side by side would have a numerical value, accordingly ⋀
and I were combined to give ⋀ .

The first appearance of the signs + and − in print is in a
book by Widman published in Leipzig in 1489.   The first
problem in which these signs are used asked the value of 13
barrels of figs at 4$\frac{1}{8}$ florins a hundred weight, the weight of
the barrels being 4 ct. + 5 lb., 4 ct. − 17 lb., 3 ct. + 36 lb., etc.
The symbols also appear in the solution of problems by the
Rule of False Position to show whether the results of the
substitution of the trial numbers are too large or too small.

Origin of the Signs + and −.   De Morgan * advanced the
theory that the signs + and − were marks used in warehouses
to show the difference in pounds between the weight of a cask
or barrel and the nearest hundredweight.   J. W. L. Glaisher,†
on the other hand, believes them to be algebraic symbols
whose use was later extended to arithmetic.   This hypothesis
is interesting in view of the fact that to-day these signs are

---

* *Transactions of the Cambridge Philosophical Society,* XI, 205.

† "On the Early History of the Signs + and − and on the Early German
Arithmeticians," *Messenger of Mathematics,* LI, 1921–22.

seldom used in commercial computation, their main applications being in algebra and in denoting the limits of error of a measurement or the fluctuations of prices on the stock market.

WIDMAN'S USE OF THE SYMBOLS + AND −

From *Behēde vnd hubsche Rechnung*, Leipzig, 1489.
Courtesy of the British Museum.

In support of his theory, Dr. Glaisher asserts that no problems containing data comparable to Widman's barrels weighing 4 cwt. − 17 lb. occur in Italian arithmetics although Italian commercial usage was at that time the model for the rest of Europe. Furthermore, a Latin manuscript on algebra known

o have been in Widman's possession contains both signs.
Dr. Glaisher concludes that Widman adopted the signs of the
now unknown author of the algebra and used them to indicate
excess or deficiency in both the Rule of False and in denominate numbers and he is of the opinion that problems of the
ype of the barrels of figs were invented simply to illustrate
he use of these symbols.

The plus sign itself may be a contraction of the Latin *et*
which was frequently used to indicate addition. The minus
sign may be contracted from the $\overline{m}$ which was one of the abbreviations for *minus*, or it may be analogous to the bar writ-
en over a letter to indicate the omission of another letter,
usually *m* or an *n*.

METHODS OF INDICATING PLUS AND MINUS

By words, initials, and abbreviations

			plus	minus
1202	Fibonacci	(Italy)	plus	minus
1494	Pacioli	(Italy)	$\bar{p}$.	$\overline{m}$.
1549	Peletier	(France)	plus	moins
			p.	m.
1556	Tartaglia	(Italy)	piu	men
1583	Clavius	(German writ-	P	M
	(Arithmetic)	ing in Italy)		

By symbols

			plus	minus
1489	Widman	(Germany)	+	−
1522	Riese	"	+	÷
c. 1542	Recorde	(England)	+	−
1568	Baker	"	×	−
c. 1590	Vieta	(France)	·	= *
1608	Clavius	(German)	+	−

The Extension of the Use of the Signs $+$ and $-$. It is
probable that the use of these signs was at first limited to
denoting excess or deficiency; that they were adopted by
German writers and extended to show addition and subtraction of algebraic numbers; but that it was not until nearly

* With Vieta, $a = b$ meant the absolute value of $a - b$, i.e., $a - b$ for $a > b$
but $b - a$ for $a > b$. Descartes (1637) used the symbol · to mean plus or
minus, but Oughtred (1631) combined the $+$ and $-$ signs as we do to-day.

fifty years after their publication by Widman that they were
used to indicate the operations of addition and subtraction in
arithmetic. In Italy, the use of the words *plus* and *minus*
and of their initial letters instead of symbols persisted for
at least a century after the publication of Widman's work.
The signs + and − were introduced into England by Robert
Recorde, but both in England and in France other symbols
were subsequently suggested by influential writers.

THE USE OF SIGNS − AND +

1489	Widman	excess or deficiency
1514	Van der Hoecke	algebraic polynomials
1525	Rudolff	rules of signs for multiplication
1536	Wälckl	operations of addition and subtraction
1545	Stifel	use of signs made popular

Signs for Multiplication and Division. The use of the sign
× for multiplication is probably due to Oughtred, who may
have adapted it from the guide lines used by many authors in
their work in fractions and in the Rule of False Position.
Leibniz objected to this notation with the plea that the sign
× was easily confused with the unknown quantity x. Of the
six signs for multiplication with which Leibniz experimented,
the dot and the × are the only ones used extensively to-day.
The others were ⌒ , ; and * .

The use of a horizontal bar to indicate division has been
discussed under the topic of arithmetic fractions. The bar
was omitted by Fibonacci who merely wrote one number
above the other. Like numerical fractions, algebraic fractions show the use of the horizontal bar about the time
of the invention of printing. A manuscript dating from
about 1460, now in Munich, for example, gives the fraction
$\dfrac{12x + 45}{x^2 + 3x}$ in the form $\dfrac{12 \text{ res et } 45}{1 \text{ census et } 3 \text{ res}}$. Leibniz, as has been
noted previously, preferred the colon (:) to the fractional
form of indicating division. The sign ÷ is of comparatively
late use, dating from the latter half of the seventeenth
century.

Equations.   The various methods of writing equations may best be studied piecemeal by considering methods of indicating relationships and methods of indicating an unknown quantity and its powers.   This plan will be followed here.   It should be noted, however, that equations were generally arranged in a horizontal line as we write them to-day.   In a few cases, however, as in the work of the Hindu writers, the two parts of an equation are written one beneath the other, corresponding terms being in the same column.

The study of the evolution of our present methods of writing equations gives an excellent basis for appreciating the comment made by J. W. L. Glaisher:

No one could have imagined that such "trumpery tricks of abbreviation"........ could have led to the creation of a language so powerful that it has actually itself become an instrument of research which can point the way to future progress.

METHODS OF REPRESENTING EQUALITY *

c. 275	ι^σ	Diophantus.	In all probability, this sign is derived from the word *isos*, "equal."

Middle Ages *aequalis* and also *ae*.

1557	=	Recorde
1559	[	Buteo
1575	‖	Xylander
1634	2|2 also ⊔	Hérigone †
1637	∝	Descartes
c. 1680	⌐ and =	Leibniz

The Sign of Equality.   The sign = is the invention of Robert Recorde (1557), who said, "I will sette as I doe often in woorke vse, a pair of paralleles, or Gemowe (i.e., twin) lines of one lengthe, thus ══, bicause noe. 2. thynges can be moare

---

* This list is meant to be suggestive of the many schemes used rather than to be a complete catalogue of the various devices.

† This writer also used 3|2 and 2|3 to signify "is greater than" and "is less than," respectively.

𝔥𝔬𝔴𝔟𝔢𝔦𝔱,𝔣𝔬𝔷 𝔢𝔞𝔣𝔦𝔠 𝔞𝔩𝔱𝔢𝔯𝔞𝔱𝔦ô 𝔬𝔣 *equations.* 𝔍 𝔴𝔦𝔩𝔩 𝔭𝔷𝔬𝔯
𝔭𝔬𝔲𝔫𝔡𝔢 𝔞 𝔣𝔢𝔴𝔢 𝔢𝔯𝔞𝔭𝔩𝔢𝔰,𝔟𝔦𝔠𝔞𝔲𝔣𝔢 𝔱𝔥𝔢 𝔢𝔯𝔱𝔯𝔞𝔠𝔦𝔬𝔫 𝔬𝔣 𝔱𝔥𝔢𝔦𝔯
𝔯𝔬𝔬𝔱𝔢𝔰,𝔪𝔞𝔦𝔢 𝔱𝔥𝔢 𝔪𝔬𝔷𝔢 𝔞𝔭𝔱𝔩𝔶 𝔟𝔢𝔠 𝔴𝔷𝔬𝔲𝔤𝔥𝔱𝔢. 𝔞𝔫𝔡 𝔱𝔬 𝔞𝔯
𝔲𝔬𝔦𝔡𝔢 𝔱𝔥𝔢 𝔱𝔢𝔡𝔦𝔬𝔲𝔣𝔢 𝔯𝔢𝔭𝔢𝔱𝔦𝔱𝔦𝔬𝔫 𝔬𝔣 𝔱𝔥𝔢𝔣𝔢 𝔴𝔬𝔬𝔷𝔡𝔢𝔰 : 𝔦𝔰 𝔠𝔯
𝔮𝔲𝔞𝔩𝔩𝔢 𝔱𝔬 : 𝔍 𝔴𝔦𝔩𝔩 𝔣𝔢𝔱𝔱𝔢 𝔞𝔰 𝔍 𝔡𝔬𝔢 𝔬𝔣𝔱𝔢𝔫 𝔦𝔫 𝔴𝔬𝔬𝔷𝔨𝔢 𝔟𝔣𝔢,𝔞
𝔭𝔞𝔦𝔯𝔢 𝔬𝔣 𝔭𝔞𝔯𝔞𝔩𝔩𝔢𝔩𝔢𝔰,𝔬𝔷 𝔊𝔢𝔪𝔬𝔴𝔢 𝔩𝔦𝔫𝔢𝔰 𝔬𝔣 𝔬𝔫𝔢 𝔩𝔢𝔫𝔤𝔱𝔥𝔠,
𝔱𝔥𝔲𝔰:════════,𝔟𝔦𝔠𝔞𝔲𝔣𝔢 𝔫𝔬𝔢.2. 𝔱𝔥𝔶𝔫𝔤𝔢𝔰,𝔠𝔞𝔫 𝔟𝔢 𝔪𝔬𝔞𝔯𝔢
𝔢𝔮𝔲𝔞𝔩𝔩𝔢. 𝔞𝔫𝔡 𝔫𝔬𝔴 𝔪𝔞𝔯𝔨𝔢 𝔱𝔥𝔢𝔣𝔢 𝔫𝔬𝔪𝔟𝔢𝔯𝔰.

$$14.z\!\!\!/\!\!-\!\!-\!\!-.15.\text{\textit{9}}======71.\text{\textit{9}}.$$

$$20.z\!\!\!/\!\!-\!\!-\!\!-.18.\text{\textit{9}}=====.102.\text{\textit{9}}.$$

$$26.z\!\!/\!\!-\!\!-\!\!+\!\!-\!\!-10z\!\!\!/\!\!=====9.z\!\!/\!\!-\!\!-\!\!-10z\!\!\!/\!\!-\!\!-\!\!+\!\!-213.\text{\textit{9}}.$$

THE SIGN OF EQUALITY

From Robert Recorde, *Whetstone of witte*, London, 1557.

equalle." * In spite of its simplicity, this sign was not widely
accepted at the time. Indeed, Cajori states that it did not
again appear in print until 1618.† The accompanying table
shows other symbols that were used subsequently by writers
of importance. The survival of the sign = may be due in part
to its simplicity but it is more probably due to the tremendous
vogue of Recorde's textbooks.

Symbols of Inequality. Oughtred (1631) used the symbols
⊏ and ⊐ with the meaning "is greater than" and "is less
than." These symbols continued in use for at least a century,
as is witnessed by their presence in notebooks kept by students
at Harvard in 1730 and 1739.‡ Prior to the publication of
Oughtred's work, however, Thomas Harriot had begun the

* Professor Cajori notes that the same sign appears on a page of lecture
notes written at Bologna prior to 1568. Thus the symbol seems to be the
almost simultaneous invention of independent workers.

† Cajori, *Notations*, i, 298.

‡ Facsimiles of pages in which these are in use in these notebooks are given
in *The Introduction of Algebra into American Schools in the Eighteenth Century*,
by Lao G. Simons, Washington, 1924.

use of the signs $>$ and $<$. Harriot (1560–1621) is particularly interesting for the fact that as a young man he went to
Virginia with an expedition sent out by Sir Walter Raleigh.
During the brief stay of the would-be-colonists, Harriot made
a survey of the surrounding country and, on his return to
England, published a report of this work. He also was an
astronomer of considerable note. His algebra which was
printed posthumously in 1631 contained several novel features, as, for example, the use of consonants for known
quantities and vowels for unknown quantities.

Unknown Quantities. All types of symbolism are represented in the ways of denoting unknown quantities. One
method was by words. Thus Ahmes referred to a "quantity"
or a "heap." * Al-Khowârizmî spoke of the first power of the
unknown as a "root" and the second power as a "square."
Fibonacci translated the Arabic names into *radix* and *quad-
ratus* and used *cubus numerus* for the third power. Later
Italian writers sometimes used *res* or *cosa* ("thing"), *censo*,
and *cubus* while German mathematicians used *Coss*, *Zenso*,
and *Cubus* for x, x^2, and x^3. As would be expected, these
words were soon abbreviated and the abbreviations and
initial letters were conventionalized into distinctive forms.
Diophantus used symbols made of the initial letters of the
words for number, power, and cube. The accompanying
table shows how these symbols were combined to indicate
higher powers.

Pictorial representation was attempted by several writers.
Ghaligai (1521) used c^0 (from *cosa*) for x, and $\square$ for x^2. Buteo
(1559) included the third power using ϱ, $\diamondsuit$, and $\square$. These
symbols were clumsy and could not be adapted to the repre-
sentation of higher powers.

The Use of Exponents. The use of numbers to indicate
powers of an unknown quantity antedated the use of literal
coefficients and of several unknown quantities. Accordingly,

* The word "'hὡ" is generally given as the equivalent of the hieroglyph in
the Ahmes Papyrus.

The Representation of Unknown Quantities

By abbreviations and initial letters:

c. 275   Diophantus (M̊) S, Δ^Y, K^Y, $\Delta^Y\Delta$, ΔK^Y ....*

   1494   Pacioli n^o, q̄drat^o

   1514   Vander Hoecke (N) Pri., Se.

   1545   Cardan   reb^s cub^s

   1551   Scheubel   R, Pri., Sec., Ter.

c. 1590   Vieta   N, Q., C., QQ.,... used in equations
                                               having numerical co-
                                               efficients.

By symbols:

   1521   Ghaligai   ɕ° ▢ ▭

   1525   Rudolff   φ ʒɹ ϫ ɾ ϫϫ β

   1554   Peletier   ℞, ξ, ϙ,   ξξ, β,

   1559   Buteo   ρ, ◇, ▢.

By exponents with no base given:

   1484   Chuquet 12°, 12^1, 12^2.... for 12, 12x, $12x^2$

   1572   Bombelli   ①, ②, ③ .... written above the co-
                                              efficient.

   1585   Stevin   ①, ②, ③, ... written above the co-
                                              efficient.

c. 1619   Bürgi   i, ii, iii, iv,... written above the co-
                                              efficient.

By exponents with the base given:

c. 1590   Vieta   a, a quad.,....

   1631   Harriot   a, aa, aaa.....

   1634   Hérigone   a, a2, a3, a4 ....

   1637   Descartes   x, xx, x^3, x^4 ....

* The symbols used by Diophantus were probably abbreviations of Greek
words meaning "unit," "number," "power," "cube." Higher powers were
represented by combinations of these symbols.

The symbols inclosed in parentheses were used to show the lack of an unknown numerical coefficient.

the base could be omitted and a number placed in some specified position indicated that the unknown was raised to that power. Thus Chuquet (1484) wrote the index of the power next to the numerical coefficient as we would write an exponent. Bombelli (1572) placed the index number in an arc above the coefficient. Stevin (1585) modified this symbol by inclosing the index figure in a circle, a notation which he also used for decimal fractions. Romanus (1593), perhaps to avoid casting new type, used an index inclosed by parentheses with a horizontal line above and below — thus $(\overline{45})$ meant x^{45}. Thomas Digges (1579) wrote an exponent by laying the index number on its side above the coefficient and drawing a line through it. Bürgi (c. 1619) wrote the index as a Roman numeral above the coefficient. These symbols belong in the main to the sixteenth century.

During the next hundred years, these ideas were modified, for literal coefficients were being introduced and several variables were needed. Girard (1629) used Stevin's notation suggesting that a $\odot$ placed at the left of a number indicated a power of that number, but placed at the right meant a power of x. Hérigone (1634) wrote coefficients and exponents in the same line. Thus $2b4$ meant $2b^4$. The Scotchman Hume, writing in Paris in 1635, used Roman numerals without any base to represent powers of the unknowns, but a year later he wrote both base and exponent.

Descartes (1637) introduced the use of Hindu-Arabic numerals as exponents, but in geometry he used A, Aq, Ac, and in algebra he wrote a, aa, a^3, a^4, etc. The use of a repeated letter for the second power of the unknown continued for many years, although Leibniz and Pascal adopted the x^2 notation at once. Gauss (c. 1800), however, preferred to write this as xx on the plea that the repeated letter occupied no more space than did x^2. The symbolism used by Descartes permitted the extension of the idea of exponents to numbers that were negative, fractional, and imaginary. Of the various notations this one was best adapted to such a generalization.

The ways of representing unknown quantities and exponents were at first identical. Prior to the sixteenth century and indeed during it, there was wide use of the initial letters of the words for *quantity*, *side*, and *square*. During the sixteenth century, there was a growing practice of using a numerical exponent without expressing the base. From the seventeenth century on, the base was generally written because the use of literal coefficients demands a means of expressing powers of these quantities as well as of unknowns.

The important steps in the use of exponents may be summarized as follows:

c. 225 B.C.	Archimedes	Use of law $a^n \cdot a^m = a^{n+m}$.
c. 1380	Oresme	Use of exponents $\frac{1}{2}2^p$ meaning $2^{\frac{1}{2}}$.
1484	Chuquet	Negative exponents $.9.^3\tilde{m}$ meaning $9\ x^{-3}$.
1544	Stifel	Laws for positive and negative integral exponents.
1572	Bombelli	Use of exponents to express powers of unknowns.
1585	Stevin	Use of fractional exponents.
1629	Girard	Use of fractional exponents. $\sqrt[6]{2000}$ written as $(\frac{1}{6})2000$
1655	Wallis	Explanation of the theory including negative exponents.
1676	Newton	Use of negative and fractional exponents in correspondence with the secretary of the Royal Society.

Radical Signs and Signs of Aggregation. Radical signs seem to have been derived from either the capital letter R or from its lower case form, the former being preferred by Italian writers and the latter by those of northern Europe.

Before the addition of the horizontal bar which showed the terms affected by the radical sign, various symbols of aggregation were developed. Stevin (1585) used a symbol of separation also. In his notation $\sqrt{9}②$ meant $\sqrt{9x^2}$, while $\sqrt{9})②$ meant $\sqrt{9}x^2$. In the early part of the seventeenth century,

parentheses were commonly used as signs of aggregation and
in the next hundred years the radical sign as we now know
it was well standardized.

VARIANTS OF THE RADICAL SIGN

Capital letter form:	Square Root	Other Roots
1484 Chuquet	R, R^2	R^3 R^4
1494 Pacioli	R. 2^a	R. 3^a
1521 Ghaligai	$R\square$	$R \square\square$
1539 Cardan	R	cu. R
1572 Bombelli	R. q.	R. c.

Small letter form:

1521 Rudolff	$\sqrt{}$	c$\sqrt{}\sqrt{}$ or $\bigwedge$
1553 Stifel	$\smile\!/$	$Z\!\!/$ $Z\!\!/$
1585 Stevin	$\sqrt{}$	$\sqrt{}$③	W
1707 Newton	$\sqrt{}$	$\sqrt{}^3$	$\sqrt{}^4$

ROOTS OF ALGEBRAIC POLYNOMIALS

1202 Fibonacci	radix de 4 et radix de 13	$\left(\sqrt{4}+\sqrt{13}\right)$
1539 Cardan	R V: cu. R 108 p:10	$\sqrt{\sqrt[3]{108}+10}$
1554 Peletier	$\sqrt{}\ 15\ p.\ \sqrt{}8,$	$\sqrt{15+\sqrt{8}}$
1556 Tartaglia	R V (R 20 min R 12)	$\sqrt{\sqrt{24}-\sqrt{12}}$
1572 Bombelli	R.q.L 20.m. $\overset{1}{6}$ p. $\overset{2}{1}$ ⌐	$\sqrt{20-6x+x^2}$
1577 Gosselin	LVL 10 PL 5	$\sqrt{\sqrt{10}+\sqrt{5}}$
1585 Stevin	$\sqrt{}$ bino $2+\sqrt{}3$	$\sqrt{2+\sqrt{3}}$
1608 Clavius	$\sqrt{}$ $(22+\sqrt{}9)$	$\sqrt{22+\sqrt{9}}$
1637 Descartes	$\sqrt{}$ C. $\frac{1}{2}$q $+\sqrt{\frac{1}{4}qq-\frac{1}{27}p^3}$	
		$\sqrt[3]{\frac{1}{2}q+\sqrt{\frac{1}{4}q^2-\frac{1}{27}p^3}}$

The RV notation is derived from the words *radix universalis*: the LV
comes from *latus universalis*, terms which are self-explanatory.

THE TOOLS OF ALGEBRA

The Rule of False Position. The equations of the Ahmes
Papyrus seem to have been solved by the method which was
later known in Europe as the Rule of False Position. The
operation of this rule was simple. To solve the equation
$x + \frac{1}{7}x = 19$, the unknown number x is assumed to be 7.
Then the sum of the number and its seventh part will be 8,
and the number of the equation is the same multiple of 7 that
19 is of the guessed number 8. This method was known to
the Hindus and to the Arabs, and it appeared in textbooks in
elementary algebra until the middle of the nineteenth century.

The simplicity of the rule when it was applied to problems
involving fractions is shown by an example from Trenchant's
work of 1566. This problem states that a cistern may be
emptied by each of three pipes in 2, 3, and 4 hours respectively. It asks the number of hours needed if all three
pipes are opened at once. The solution is as follows: If the
time were 12 hours, the first pipe would empty the cistern 6
times, the second 4 times, and the third 3 times. Thus in
12 hours, the pipes would empty the cistern 13 times. Ac-
cordingly, they would empty it once in $\frac{12}{13}$ hours or in $55\frac{5}{13}$
minutes.

The Rule of Double False. A variant of the Rule of False
necessitated making two trials and noting the error due to
each. It was applied to the solution of many types of problems, one of which indicates the general plan of the group.
This particular problem and its solution are from Robert
Recorde's *Grovnd of Artes* (*c.* 1542).

One man said to another, I think you had this year two thousand
Lambes: so had I said the other; but what with paying the tythe
of them, and then the several losses they are much abated: for at
one time I lost half as many as I have now left, and at another time
the third part of so many, and the third time ¼ so many. Now
guesse you how many are left.

It was clear that after the tithe was deducted, 1800 lambs
were left. If the man had had 12 at the end, he would have

had $12 + 6 + 4 + 3$ or 25 at the beginning. This is 1775 too
few. On the other hand, if he had 24 at the end, he would
have had $24 + 12 + 8 + 6$ or 50 at the end which again is 1750
too few. The guesses and errors are then written down and
the cross-products are found by multiplying along the guide
lines thus:

Then the difference of these products is divided by the difference of the guesses and the quotient is the required number.
In this case it is

$$\frac{42600 - 21000}{1775 - 1750} = \frac{21600}{25} = 864.$$

The form of the work is important in the development of
symbolism for the guide lines may be the origin of the sign $\times$
for multiplication, and the principal occasion for the use of the
signs $+$ and $-$ for many years was to indicate whether the
errors in the Rule of False exceeded the true amount or fell
short of it.

The name of this process was considered misleading and
many authors tried to explain the true meaning of the word
"False" as used in this connection. Humphrey Baker (1568)
puts it this way:

The Rule of falsehoode is so named not for that it teacheth anye
deceyte or falsehoode, but that by fayned numbers taken at all
aduentures (*i.e.*, by chance), it teacheth to finde out the true number
that is demaunded, and this of all the vulgar Rules which are in
practice is ye most excellence.

It is stated that Robert Recorde astonished his friends by
proposing difficult questions and by finding the true result
by this rule from the chance answers of "suche children or
ydeotes as happened to be in the place."

Practice in using the Rule of False was provided by problems which contained both the trial numbers and their corresponding errors thus permitting the reader to concentrate his attention on fitting the trials and errors into his scheme for finding the true answer. Humphrey Baker (1568) gives one of these as follows:

A Burgeois would distribute a certayne summe of pence vnto dyuers poore men equally, but after that hee had counted howe manye they were in number, he perceiued that if he should giue vnto euery man 6 d. hee shoulde want 14 pence. But if he should giue every man 5 pence the peece, he should have 9 pence remayning the question is to knowe the number of poor men.

The Rule of False was applied to many types of problems and, as a result, it occupied many pages in the early printed arithmetics. Indeed Gemma Frisius (c. 1540) stated that "These and infinitely many other problems may be solved by the Rule of False; but to list all of these applications would require infinite labor as well as being intolerably wearying." *

The difficulty experienced in dealing with negative numbers gave rise to the practice of citing specific rules for each case: when both products were plus, when both were minus, and when one was plus and the other minus. This offers another illustration of the slowness with which men accepted the idea of new numbers, for if the multiplication and subtraction of negative numbers is understood, a single rule covers all cases.

The Rule of Three. The Rule of Three and its variants, the Inverse Rule of Three, the Rule of Five, and the Rule of Seven, were devices for the mechanical solution of problems in the form:

$$\frac{a}{b} = \frac{c}{x}, \frac{a}{b} = \frac{x}{c}, \frac{ab}{cd} = \frac{e}{x}, \text{ and } \frac{abc}{def} = \frac{g}{x}.$$

* "Haec atque infinita alia exempla licet per Regulam Falsi perficere; quae omnia recensere infiniti laboris ac intolerabilis nausea."

Typical problems read:

If a hundred pounds of cinnamon cost 32 ducats, what will be the value of 987 pounds?

If ten men can cut a meadow in twenty-five days, how many days will it take thirty men to cut it?

A certain king sent thirty men into his orchard to plant trees. If they could set out a thousand trees in nine days, in how many days would thirty-six men set out four thousand four hundred trees? *

Problems of this sort are solved by writing the given information according to fixed rules and following guide lines in combining terms. The rules were frequently given with no explanation of the theory involved. To solve the first problem, one merely learned to write the terms in the given order 100 lbs. —— 32 ducats —— 987 lbs. and to multiply the second and third and divide by the first. In more complicated cases, as in the third example given above, the same type of procedure was followed. Fibonacci's solution reads:

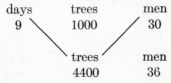

days	trees	men
9	1000	30

trees	men
4400	36

Then the product of 9, 4400, and 30 is divided by the product of 1000 and 36.

Although the Rule of Three was known to the Hindu writer Brahmagupta in the seventh century, and although it was given in great detail and with many applications in the work of Fibonacci (1202), the connection between this rule and the idea of ratio and proportion was not appreciated until toward the close of the fifteenth century. Even then few writers called the reader's attention to the fact. In short, the Rule of Three and its variants belonged to the period in which

* These problems are from the work of Pacioli (1494), Köbel (1514), and Fibonacci (1202). Problems illustrating the same processes may be found in the works of any of the writers on elementary arithmetic and algebra prior to the nineteenth century, and in the work of many people subsequently.

arithmetic devices with their many special cases were preferred to algebraic methods with their clumsy symbolism.

The Solution of Linear Equations. The methods of dealing with linear equations in one unknown that have been outlined in the preceding sections make it evident that, in general, writers advocated arithmetic methods in preference to algebraic ones. It was not until the middle of the sixteenth century that Peletier proposed a "General Rule of Algebra" and this was simply the method of solving problems by setting up an equation and finding its root. The solution of quadratic and cubic equations had taken shape long before writers of elementary texts had reduced the solution of all linear equations in one unknown to a single case. The whole movement is like the experience of a group of clever children who solve simple equations with great facility by trial and error methods of which they are scarcely conscious and who can be brought to the use of algebraic methods only when they encounter difficult cases in which the arithmetic scheme proves too laborious.

Simultaneous Equations. Equations that involve several unknown quantities were known in Egypt, in Greece, and in India. Diophantus (c. 275) gave these quantities the names of "the first number," the "second number," etc., and in his solutions, the first step was to express each quantity in terms of a single quantity. The Chinese seem to have avoided the difficulty by using computing rods to denote the coefficients of the quantities. When these were laid out in parallel columns the position of the rods on the computing board was a sufficient symbol of the unknowns. The Hindus wrote their equations one below the other, using the names of colors to distinguish between the unknowns. In Europe, each variable was expressed in terms of a single quantity until Buteo introduced the use of different letters for the different unknowns and solved the equations by addition and subtraction as we would to-day. This was in 1559. Other writers copied this device, using the letters in the first part of the alphabet until Descartes (1637) abandoned this system and used the final letters of the alphabet for the unknowns thus leaving the first letters to represent literal coefficients.

THE REPRESENTATION OF SEVERAL
UNKNOWN QUANTITIES

1559	Buteo	$A, B, C, \ldots$
c. 1590	Vieta	$a, b, c, \ldots$
1637	Descartes	$x, y, z, \ldots$

One of the first writers to make extensive use of literal coefficients in writing algebraic polynomials and in the statements of problems was Sir Isaac Newton. His *Arithmetica Universalis* (1707) contains many instances of this, none perhaps more striking than the following problem which is quoted from the second edition in English (1728).

If the Number of Oxen a eat up the Meadow b in the Time c; and the Number of Oxen d eat up as good a Piece of Pasture e in the Time f, and the Grass grows uniformly; to find how many Oxen will eat up the like Pasture g in the time h.

Quadratic Equations. Equations of the second degree were solved arithmetically by the Egyptians, geometrically by Euclid and his followers, and algebraically by the Hindus. The Arab writer al-Khowârizmî gave arithmetic rules whose validity was demonstrated by geometric methods and the use of these rules was followed in Europe until, toward the close of the sixteenth century, writers began to consider the solution of general equations with literal coefficients. Even then, zero and negative roots were neglected and the complete solution of the quadratics was not given until negative and irrational and complex numbers had become the common stock-in-trade of the mathematician.

Arithmetic Treatment of Quadratics. The Berlin Papyrus (c. 2160–1700 B.C.) contains instances of quadratic equations that seem to have been solved by the Rule of False. The method of attacking one of them seems to have been substantially as follows:

Given $$x^2 + y^2 = 100$$
and $$y = \tfrac{3}{4}x$$
Then if $x = 1$, $y = \tfrac{3}{4}$ and $x^2 + y^2 = 1 + \tfrac{9}{16} = \tfrac{25}{16}$.
The true value of x is then the square root of $100 \div \tfrac{25}{16}$ or 8.*

Geometric Treatment of Quadratics. A single example will illustrate the character of the geometric solution of quadratics. The idea of using areas for this purpose orig-

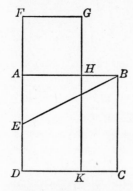

inated with the Pythagoreans and it formed an important part of Euclid's *Elements*. This particular example is Proposition 11, Book II.

To cut a given straight line so that the rectangle contained by the whole line and one of its segments is equal to the square on the remaining segment. That is: to divide a into two parts x and $a - x$ such that $a(a - x) = x^2$.

On the given line AB construct a square $ABCD$. Bisect AD at E and draw EB. Extend AD through A to F making $EF = EB$. On AF construct a square $AFGH$ and extend GH to cut DC at K. Then the rectangle HC equals the square AG.

The proof consists of applying area theorems to the figure. Using modern symbols, this would appear as follows:

Since $AE = ED$, then
$$FGKD = (EF + ED)\,(EF - ED)$$
$$= EF^2 - ED^2$$
$$= EF^2 - AE^2.$$
Therefore $FGKD + AE^2 = EF^2$.
But since $EF = EB$ and since AEB is a right triangle,
$$AB^2 + AE^2 = EB^2 = EF^2.$$
It follows that $AB^2 + AE^2 = FGKD + AE^2$, $AB^2 = FGKD$, and, subtracting, $AH^2 = HBCK$.
In other words, the given line segment AB has been divided

* See also a bibliography by R. C. Archibald in A. B. Chace, *The Rhind Mathematical Papyrus*, Chicago, 1927–1929.

into segments x and $a - x$ such that $x^2 = a \, (a - x)$ and the segment AH is the number x that was required. The study of the figure shows that $x = \sqrt{a^2 + \frac{1}{4}a^2} - \frac{1}{2}a$.

Work of Diophantus. Diophantus may have given a discussion of the solution of a quadratic equation but, if so, this is no longer extant. In working with quadratics, he seems to have used a method of completing the square, but he rejects negative or irrational roots as impossible and uses only one solution even in cases where both are positive and rational.

Algebraic Treatment by the Hindus. In India, quadratics were treated algebraically. Āryabhata (c. 510) was familiar with the equations of the form $ax^2 + bx + c = 0$, but he did not tell how he approached their solution. Brahmagupta (c. 628) solved the equation $x^2 - 10x = -9$ by a rule that is equivalent to the quadratic formula. He multiplied the constant term by the coefficient of x^2, added the square of half the coefficient of x and found the square root of this sum. He then subtracted half the coefficient of x and divided by the coefficient of x^2. The quotient gave the solution of the equation.

The "Hindu Method" was given by Śrīdhara (c. 1020). It consisted of multiplying both sides of the equation by 4 times the coefficient of x^2, adding the square of the original coefficient of x to both sides, and extracting the square root.

Geometric Demonstration of the Algebraic Rule. Al-Khowârizmî (c. 825) classified equations in six divisions according to their form, calling the first power of the unknown a "root," the second power a "square." His classification * is interesting for its detail and for the emphasis it gives to special cases all of which we would put under the two heads: linear equations and quadratics. The six groups are:

squares equal to roots	i.e., $x^2 = 5x$
squares equal to numbers	$x^2 = 9$
roots equal to numbers	$4x = 20$
squares and roots equal to numbers	$x^2 + 10x = 39$
squares and numbers equal to roots	$x^2 + 21 = 10x$
roots and numbers equal to squares	$3x + 4 = x^2$

* See Karpinski, *Al-Khowarizmi*.

Al-Khowârizmî's geometric demonstration of his algebraic rules for solving quadratic equations may be illustrated by his discussion of the solution of the equation $x^2 + 10x = 39$, a problem that was to become the type equation of later discussions. In proving the rule, a square was to be constructed whose side should stand for the unknown quantity. Add to each side of this square a rectangle equal to one fourth of the number of given roots (i.e., $\frac{1}{4} \cdot 10$). The figure then represents the expression $x^2 + 10x$ and its value accordingly is 39. By adding four squares of side $2\frac{1}{2}$, the figure is made into a square of area $39 + 25$ or 64. But if the area of a square is 64, its side must be 8. The side of the square, however, is known to be $x + 5$. Accordingly, x must equal 3.

Later Solutions of the Quadratic. Stevin (1585) seems to have been the first to use a single formula for all quadratics. Vieta (c. 1590) reduced a general quadratic to a pure quadratic by an ingenious substitution. His equation reads:

A quad. $+ B2$ in A aequantur Z plano $(x^2 + 2ax = b)$.

Using modern symbols, his work would consist of substituting $u + z$ for x and letting $z = \frac{1}{2}a$. This changes the equation to the form $u = +\frac{1}{2}\sqrt{a^2 - 4b}$ and $x = \frac{1}{2}a + \sqrt{a^2 - 4b}$.

Solution by Factoring. In view of the present emphasis given to the solution of quadratic equations by factoring, it is interesting to note that this method was not used until Harriot's work of 1631. Even in this case, however, the author ignores the factors that give rise to negative roots.

Special Cases of the Cubic Equation. By reason of the difficulty of their solution, cubic equations have a more interesting history than have quadratics. In substance, this subject was known to the Greeks at an early date, as is indicated by the fact that the geometric solution of the equation $x^3 = 2a^3$ constituted one of the three most famous problems of antiquity.

Archimedes (c. 225 B.C.) met with a cubic equation in his work on the segments of a sphere, the problem being to pass a plane through a sphere in such a way that the segments cut off should be in a given ratio. Many years later Diophantus encountered one in finding the sides of a right triangle whose perimeter is a cubic number and whose area and hypotenuse add together to give a square number. The method he used is not known but it is possible that he reduced the equation to a linear one by removing a common factor.

Arab writers contributed solutions of special cases but they seem to have believed that many cubics could not be solved. The Persian poet and algebraist Omar Khayyám (c. 1100) classified thirteen cases of cubics that could be solved, but the treatment of the general case, like that of the quadratic, was delayed until men recognized numbers that were negative, irrational, or complex.

It was perhaps due to Arab influence that John of Palermo challenged Fibonacci to solve the equation

$$x^3 + 2x^2 + 10x = 20$$

in their mathematical contest in the thirteenth century. It is interesting that the first mention of a cubic in Europe after the time of the Greeks should have come in this way, for it was in connection with a mathematical contest that the greatest contribution to the solution of the cubic was made.

The Cardan Controversy. In the early part of the sixteenth century, a mathematician of Bologna, named Scipione del Ferro, solved cubic equations of the form $x^3 + ax = b$, possibly basing his work on Arab sources. He followed the custom of his time in not revealing his method to scholars at large although he told it to his pupil, Antonio Maria Fior. Some twenty years later, Tartaglia and Fior arranged to meet in a mathematical contest. Each was to set thirty problems for the other and the man who solved the greatest number of problems in fifty days was to be considered the victor. Being anxious to defeat Fior and knowing that his opponent had a scheme for solving a particular type of cubic equation, Tartaglia devoted his time to devising a method for solving cubics in which the first degree term was missing. Having done that, he turned his attention to the type which lacked a term of the second degree. According to his own story, he perfected a solution of the equation less than two weeks before the contest. Equipped with two pieces of theory, one which

NICOLO TARTAGLIA
From the collection of Professor David Eugene Smith.

Fior knew and one which he did not know, Tartaglia succeeded in solving all the problems set him by Fior in less than two hours and thus he completely vanquished his opponent.

According to the account given in Ball's *History of Mathematics*, Cardan asked Tartaglia to show him his discovery. Tartaglia refused. Thereupon, Cardan informed him that a wealthy nobleman was interested in it and he arranged a meeting at Milan between the mathematician and his would-be patron. On reaching Milan, Tartaglia found that it was all a hoax, but he was finally persuaded to give Cardan the information he desired, pledging him to secrecy.

JEROME CARDAN
From the collection of Professor David Eugene Smith.

Tartaglia subsequently claimed that he divulged the entire theory. Cardan (1545) then published a treatment of the cubic covering Tartaglia's contributions as well as other points. When Tartaglia protested, Cardan's most capable pupil, Ferrari, entered a claim that Cardan had received his information from Ferro by way of a third party, not Tartaglia, and he accused Tartaglia of plagiarizing work he had had from the same source through Fior. Tartaglia then challenged Cardan to a mathematical duel. Cardan failed to appear but sent Ferrari instead. Whatever may have been the outcome of the duel itself, Ferrari's followers were so acrimonious that Tartaglia counted himself lucky to escape alive.

The method has since been called by Cardan's name, but it is a question whether either man originated it. Tartaglia's statements were often unreliable. Cardan himself was known to be a scoundrel. It seems clear, however, that Cardan made notable additions to the theory, particularly in his treatment of negative roots and his discovery that the sum of the roots of an equation is equal to the coefficient of x^{n-1} with the sign changed provided the coefficient of x^n is unity.

Cardan's Solution of the Cubic. In solving the cubic, Cardan first eliminated terms of the second degree. If the given equation was $x^3 = ax^2 + c$, the substitution was $x = y + \frac{1}{3}a$. If the given equation was $x^3 + ax^2 = c$, the substitution was $x = y - \frac{1}{3}a$. With the equation changed to the form $x^3 + bx = c$, he found the quantities that satisfied the equations $u - v = c$ and $uv = (\frac{b}{3})^3$. Then $x = \sqrt[3]{u} - \sqrt[3]{v}$.*

Other Solutions of the Cubic. Vieta (1615) attacked the cubic in a different manner. He first eliminated the quadratic term of $x^3 + px^2 + qx + r = 0$ by substituting the value $y - \frac{1}{3}p$ for x. He then had an equation in the form $y^3 + 3by = 2c$. By taking $\dfrac{b - z^2}{z}$ as the value of y, he changed the solution to the form $z^6 + 2cz^3 = b^2$ which could be solved for z^3. Hudde (c. 1658) took the important step of letting a letter stand for any number whether positive or negative. In solving $x^3 = qx + r$, he set $x = y + z$, choosing y and z so that $y^3 + z^3 = r$. He then solved for y^3 and z^3 and finally found x.

Equations of Higher Degree. Certain fourth degree equations were solved by the Arabs by the intersection of conics

* For a translation of Cardan's work on the cubic see Smith, *Source Book in Mathematics.*

In 1530, da Coi, an Italian mathematician, challenged Tartaglia to solve certain cubics, thus rousing the Venetian's interest in the matter. Ten years later, da Coi proposed a biquadratic to Cardan. Cardan was unable to solve it, but his pupil Ferrari completed the task and Cardan published his solution in the *Ars Magna* (1545), in which Tartaglia's solution of the cubic also appeared. Vieta (*c.* 1590) and Descartes (1637) added to the subject, as did Simpson (1745).

Having used a cubic in solving a biquadratic, Euler (*c.* 1750) attempted to find a scheme to solve an equation of the fifth degree by means of one of the fourth. Lagrange (*c.* 1780) made an unsuccessful attempt to do this also, but it was later proved that such a solution was impossible for the general equation.

Determinants. The study of determinants seems to have originated simultaneously in Europe and in Japan. In the latter country, Seki Kōwa* used the general idea of determinants in 1683. In 1693 Leibniz employed them to solve simultaneous equations. The formal study of determinants belongs to the eighteenth and nineteenth centuries, contributions to this work having been made by Vandermonde (1735–1796), Laplace, and Lagrange. Gauss (1801) introduced the word *determinant*, and Cauchy summarized the existing knowledge of the subject and introduced the multiplication theorem in 1812.

Theory of Equations. Cardan had noticed certain facts relating to the roots of an equation, but these were not actually stated as theorems until the time of Harriot and Descartes. The latter author was hampered by his difficulty with negative roots, and accordingly his statements read "can have" where later writers were able to say "must have." In the third book of *La Géométrie* (1637) Descartes states:

Every equation can have as many distinct roots (values of the unknown quantity) as the number of dimensions of the unknown quantity in the equation....

* See D. E. Smith and Y. Mikami, *A History of Japanese Mathematics.*

It often happens, however, that some of the roots are false or less than nothing....

It is evident from the above that the sum of an equation having several roots is always divisible by a binomial consisting of the unknown quantity diminished by the value of one of the true roots, or plus the value of one of the false roots.   In this way, the degree of an equation can be lowered....

We can determine also the number of true and false roots that any equation can have, as follows: An equation can have as many true roots as it contains changes of sign from + to − or from − to +; and as many false roots as the number of times two + signs or two − signs are found in succession.*

Descartes then discusses changing false roots to true ones and vice versa by changing alternate signs in the equation. He also shows how to increase or decrease the roots of an equation by a given amount.

The Fundamental Theorem of Algebra.   The theorem that every algebraic equation has a root leads to the corollary that every algebraic equation of the nth degree has n roots. This was first established by Gauss ($c.$ 1799), but the Italian writers of the sixteenth century knew the fact for quadratics, cubics, and fourth-degree equations.   Descartes, as we have seen, said that equations *can* have this number of roots. Attempts at proving the hypothesis were made by Newton, D'Alembert, Euler, and Lagrange.

Arithmetic and Geometric Series in the Ancient World. The presence of geometric progressions on Babylonian tablets ($c.$ 2000 B.C.) and the use of problems involving both arithmetic and geometric progressions in the Ahmes Papyrus, places series among the earliest bits of mathematical theory, not primarily utilitarian, which are now known.   The Egyptian method of multiplying by repeated doubling naturally introduces a geometric series in which the common ratio is 2, and the Ahmes Papyrus includes a problem in which the common ratio is 7.   This problem and a later variant appear on page 210.

The Greeks studied arithmetic progressions by means of

* Smith-Latham, *Descartes*, 159–60.

figurate numbers, and Euclid gave a formula for the sum of a geometric progression also.   Furthermore, the Pythagoreans had arrived at the idea of a harmonic series in connection with their research in music.

Recreations Based on Progressions.   The mystery of a rapidly increasing series is probably responsible for the Arab problem of the caliph who promised the inventor of the chess-board 1 grain of wheat for the first square, 2 for the second, 4 for the third, and so on for the sixty-four squares.   It was a practical European who supplemented this problem by calculating the number of ships needed to carry the grain.

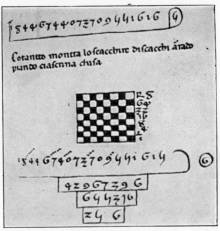

THE CHESSBOARD PROBLEM

From the Columbia Algorism (fourteenth century). The method of pointing off the digits of the result in groups of three should be noted.

The Hindus used progressions as the basis of recreational problems at an earlier date.   These questions were extensively copied by European writers, who seemed to be more interested in mystifying their readers than in giving them training in summing the various series.   The problem of the number of times a clock strikes in twenty-four hours is almost as old as the first clock that struck.   The potato race problem appeared in the sixteenth century under the guise of an egg race, thus antedating the introduction of the potato.   The purchase of a horse at 1, 2, 4, 8,....... pence for each of his thirty-two horseshoe nails is a similar case.   These problems should be contrasted with one from Hindu mathematics; for while the European problem was framed to interest and amuse the reader, the Hindu ones were made to illustrate important properties of progressions. Among the problems given by Bhāskara is the following:

In an expedition to seize his enemy's elephants, a king marched 2 yojanas the first day. Say, intelligent calculator, with what increasing rate of daily march did he proceed, since he reached his foes' city, a distance of 80 yojanas, in a week? *

Progressions and Exponents. The association of progressions with recreations was so well fixed in people's minds that they failed to see other values inherent in them. The parallel arrangement of two series was well known in the sixteenth century, the series generally appearing as follows:

0	1	2	3	4	5	6	7	8	9	10
1	2	4	8	16	32	64	128	256	512	1024

Even in 1484, Chuquet had noticed the fact that the product of two numbers in the lower line lay beneath the sum of the corresponding numbers in the upper line. Rudolff stated this principle explicitly in 1526. Adam Riese used the idea in his solution of the horseshoeing problem. Stifel (1544) called the upper set of numbers *exponents* and extended both series to the left, thus including negative exponents; and he said: "I might write a whole book concerning the marvelous things relating to numbers, but I must refrain and leave these things with eyes closed."

Close as this was to the idea of logarithms, Napier's invention was the result of a very different line of thought. It is an interesting speculation to try to gauge the influence of the recreational aspects of this subject in inhibiting the use of the idea in the earlier invention of logarithms. Had Napier's invention not come when it did, it is highly probable that logarithms would have come by way of Stifel's *exponents*. Even before Napier's work, men were using the ideas of compound interest and annuities about which so much work in

* Colebrooke, *Bhāskara*, 54.

progressions may well be centered, but they paid no attention to these possibilities.

Theoretical Work with Power Series. Euclid had given a formula for the sum of a geometric progression. Archimedes (c. 225 B.C.) had summed the infinite series $1 + \frac{1}{4} + (\frac{1}{4})^2 + \ldots\ldots(\frac{1}{4})^n$. Clavius in 1583 gave a general rule for the sum of n terms. Vieta (c. 1590) gave the formula for the sum of an infinite geometric series. The work with other series is in general beyond the scope of elementary mathematics, but it is interesting to note the steps in the development of the formula for the sum of the mth powers of the first n integers. This may be summarized as follows: squares, Archimedes (c. 225 B.C.); cubes, Nicomachus (c. 100); fourth powers, al-Karkhî (c. 1020); mth powers, Jacques Bernoulli (*Ars conjectandi*, 1713).

The Binomial Theorem. The development of the Binomial Theorem, beginning with Euclid's formula for $(a + b)^2$ and culminating in Abel's proof of the theorem for any value of the exponent, covers a period of over two thousand years. As would be expected, mathematicians were first concerned with finding formulas for the expansions of the various powers. Proofs of these formulas were developed later.

The Pascal Triangle. The array of numbers which gives the coefficients of the exponents of $(a + b)^n$ where n is a positive integer was known to the Chinese in the early fourteenth century. Its first appearance in print in Europe was in a work of Apianus * published in 1527, but it seems to have been invented almost simultaneously by several writers of the sixteenth century. Tartaglia, for example, claimed it as his own. A century later, Jacques Bernoulli (1654–1705) noted the same array of numbers, saying that he wondered that no one had pointed out the properties of this table before his time.

* Petrus Apianus (1495–1552) was professor of astronomy in the University at Ingolstadt in Germany. His work is interesting for the fact that, contrary to the prevailing custom, he taught in the German tongue instead of in Latin. His arithmetic is chiefly important for its use of the triangle mentioned above.

THE FIRST APPEARANCE OF THE PASCAL TRIANGLE IN PRINT
Title-page of the arithmetic of Petrus Apianus, Ingolstadt, 1527.

The writer whose name is given to this series of numbers made no claim to originality, for he says, "I have not given a proof for all of this because others as Hérigone have already treated it, besides the work is self-evident." Pascal, however, used the method of mathematical induction to derive several theorems of importance from this triangle,* and he showed how it might be applied to solving questions in combinations, applying it in particular to the gambling problem proposed by the Chevalier de Méré (see page 200).

Newton's Statement of the Binomial Theorem. Pascal's work had been to draw inferences from a device long used in practice. Newton's contribution was the formulation of a law of whose existence people were not aware. He developed this law while a student at Cambridge, and it has been asserted that, owing to the importance of the discovery, the theorem was carved on his tomb in Westminster Abbey. This appears to be doubtful — at least no vestige of such an inscription appears there to-day.

Newton discovered the Binomial Theorem through the problem of finding the area under the curve $y = (1 - x^2)^{\frac{1}{2}}$. The values for the areas under the curves $y = (1 - x^2)^0$, $y = (1 - x^2)^1$, $y = (1 - x^2)^2$ and $y = (1 - x^2)^3$ had been shown by Wallis† to be $\qquad x - \frac{1}{3}x^3, \qquad x - \frac{2}{3}x^3 + \frac{1}{5}x^5$ and $\qquad\qquad\qquad x - \frac{3}{3}x^3 + \frac{3}{5}x^5 - \frac{1}{7}x^7$.

In previous work, Wallis had made considerable use of general expressions for various formulas, and this may have provided Newton with the suggestion of finding a general expression for these areas from which the area under the curves $(1 - x^2)^{\frac{1}{2}}$, $(1 - x^2)^{\frac{3}{2}}$, and the like, could be calculated. The first term of each expansion was x. The signs were alternately plus and minus. The denominators were in arithmetic progression, and the exponents of the x in each series were in the same progression. It remained to compute the

---

* These are given in his *Traité dv triangle arithmétiqve, avec qvelqves avtres petits traitez svr la mesme matière.* This was written in 1653, but it was not published until 1665. Excerpts from this are given in Smith, *Source Book in Mathematics.*

† This work is found in Wallis's *Arithmetica Infinitorum, Sive Nova Methodus Inquirendi in Curvilineorum Quadraturam, aliaque difficiliora Matheseos Problemata*, Oxford, 1655. Excerpts from the English translation appear in Smith, *Source Book in Mathematics.*

numerators. The general formula for the numerators was found to be the continued product

$$\frac{1}{1} \times \frac{m-0}{1} \times \frac{(m-1)}{2} \times \frac{(m-2)}{3} \times \frac{(m-3)}{4} \times \ldots\ldots$$

where the numerator of the first term was equal to the first fraction; the numerator of the second term, the product of the first two fractions; the numerator of the third, the product of the first three, and so forth.

In 1674, Leibniz mentioned work with infinite series in course of some correspondence with Oldenburg, the secretary of the Royal Society. In reply, Oldenburg told him that other work in the subject was then in progress in England. Leibniz at once asked for information about it, and Newton sent a preliminary statement of his work to Oldenburg in June, 1676. This statement was forwarded to Leibniz, who at once begged for further particulars. Newton then described the course of his discovery in another letter in October of that year.* In the second of these letters, Newton gave something of the history of his work:

This [referring to the work summarized above] was my first entry into these studies; which would surely have slipped from my memory had I not referred to certain notes a few weeks ago.

But when I had learned this, I soon considered that the terms $\overline{1-xx}\vert^{\frac{0}{2}}$, $\overline{1-xx}\vert^{\frac{2}{2}}$, $\overline{1-xx}\vert^{\frac{4}{2}}$, $\overline{1-xx}\vert^{\frac{6}{2}}$, etc., that is, 1, $1-xx$, $1-2xx+x^4$, $1-3xx+3x^4-x^6$, etc., could be interpolated in the same way and areas could be derived from them; and that for this nothing more is required than the omission of the denominators 1, 3, 5, 7, etc., in the terms expressing the areas, that is, the coefficients of the terms of the quantity to be intercalated $\overline{1-xx}\vert^{\frac{1}{2}}$, or $\overline{1-xx}\vert^{\frac{3}{2}}$ or more generally $\overline{1-xx}\vert^{m}$ could be produced by continuous multiplication of the terms of this series
$$m \times \frac{m-1}{2} \times \frac{m-2}{3} \times \ldots.$$

* Both letters appear in their original Latin in the *Commercium Epistolicum*, London, 1712. Translations are given in Smith, *Source Book in Mathematics*. The section quoted here is from this translation.

And therefore (for example) $\overline{1-xx}\rvert^{\frac{1}{2}}$ would amount to $1 - \frac{1}{2}x^2 - \frac{1}{8}x^4 - \frac{1}{16}x^6$ etc., and $\overline{1-xx}\rvert^{\frac{3}{2}}$ would be $1 - \frac{3}{2}x^2 + \frac{3}{8}x^4 + \frac{1}{16}x^6$ etc. And $\overline{1-xx}\rvert^{\frac{1}{3}}$ would be $1 - \frac{1}{3}\,xx - \frac{1}{9}x^4 - \frac{5}{8}x^6$ etc.

Thus the general reduction of radicals into infinite series became known to me through the rule which I set at the beginning of the former letter before I knew the extractions of roots.

As given in the June letter to Oldenburg, the Binomial Theorem was written in the following form:

$$(P+PQ)^{\frac{m}{n}} = P^{\frac{m}{n}} + \frac{m}{n}\,AQ + \frac{m-n}{2\,n}\,BQ + \frac{m-2n}{3\,n}\,CQ$$

$$+ \frac{m-3n}{4\,n}\,DQ + \dots.$$

where A, B, C, D ... stand for the first, second, third, and fourth terms, respectively.

Further Work on the Binomial Theorem. The proof of the Binomial Theorem was developed slowly. Among those who worked on it were Maclaurin (1742), Salvemini (1742), and Kästner (1745), these men treating integral values of the exponent. The work was completed by Euler (1774), who proved the theorem under the proper conditions for fractional exponents, and Abel (c. 1825), who extended the proof to include exponents that are complex.

STEPS IN THE DEVELOPMENT OF THE BINOMIAL THEOREM

c. 300 B.C.	Euclid, expression for the value of $(a+b)^2$
c. A.D. 1100	Omar Khayyám, $(a+b)^4$, $(a+b)^5$, $(a+b)^6$
c. 1300	Chinese writers, diagram for coefficients of $(a+b)^n$ for n a positive integer
1527	Apianus, triangular array for coefficients
1654	Pascal, theorem for positive integral exponents. Other theorems derived from the triangle
1655	Wallis, virtual integration of $\int (1-x^2)^m dx$
1676	Newton, theorem for negative and fractional exponents
1742	Salvemini, proof for integral exponents
1774	Euler, proof of theorem for fractional values of n
c. 1825	Abel, proof of theorem for general value of n

ALGEBRAIC AND TRANSCENDENTAL NUMBERS

Introduction. The study of algebraic equations necessitated one of two things: either the admission that certain equations could not be solved or else the invention of negative, irrational, and complex numbers. For a long time the first of these alternatives was adopted, mathematicians being unaware of the second, and certain equations were considered as being impossible of solution. Gradually, however, the new numbers were admitted into algebra and, this done, the solution of many separate cases could be treated under one general head. It was also assumed that a suitable selection of integral coefficients would make the equation $a_0 + a_1x + a_2x^2 + \ldots + a_nx^n = 0$ have a given number as its root. It developed, however, that certain numbers existed for which this was not the case. Perhaps it would be more exact to state that it later was realized that certain numbers with which people had long been familiar lay beyond the pale of algebraic equations with integral coefficients. For this reason, these particular numbers were given the name "transcendental." Among them were the number π and most of the values of the trigonometric functions. These may be expressed as the limits of certain infinite series, or they may be given decimally to any required degree of accuracy, but they can never appear as the roots of algebraic equations with integral coefficients.

It is the purpose of this section to show the steps by which the various types of algebraic numbers were accepted as a part of the number system and then to outline the efforts to find the value of the number π. Following this, the discovery of a second great transcendental number e will be discussed and, finally, the group of numbers many of which are transcendental which we call logarithms. Trigonometric functions will be treated in Chapter VIII.

Negative numbers. Although the Greeks had invented a geometrical representation for $(a - b)^2$ and for $(a - b)(a + b)$, they had no conception of a negative number, and Diophantus (*c.* 275) called an equation "absurd" if its roots were negative. The Hindus, on the other hand, discussed affirmative and negative quantities as early as the seventh century, when Brahmagupta gave the rules of signs for their operation and distinguished between the two classes of numbers by writing a dot or a small circle over those that were negative. The Arabs added nothing to the knowledge of negative numbers which they obtained from the Hindus.

In Europe, Fibonacci (1225) interpreted the negative answer to a problem that asked for a man's profit by saying, "I will show that this question cannot be solved unless it be conceded that the man might be in debt." Chuquet (1484) gave a negative root to a quadratic. It is true that Cardan (1545) classed numbers as *numeri ueri* (true numbers) and *numeri ficti* (false numbers), but by the close of the sixteenth century negative numbers were no longer considered absurd, and in 1659 Hudde took the final step of allowing a letter in a formula to represent any number whether positive or negative, thus permitting a single rule to cover many special cases.

Irrational Numbers. The Pythagoreans formulated a theory of proportion that applied only to commensurable quantities. Accordingly, the discovery that the length of the diagonal of a square is incommensurable with the length of its side gave rise to a "logical scandal," as the French writer Tannery put it. As a consequence of this discovery, all propositions relating to proportions had to be restricted to commensurable magnitudes, and tradition claims that Hippasus was drowned by his fellow Pythagoreans for speaking of the irrationality of the square root of 2 outside that society. For some time, this was the only known instance of an incommensurable quantity, but the single case was sufficient to hamper the development of geometry by causing scholars to avoid proportions wherever possible. According to Plato, Theodorus (*c.* 425 B.C.) extended the idea of irrationals to include the roots of 3, 5, 6, 7,.... 17. Plato himself added to the theory by showing that a rational number might be the sum of two irrationals, as is the case in dividing a line into the Golden Section. The difficulties of working with incommensurables in geometry were settled by the definition of proportion advocated by Eudoxus, a pupil of Plato (see page 274). Euclid himself (*c.* 300 B.C.) gave a detailed discussion of expressions such as $\sqrt{\sqrt{a} + \sqrt{b}}$.

Thus the subject of irrationals belongs to the theory of numbers, and accordingly it was included in the algebras of the sixteenth century, together with other parts of the Greek *arithmetica*. It had another application, however, in the solution of equations, especially quadratics, and the evaluation of irrationals formed the basis for the topic of approximate mathematics as distinguished from the precise mathematics where all coefficients are rational.

The Name "Surd." The Greek name for irrational numbers, *alogos*, meant "without a ratio" or "without a name." With the Arabs this became a "non-expressible number," and al-Khowârizmî called them "inaudible," a phrase that became *surd* (deaf) in the work of Gherardo of Cremona (*c.* 1150).

The Approximate Value of Irrationals. One important method of approximating the square roots of irrational numbers is due to Heron of Alexandria (*c.* 50). This corresponds to the trial and error method frequently taught in the United States to-day. In brief, it is to divide the given number by the square root of the perfect square nearest the number. The average of the quotient and the divisor is the first approximation. This number is then used as the divisor and the process is repeated as often as is desired.

There were several other methods of finding the approximate value of a surd. Archimedes (*c.* 225 B.C.) seems to have used a formula equivalent to $\sqrt{a^2 \pm b} = a \pm \dfrac{b}{2\,a}$.

Fibonacci found the square root of a number as accurately as he wished by subtracting the next smaller perfect square and dividing the remainder by twice the root of that square. The quotient added to the square root of the lower number gave an approximation to the square root of the original figure. John of Seville (1140), borrowing a device from the Arab writers, added an even number of zeros to the number, found the root of this product, and divided by 1 with half the number of zeros added. Thus if he added $2n$ zeros, he would divide by 10^n. In this way, he virtually found the root to any required number of decimal places.

Approximate Solutions of Quadratic Equations. In solving quadratic equations whose roots were irrational, the Hindu writers had a scheme equivalent to applying the Rule of False Position twice. Chuquet (1484) solved the problem by finding two numbers $\dfrac{a}{c}$ and $\dfrac{b}{d}$, one too large and the other too small. He then used the intermediate fraction $\dfrac{a+b}{c+d}$ as his first approximation. If this was too small and $\dfrac{b}{d}$ too large, his next approximation would be $\dfrac{a+2b}{c+2d}$. On the other hand, if $\dfrac{a+b}{c+d}$ was too large, his next approximation would be the fraction $\dfrac{2a+b}{2c+d}$, which is intermediate between $\dfrac{a}{c}$ and $\dfrac{a+b}{c+d}$. The process could be continued indefinitely. In solving the equation $x^2 + x = 39\frac{13}{81}$, for example, he found that 5 was too small and that 6 was too large. His next approximation, $5\frac{1}{2}$, was too small. He then combined $\frac{11}{2}$ and 6 to find a closer result. The same principle may be applied to the evaluation of square roots.

Approximate Solutions of Equations of Higher Degree. In solving the equation $x^3 + 2x^2 + 10x = 20$, Fibonacci seems to have reasoned that the unknown quantity lay between 1 and 2; for, if it were 1, the value of $x^3 + 2x^2 + 10x$ would be less than 20, while if it were 2, this value would be greater than 20. He then states a value of x in sexagesimals whose value is correct to within 10^{-10}, but he gives no explanation of the method by which he reached this result.

Stevin (1585) used a method of substitution to tell first whether the root of an equation lay between 1 and 10, 10 and 100, 100 and 1000, etc. He then substituted values intermediate between the limits which he had found. The process was a laborious one.

Newton devised a method of finding the root to within one tenth of its true value, and he then changed his equation so that the roots would each be diminished by that quantity. He obtained his next approximation by neglecting all terms of this equation whose degree is higher than the first, and then solving for the unknown quantity. He continued this process until the required degree of accuracy was reached.

Complex Numbers. The square root of a negative number was avoided by many writers, some of whom stated the relations between the coefficients of a problem that would permit the solution of the equation. Cardan (1545) was notable for finding the complex solution of the problem to find two numbers whose sum is 10 and whose product is 40.* He checked his work by multiplication, but he elsewhere called such roots "fictitious" and did nothing to develop them further. Bombelli (1572) and Stevin (1585) spoke of imaginary numbers but did not explain them. Girard (1629), on the other hand, claimed that there were three reasons for considering solutions that were "impossible." These were: for establishing a general rule concerning the roots of an equation, for supplying the lack of other solutions, and for their own usefulness.

Wallis (1673) claimed that the idea of an imaginary quantity was no more unreasonable than that of a negative one. He attempted to explain an imaginary quantity as being the side of a square whose area is negative, and he explained the meaning of the square root of $- bc$ as being the mean proportional between $- b$ and c. It remained for Wessel, a Nor-

* A translation of this particular problem appears in Smith, *Source Book in Mathematics.*

wegian surveyor (1797), to represent these numbers graphically by using a perpendicular to the axis of real numbers at
the origin to represent the square root of negative numbers.
Pure imaginaries were plotted on this axis while the sum or
difference of a real and an imaginary number were indicated
in the various quadrants.*

It is interesting to note in this connection that Leibniz
(1702) characterized imaginaries as "a fine and wonderful
invention of a marvelous mind, almost an amphibian between
things that are and things that are not." †

The symbolism and the names for these quantities were
standardized soon after the numbers were accepted as being
worthy of notice.   Descartes (1637) was the originator of the
words *vraye* (real) and *imaginaire* (imaginary) in this connection.   Euler (1748) used the letter i for $\sqrt{-1}$.   Cauchy
(1821) used the word *conjugate* for the pair of values $a + bi$
and $a - bi$, and the word *modulus* for the distance from the
origin to a point in the complex plane.

Imaginary Roots of an Equation.   The question of the
imaginary roots of an equation was the subject of discussion
by the Academy at Paris in the eighteenth century; but by
the close of this period (1798), when Lagrange summarized
previous investigations, the solution of numerical equations
had been accomplished and mathematicians were able to find
the approximate values of all roots of algebraic equations
that had numerical coefficients.   It is true that refinements of
the process were added by Horner (1819) and by others, but
the problem was virtually completed before 1800.

The Number π.   No part of the arithmetic that deals with
approximations is more interesting than is that which seeks to
find the ratio of the circumference of a circle to its diameter.
This ratio has been studied from both a practical and a
theoretical standpoint.   Under the name of the "quadrature

---

* Translations of pertinent sections of Wessel's memoir and of Horner's
work are given in Smith, *Source Book in Mathematics.*

† "beinahe ein Amphibium zwischen Sein und Nichtsein."

of the circle " it occupied mathematicians for many years, but it was not until the nineteenth century that it was actually proved that the value of π is transcendental. This was done by Lindemann in 1882.

TABLE SHOWING THE APPROXIMATIONS TO THE VALUE OF π

China — Ancient Chinese works.............................. 3 [a]
Egypt — Ahmes Papyrus (*c.* 1650 B.C.)................. 3.1605 [b]
Greece — Archimedes (*c.* 225 B.C.)................... $3\frac{10}{17} - 3\frac{1}{7}$ [c]
    (i.e., between 3.1408 and 3.1428)
    Ptolemy (A.D. *c.* 150)................. 3 8′30″ (3.1416)
Rome — Vitruvius (*c.* 20 B.C.)...................... $3\frac{1}{8}$ (3.1250)
India — Brahmagupta (*c.* 628).................... $\frac{22}{7}$ [d] (3.1428)
    Bhāskara (*c.* 1150).................... $\frac{3927}{1250}$ (3.1255)[e]

Europe (before the invention of decimals) —
    Fibonacci (1220).............................. $\frac{864}{274}$ (3.1418)
    Tycho Brahe (*c.* 1580)........................ $\frac{88}{\sqrt{785}}$ (3.1409)

Europe (after the invention of decimals) —
    van Ceulen (1540–1610)........ π carried to 35 decimal places
    Vega (1756–1802)............. π "   " 140   "   "
    Dase (*d.* 1861)................. π "   " 200   "   "
    Richter (*d.* 1854).............. π "   " 500   "   "
    Shanks (*c.* 1853).............. π "   " 707   "   "

EXPRESSIONS WHICH SHOW THE ARITHMETIC NATURE OF π

Vieta (*c.* 1593)..$\dfrac{2}{\pi} = \sqrt{\frac{1}{2}} \cdot \sqrt{\frac{1}{2} + \frac{1}{2}\sqrt{\frac{1}{2}}} \cdot \sqrt{\frac{1}{2} + \frac{1}{2}\sqrt{\frac{1}{2} + \frac{1}{2}\sqrt{\frac{1}{2}}}} \cdots$

Wallis (1655)..$\dfrac{4}{\pi} = \frac{3}{2} \cdot \frac{3}{4} \cdot \frac{5}{4} \cdot \frac{5}{6} \cdot \frac{7}{6} \cdot \frac{7}{8} \cdot \frac{9}{8} \cdots$

Leibniz (1673)..$\dfrac{\pi}{4} = 1 - \frac{1}{3} + \frac{1}{5} - \frac{1}{7} + \frac{1}{9} - \frac{1}{11} + \cdots$

[a] This is the value given in the *Old Testament* also, as is shown in I Kings, VII, 23: "And he made a molten sea, ten cubits from the one brim to the other; it was round all about ..... and a line of thirty cubits did compass it round about."
[b] The Ahmes Papyrus gives the area of a circle as the square of $\frac{8}{9}$ of the diameter. This is equivalent to giving π the value noted above.
[c] Archimedes obtained his results by considering inscribed and circumscribed polygons of 96 sides each.
[d] Brahmagupta gave 3 as a "practical value."
[e] Bhāskara gave $\sqrt{10}$ for ordinary work.

The symbol π was first used to mean the circumference or periphery of a circle. It appears in this form in Oughtred's *Clavis Mathematicae* (1647 ed.). Other writers copied this, but in 1707 William Jones gave the symbol its present meaning of the ratio of the circumference to the diameter. Euler's adoption of the symbol in 1737 brought it into general use.

The Number *e*. If the problem of squaring the circle had not focussed the interest of mathematicians on the number π, they would have been obliged to find an approximate value for this number because of its importance in other connections. This fact is frequently overlooked, because the experience of both the race and the individual links the value of π with the circle before it makes any bond between it and its other applications. In contrast to π, whose value in mathematics was at first limited to a single problem, the number *e* came into notice through several different channels at about the same time. Certain of these will be outlined here.

A great amount of attention was paid to the study of the compound-interest law in the seventeenth and eighteenth centuries. Oughtred, Halley, Jacques Bernoulli, and Euler were all interested in this matter. It was discovered that the expression $\left(1 + \dfrac{1}{n}\right)^n$ approached a limit as n became infinite. This could be considered as a special case of the compound interest law $A = P\left(1 + \dfrac{r}{n}\right)^{nt}$ where P is the principal, r the interest rate, and n the number of times the interest is compounded yearly for t years. Thus the expression $\left(1 + \dfrac{1}{n}\right)^n$ for $n = \infty$ may be interpreted as being the amount of \$1 invested at 100 per cent in one year, the interest being compounded every instant. The expansion of this binomial may be greatly simplified by consideration of the fact that when n is very large $\dfrac{n-1}{n}, \dfrac{n-2}{n}, \dfrac{n-3}{n}$, etc., are each approximately equal to 1. Thus the expansion

$$1 + \frac{n \cdot 1}{n} + \frac{n(n-1)}{1 \cdot 2\, n^2} + \frac{n(n-1)\,(n-2)}{1 \cdot 2 \cdot 3\, n^3} + \cdots$$

becomes
$$1 + \frac{1}{1} + \frac{1}{2!} + \frac{1}{3!} + \cdots$$

a series whose value is $2.71828\ldots$ to which the letter e has been applied. This symbol was first used by Euler ($c.$ 1727), who developed the formulas $e^z = \left(1 + \dfrac{z}{n}\right)^n$ for $n = \infty$, and $i^i = e^{-\pi/2}$.

Roger Cotes (1682–1716), a brilliant professor at Cambridge, linked exponential and trigonometric functions in a formula which we would write as: $e^{ix} = \cos x + i \sin x$. By substituting π for x, this becomes $e^{\pi i} = -1$, a formula interesting for its combination of artificial numbers.

The quantity e is closely connected with the calculus, and the function $y = e^x$ has the peculiar property that its derivative is e^x also.

Geometrical Considerations. Galileo had supposed that the curve of a flexible chain hung from two fixed points was a parabola; but later writers doubted this conclusion, and in 1690 Jacques Bernoulli proposed the problem of finding the true equation of this curve. This was solved by Leibniz in the following year. In modern symbols the equation reads:

$$y = \frac{a}{z}(e^{\frac{x}{a}} + e^{-\frac{x}{a}}).$$

Other Considerations. The connection of π with a problem that arose naturally in the study of elementary geometry gave this number a popular interest which the number e has never had. In fact, many people think of e as the base of Napier's logarithms and as nothing else — yet Napier used no base in computing his logarithms so this information is completely erroneous. The fact that the number e is transcendental, however, was proved by Hermite [*] in 1873, nine

* 1822–1901. See Smith, *Source Book in Mathematics.*

years earlier than Lindemann's proof of the transcendence of π.

Logarithms.   Until the early part of the seventeenth century, all astronomical computations were performed by arithmetic.   The work of Copernicus and Tycho Brahe * was rendered very laborious through their lack of logarithms. It should be remembered that the first half of the seventeenth century was the period of the invention of the telescope and of the beginning of the more accurate observation that this made possible.   It was also close to the time of Torricelli's † work with the barometer, to Newton's study of the Law of Gravitation, and, in short, to the first contributions to mathematical physics.   It is certain that much of this work would have been delayed had no quick method of computation been invented.

Napier.   Prior to the invention of logarithms, no major contribution to mathematics had been made by any native of Scotland and, with the exception of Michael Scot, to whom Fibonacci addressed his *Liber Abaci*, there had been no notable mathematicians in that country.   John Napier,‡ Laird of Merchiston, was perhaps the least likely of the scholars of the time to produce this work.   He belonged to the landed aristocracy of Scotland.   He was educated in the University of Saint Andrews and perhaps also in France.   He took an active part in the religious and political disturbances of his day, championing the cause of King James, Knox, and Protestantism against Mary Stuart and the Roman Catholic faction, and he supposed that his reputation with posterity would rest on his theological work, *A Plaine Discouery of the whole Reuelation of Saint Iohn*, a volume of which at least ten editions appeared in his own lifetime.

Napier seems to have paid considerable attention to the

* An astronomer working in Denmark, *c.* 1580.

† 1608–1647.   Torricelli was a pupil of Galileo.   He invented the barometer and made contributions to mathematics also.

‡ 1550–1617.   For Napier's life and works, see E. S. Knott, *Napier Tercentenary Memorial Volume*, London, 1915.   This contains essays by Lord Moulton, J. W. L. Glaisher and others to which later reference will be made.

improvement of agriculture. He also contributed to military
science, writing of "devises of sayling under water" and making various war chariots and other infernal engines. His
ability won him notoriety as a magician and various stories
are told to substantiate this point. These are probably pure
fiction, but one of them might well be mentioned to show their
general tenor. It tells that Napier, who was Hereditary

JOHN NAPIER
From the collection of Professor David Eugene Smith.

Poulterer to the king, had a coal-black rooster for his familiar
spirit. Suspecting that one of his servants had been cheating
him, Napier announced that the rooster knew which one was
guilty. He sent the servants one by one into a darkened room
with instructions to pat the rooster, who would then identify
the culprit. The rooster, meantime, had been well coated
with lamp black and the guilty servant, being afraid to touch
him, came out with clean hands.

The Discovery of Logarithms.   Napier's Rods for mechanical multiplication are described elsewhere (see page 339). Their invention was a simple matter, for the idea had been in use for many years in the "Gelosia" multiplication of the Italian writers.   The discovery of logarithms, on the other hand, has long been thought to have been independent of contemporary work, and it has been characterized as standing "isolated, breaking in upon human thought abruptly without borrowing from the work of other intellects or following known lines of mathematical thought."   The study of Clavius's work on Prosthaphaeresis suggests a possible origin for Napier's concept.*   Prosthaphaeresis was a device used by Clavius, Pitiscus (1595) and possibly by others for finding the product of two trigonometric functions by addition formulas.

In an address given at the Napier Tercentenary in 1914, Lord Moulton reconstructed Napier's line of thought in the invention of logarithms.†   It is evident that at first Napier was attempting a simplification of trigonometric computation, for he refers to "sines" rather than to "numbers."   He seems to have begun with the then recently discovered formula

$$\sin A \sin B = \tfrac{1}{2} \left[\cos \left(A - B \right) - \cos \left(A + B \right) \right].$$

The possibility of finding this product by means of the simpler operation of subtraction was undoubtedly the clue that started him on his investigations.   Napier was familiar with the use of an arithmetic series paired with a geometric one in multiplication.   But he realized that the difficulty of any extensive use of this device was that as the exponents increased, the numbers they represented differed by wider and wider intervals.   At this period, however, trigonometric tables gave the series of angles in terms of the length of the

* See Jekuthiel Ginsburg, "Clavius on Prosthaphaeresis" and "Clavius on Prosthaphaeresis as Applied to Trigonometry," in Smith, *Source Book in Mathematics.*

† "The Invention of Logarithms: its Genesis and Growth," *Napier Tercentenary Memorial Volume*, 3.

half chord of a double angle placed in a circle whose radius was 10 000 000. This may have suggested building the geometric series with $1 - \frac{1}{10\ 000\ 000}$ as the common ratio, the difference between successive terms being less and less.

Napier's Definition of Logarithms. From this beginning, Napier passed to the idea of representing numbers and logarithms by the segments of lines cut off by moving points. This represented a great advance over his previous idea, for

NAPIER'S GEOMETRIC DEFINITION OF LOGARITHMS

by it each number whether integral or fractional has a logarithm. In describing this motion, he used two line segments. The point P moves from A to B with a velocity proportional to the distance PB. The motion of the point P' begins simultaneously with that of P. This point moves on the line l from the fixed point A', keeping always a constant velocity which is equal to the initial velocity of the point P. By this motion, a length $A'P'$ corresponds to every length PB. As the velocity of P' is continually decreasing, P never reaches B. The position of P' serves as a counting device for the motion of P and the distance $A'P'$ corresponding to a large value of PB is less than the distance $A'P'$ that corresponds to a small value of PB. It develops that successive values of the segment PB are in geometric progression. Napier's definition of a logarithm states this idea in general terms:

The Logarithme therefore of any sine is a number very neerely expressing the line, which increased equally in the meane time, whiles the line of the whole sine decreased proportionally into that sine, both motions being equal-timed, and the beginning equally swift.

It then developed that if four numbers form a proportion, their logarithms differ by equal amounts. That is, if $a:b = c:d$, $\log a - \log b = \log c - \log d$. Accordingly when the number whose logarithm was 100 had been discovered, it was relatively simple to find the numbers whose logarithms were 200, 300, 400, etc.

Computation of Logarithms. Napier's logarithms were computed in the following manner: The first number of his geometric series was 10 000 000 and the common ratio was $(1 - \frac{1}{10\,000\,000})$ or 0.999 9999. The logarithm of 10 000 000 was 0; the logarithm of (10 000 000 − 1) was 1; that of the next term, 9999998.0000001, was 2; etc. The number whose logarithm was 100 was not precisely 9999900, but it was so close to this number that the proper logarithm could be found by approximation. Since this number differs from 10 000 000 by $\frac{1}{100000}$ of itself, a new geometric series could be formed whose ratio was $(1 - \frac{1}{100\,000})$. The logarithms of these numbers differ by a number equal to the logarithm of the last number. By finding successive terms, the logarithm of 10 000 000 − 5 000 could be determined. This made possible the use of the new ratio $(1 - \frac{1}{2\,000})$, and more terms were computed on this basis.

In making up tables of logarithms, Napier chose the number of his geometric progressions which was closest to the sine of a given angle if the position of the decimal point be disregarded. He then found the logarithm of the sine by interpolation.

Publication of Logarithms. Napier's discussion of logarithms appeared in 1614 with the title *Mirifici Logarithmorum Canonis Descriptio*, i.e., "A Description of the Wonderful Law of Logarithms." This included tables which were arranged in seven columns which gave the logarithms of the sines of different angles differing by minutes. The first and seventh of these columns contained the size of the angle in question and its complement. In the words of the text: "Arches" from 0–45, or the "less sharp angle of any right lined right angled triangle," and "Arches" from 90–45 and the "greater sharpe angle of the same right triangle." The next columns gave the sines of these angles; the third and fifth columns gave the logarithms of these sines; and the middle column gave the difference between these logarithms. The table for 30° 0′ appeared as follows:

Gr.   30

30

min.	Sinus	Logarithmi	Differentiae	Logarithmi	Sinus	
0	5000000	6931469	5493059	1438410	8660254	60

In describing these columns, Napier calls the sine of the complementary angle the *Antilogarithm*.

It is evident, then, that Napier's logarithms differ from those with which we are familiar in that they had no base and that the value of a logarithm *decreased* as the number *increased*. Napier's logarithms may be formed from a table of logarithms with the base e by using the formula:

$$\text{Nap. log } y = m \text{ nat. log} \left(\frac{m}{y} \right), \text{ where } m = 10^7.$$

The year after the publication of the *Descriptio*, Henry Briggs, then professor of geometry in Gresham college in London, traveled to Edinburgh and spent upwards of a month with Napier discussing this work. Both agreed that the tables would be more useful if they were changed so that the logarithm of 1 would be 0. In 1619, there was published posthumously a description of the construction of Napier's tables with the title: *Mirifici Ipsius Canonis Constructio.* This contained the following Appendix:

On the construction of another and better kind of Logarithms, namely one in which the Logarithm of unity is 0.

Among the various improvments of Logarithms, the more important is that which adopts a cypher as the Logarithm of unity and 10 000 000 as the Logarithm of either one tenth of unity or ten times unity. Then these being once fixed, the Logarithms of all other numbers necessarily follow.

In 1620, a colleague of Briggs's named Gunter, published a table of logarithms of trigonometric functions using the base 10. Four years later, Briggs published a table of logarithms of numbers with the base 10, thus completing the task which Napier had seen advisable ten years previously and using the word *mantissa* to mean the fractional part of a logarithm.

TABLES OF LOGARITHMS

	In England	*In Other Countries*
1614	Napier, *Descriptio*	
1620	Gunter, Logarithms of trigonometric functions	Bürgi, *Progress Tabulen* (Prague), antilogarithms with the base 1.0001.
1624	Briggs, Logarithms with base 10	Kepler's Tables
1625		Wingate's Tables (Paris)
1626		Vlacq's Tables (Holland)
1630		Faulhaber's Tables (Germany)
1646	Logarithms appear in the edition of the *Grovnd of Artes* of this date.	

Bürgi's Invention of Logarithms. Logarithms seem to have been developed independently by a Swiss watchmaker Jobst Bürgi, who approached the subject through the idea of exponents, influenced probably by the German writers of the sixteenth century. Kepler says of this invention that Bürgi "deserted the child at its birth and failed to educate it for the public good." At all events, it seems evident that the two men, Napier and Bürgi, worked independently but that by delaying the publication of his tables until 1620, Bürgi lost the right to a possible claim to priority.

PROBABILITY AND STATISTICS

Introduction. School courses in algebra are principally concerned with the behavior of variable quantities whose relation to one another is stated in laws drawn from the sciences or from business and economics. There is, however, another aspect of the work whose importance is daily becoming more apparent and which should be included in a discussion of the history of algebra. This branch of the subject deals with the discovery and formulation of the relationships between the variable quantities involved in the phenomena of business, economics, or science by applying the methods of statistics to data obtained by experiment or by observation. An account of the development of the theory of statistics is beyond the scope of this work, yet it is desirable to note certain steps in the evolution of its methods. Among these are the topics permutations, combinations and probability.

Permutations and Combinations. The first evidence of the study of permutations comes in the mystic trigrams of the Chinese and Japanese, which appear in one of the oldest of the Chinese classics, the *I-king*. This consists of the various permutations of straight and broken lines taken three at a time. This arrangement of lines is seen on amulets and charms in China and in India, and it is also used as an ornament on objects where it can have no mystical significance whatever. Interest in the subject of permutations was relatively slight among the Greeks, but in late Roman times Boethius (*c.* 510) gave a rule for the number of combinations of *n* things taken 2 at a time.

The Hindu writer Bhāskara (*c.* 1150) paid considerable attention to the subject of permutations, as is evidenced by the following problem from the *Lilāvati*:

How many are the variations in the form of the god Sambu (Síva) by the exchange of his ten attributes held reciprocally in his several hands: namely, the rope, the elephant's hook, the serpent, the tabor, the skull, the trident, the bedstead, the dagger, the arrow, the bow: as those of Hari by the exchange of the mace, the discus, the lotus, and the conch? *

This problem was not entirely an innovation, for the Hindus had different names for the god Hari according to the vari-

* Colebrooke, *Bhāskara*, 124.

ous arrangements of his four attributes in his four hands. We may imagine that Bhāskara had this in mind, and thought to astound his readers by the number of names that would have to be invented for Síva had that god been given a name for each of the ways in which his ten attributes could be placed in his ten hands.

The Hebrew writers of the Middle Ages were interested in the matter of permutations. This was largely due to the connection between this subject and astrology; for since the planets were supposed to have an influence on the course of events, the conjunction or coming together of two planets was indicative of the combination of two sets of circumstances; the conjunction of three planets was even more potent; and the conjunction of all seven planets is exceedingly significant. Rabbi ben Ezra (c. 1140) is known to have written on the subject, but, although he was justly noted for his ability in mathematics, he seems to have failed to realize that his study of the number of possible combinations of the planets was really mathematical in character.

By the time of the first printed books, European writers were discussing such problems as the number of permutations of n people seated at a table. In the sixteenth century, Tartaglia (1556) gave problems connected with the throwing of dice, and Buteo (1559) discussed the number of combination locks that could be made by a given number of movable cylinders each of which could be set in any one of six given positions. It should be noted that Buteo's treatment consisted in listing all possible combinations with no attempt at solving the problem algebraically.

During the seventeenth century, permutations and combinations were treated algebraically, with Pascal, Wallis, and Fermat as the chief contributors to the theory. Pascal, for example, realized the connection between the coefficients of the Binomial Theorem as given in the Pascal triangle and the number of combinations of two groups of things taken n at a time. Hérigone (1634) had previously developed a general formula for this case.   Leibniz, who was noted for his interest in symbols and in terms, suggested that the word com*bina*tions be used for groups of two each, con*terna*tions for groups of three each, and that these be written as *con2natio, con-3natio*, with the extensions *con4natio*, etc.   The word *permutations* was first used as a mathematical term in Jacques Bernoulli's *Ars conjectandi* (1713).

Probability.   Except for a problem of Chinese mathematics dating from about the beginning of the Christian era, there seems to be no reference to the subject of probability prior to the latter part of the fifteenth century.   Pacioli (1494) was among the first to introduce the "Problem of the Points" into a work on mathematics.   The substance of this problem was as follows: Two men are forced to quit their game of chance before either has won.   If the number of points each has is known and if the number of points required to win is also known, how shall the stake be divided?   The problem was discussed by Tartaglia and by Cardan.   The latter author, himself an inveterate gambler, actually wrote a handbook of games of chance.

The Problem of the Points was proposed to Pascal in 1654 by the Chevalier de Méré, a gambler who was said to have unusual ability "even for the mathematics."   Pascal interested himself in the question and sent the problem to Fermat.*   The solutions given by the two scholars differed in method but agreed in the result.   As a consequence of this study, Pascal and Fermat extended the problem from a particular case to the general one.

Shortly after this, Huygens † published a mathematical discussion of the winning of certain games of chance, and in the *Ars conjectandi* (1713), Jacques Bernoulli gave a de-

* The correspondence which ensued appears in Smith, *Source Book in Mathematics*.   For the history of these topics, see also Helen M. Walker, *Studies in the History of Statistical Method*, Baltimore, 1929.

† 1629–1695. Christaan Huygens was a Dutch mathematician and physicist interested in the study of the pendulum, writing on the cissoid, catenary, cycloid, and other curves, and making contributions to the calculus.

tailed treatment of the subject together with the interesting suggestion that these ideas might be applied to civil, moral, and economic affairs.

The Doctrine of Chances (1718) published by Abraham de Moivre was probably the outgrowth of the problems solved

ABRAHAM DE MOIVRE
From *Biometrika*, XVII, by the kind permission of Professor Karl Pearson.

by De Moivre for the gentlemen in the London coffeehouses. The important thing for the history of probability is that this study led him to the discovery of the normal distribution curve which he published in 1733, with the statement that he had come upon it some twelve years earlier.

An application of the ideas of probability to a different type of problem had been made by Halley in 1693. Halley published a mortality table which included an attempt to ascertain the prices of annuities on lives. It should be noted that life annuities had been bought and sold previously. Indeed, during the seventeenth century, the Government of Holland had had this as its favorite method of floating loans. A certain amount of money purchased a life income for the purchaser or for the beneficiary whom he named, the rate being reckoned as half that of a perpetuity for the same amount. Halley's attempt, then, is important as a beginning toward the mathematical calculation of life insurance, but it was only a beginning. The task of compiling mortality tables had to be carried much further before work based on them could be considered valid.

The most notable contribution of all was made by Laplace, whose *Théorie analytique des probabilités* was published in 1812. His important work in probability was but a part of his activities, for he wrote on celestial mechanics, the calculus, and differential equations.

The great German mathematician Gauss applied the theories of probability to practical work in astronomy. It was indicative of the general tendency of scientists and mathematicians that most of the important astronomers of the nineteenth century followed his example and studied the mathematical theory of probability in its applications to their particular fields.

From beginnings that were closely associated with number mysticism and with recreational problems, the study of permutations and combinations merged in the study of probability in connection with a gambling question of the fifteenth century. Having attracted the attention of mathematicians for over a hundred years, this problem was put on a scientific basis by Pascal and Fermat. The subject of probability was treated in detail by Jacques Bernoulli and De Moivre. During the eighteenth century it developed rapidly, and in the nineteenth it found application in the mathematical study of statistics whose development has been rapid in recent years, and whose applications are found in many apparently unrelated fields.

SUMMARY

Almost all of the great topics of algebra have had their origin in the early days of the history of mathematics. The Egyptians, for example, were acquainted with linear and quadratic equations and with progressions, and they applied this knowledge to verbal problems. Archimedes virtually knew the laws of multiplication for exponents. Cubic equations arose in connection with the problem of duplicating the cube, and a large amount of work that was algebraic in its content was accomplished by methods that were geometric in nature.

If we except the work of Diophantus, no notable suggestions in the way of symbolism in algebra were made prior to the invention of printing. Yet by that time, Hindu writers had developed the solution of the quadratic and had made a beginning in the study of negative numbers; Fibonacci had solved a special case of a cubic; and Oresme had invented exponents. The work of these scholars should not be belittled, nor should Euclid's ingenuity in solving algebraic problems by geometry be overlooked, but the fact must be admitted that rapid progress in algebra was contemporaneous with the development of symbolism and that this was the contribution of the sixteenth and seventeenth centuries. The use of symbols has not only facilitated work along lines already developed, but the symbols themselves have frequently suggested extensions of the theory in new and important directions. It was independence of symbolism that permitted the rapid growth of geometry: it was the dependence of theory upon symbolism that retarded the development of algebra.

CHAPTER V

VERBAL PROBLEMS

Uses of Problems in Textbooks — Problems Typical of Different
Races and Epochs — History of Certain Standard Problems —
Puzzles and Recreations — Summary.

USES OF VERBAL PROBLEMS IN TEXTBOOKS

General Considerations. The problem content of a textbook in arithmetic or in algebra is a measure of the mathematical interests and accomplishments of the group for whom
it is written. To a somewhat less degree, it is also an indication of the ability and interest of the author, for these problems include the matter-of-fact question of the merchant, the
puzzle of the scientist, the imagination of the poet, the spec-
ulations of the philosopher, the verbose trivialities of the amateur, and the absurd variants of the copyist. In general, the
more elementary a text, the more abundant are its problems:
the more advanced a treatise, the less the repetition in the
fundamental pattern of the questions.

In an effort to make problems appeal to the reader, authors
have utilized subject matter of current or of local interest to
such a degree that it is often possible to give the approximate
date and place of publication of their works on this basis alone.
They have also clothed problems in extraneous details, perhaps merely to give variety or to disguise a standard question,
perhaps to catch the reader's attention.

Three Types of Problems. Certain verbal problems have
been drawn from real situations, others have been invented to
resemble these situations without reproducing them, and still
others have been framed with the sole object of mystifying or
amusing the reader. These groups of problems will be referred to as genuine, pseudo-real, and recreational.*

* See Vera Sanford, *History and Significance of Certain Standard Problems
in Algebra*, New York, 1927.

The Purpose of Problems.   Since genuine problems are the creatures of our external surroundings, their presence in textbooks in mathematics is due to a desire to link reality to theory, thus justifying the subject matter of the mathematics on the one hand, and, on the other, showing how mathematical ideas are of assistance in interpreting the life about us.   The existence of puzzle problems is due to man's innate curiosity and to the fascination which he feels for riddles.   In fact, even if textbooks contained no genuine problems and no recreational ones, both groups would nevertheless exist; the one because of the demands of our environment, and the other because of its appeal to our imagination.   The presence of these problems in textbooks in mathematics is largely due to an opportunism which seeks to give material which men know to be of intrinsic worth or which they must admit is of inherent interest.

Problems of the genuine or pseudo-real type have frequently been used to introduce new subject matter.   Köbel (1514), for example, introduces the topic of division by referring to a schoolmaster who purchased a cask of 180 herring for 18 pence in the Friday fish market, and who asked how many herring he had bought for a penny.

Besides these problems whose use is apparent, many writers have further applications grouped according to the problem material.   A section of an arithmetic would be devoted to alligation, another to the Rule of the Fairs, etc., while problems that were patently recreational in character would be put together under such captions as "accomplishments" in the Treviso Arithmetic, or "Pleasing and Diverting Questions" as in Baker's *Well Spring of Sciences* (1568).

The practical reasons for teaching such problems have been given above.   In contrast to these, it is interesting to note the comment of one who was interested in the question from another point of view.   Sir Isaac Newton puts the matter in this way:

After the Learner has been some time exercised in managing and transforming Equations, Order requires that he should try his Skill in bringing Questions to an Equation. And any Question being proposed, his Skill is particularly required to denote all its Conditions by so many Equations. To do which he must first consider whether the Propositions or Sentences in which it is expressed, be all of them fit to be denoted in Algebraick Terms, just as we express our Conceptions in *Latin* or *Greek* Characters. And if so, (as will happen in Questions conversant about Numbers or abstract Quantities) then let him give Names to both known and unknown Quantities, as far as the occasion requires; and express the Sense of the Question in the Analytick Language if I may so speak...

But it may sometimes happen, that the Language or the Words wherein the State of the Question is expressed, may seem unfit to be turned into the Algebraical Language; but making Use of a few Changes, and attending to the Sense, rather than the Sound of the Words, the Version will become easy. Thus, the Forms of Speech among different Nations have their proper Idioms; which, where they happen, the Translation out of one into another is not to be made literally, but to be determined by the Sense.*

It was characteristic of mathematical works until the close of the eighteenth century to give the full solutions of all problems, or at least to indicate the method and supply the result. The authors seem to have been of the same opinion as was Newton when, following the remarks given above, he said "Since Arts are more easily learned by Examples than Precepts, I have thought fit to adjoin the Solutions of the following Problems." A few authors expressed the hope that the reader would frame other similar problems for himself, but they seldom provided additional practice in their texts. It is perhaps reasonable to suppose that this was the result of the teaching methods in the schools and universities, or of the concept of a textbook as a handbook and not a workbook.

Plagiarism. Certain types of experience are so universal that it is not surprising that problems based on these situations should appear independently in many works. On the other hand, writers of all ages have borrowed extensively

* *Arithmetica Universalis*, London, 1707. The quotations above are taken from the second edition in English which was published in London in 1728 under the title *Universal Arithmetick*.

from the works of their predecessors and contemporaries, rarely stating the immediate source of a problem. In the sixteenth century it became fashionable to use problems from various authors of classic times and few writers failed to mention that the problem of Hiero's crown was taken from the work of Vitruvius. Scheubel even attributed the problem of the mule and the ass to Euclid. As Clavius (1608) gives this problem, it reads:

A mule and an ass were laden with wine, and the ass groaned under the weight of her burden. Seeing this, the mule said to the ass, "Mother, why do you weep? Why do you thus bathe your daughter with your tears? If you give me one measure of wine, I will have double your load but if you take one from me we shall have equal burdens." Most skilled Geometer, I ask that you tell me the size of their burdens.

In some cases, however, the plagiarism was most pronounced. For example, Trenchant writing in France (1566) and Humphrey Baker (1568) writing in England give groups of recreations whose phraseology and sequence clearly indicate that they are drawn from a common source.

Variants of Problems. In an effort either to disguise a borrowed problem or to make it appeal to the reader, time-honored questions were given new details which were often carried to ridiculous extremes. An example of this is in the puzzle of the frog in the well. An early form appears in Fibonacci's *Liber Abaci* (1202). Using modern units of measure, the problem reads as follows: "A lion is in a well whose depth is 50 ft. Every day, he climbs up $\frac{1}{7}$ of a foot and slips back $\frac{1}{9}$ of a foot. In how many days will he get out of the well?" A late variant concerned a frog who gained three feet each day and lost two feet each night. The problem was exceedingly popular, both in its simple form and with many additional details, but the tendency to elaboration was checked when Pacioli (1494) gave his version:

A mouse is at the top of a poplar tree that is 60 ft. high, and a cat is on the ground at its foot. The mouse descends $\frac{1}{2}$ of a foot each day and at night it turns back $\frac{1}{6}$ of a foot. The cat climbs one foot a day and goes back $\frac{1}{4}$ of a foot each night. The tree grows $\frac{1}{4}$ of a foot between the cat and the mouse each day and it shrinks $\frac{1}{8}$ of a foot every night. In how many days will the cat reach the mouse and how many ells has the tree grown in the meantime, and how far does the cat climb?

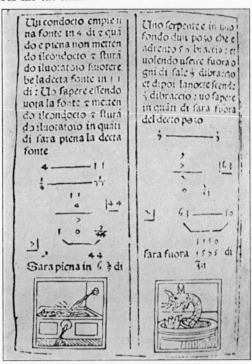

A PAGE FROM CALANDRI'S ARITHMETIC OF 1491

The questions shown here are the pipes filling the cistern and the serpent in the well.

PROBLEMS TYPICAL OF DIFFERENT RACES AND EPOCHS

Egyptian Problems. As has been noted above, the Ahmes Papyrus (*c.* 1650 B.C.) is in two sections: an addition table of fractions and a collection of problems. These questions are both algebraic and geometric, the former dealing with a wide variety of subject matter and giving correct solutions while the latter is concerned with the use of formulas which are applicable only to special cases. The algebraic questions give several examples which seem to have been solved by a method resembling the Rule of False Position. A typical problem of this group reads: "Find the quantity such that its $\frac{2}{3}$, its $\frac{1}{2}$, its $\frac{1}{7}$, and its whole make 37." A somewhat similar problem has greater detail, as if the author intended to give practice with a sample form before he disguised the fundamental idea with a clothing of extraneous circumstances. The problem is as follows:

Behold now this herdsman came to the numbering of cattle with 70 oxen: said this accountant of cattle to the herdsman, How few are the head of oxen which thou hast brought! Where then are thy numerous head of oxen? This herdsman said to him, what I have brought thee is $\frac{2}{3}$ of $\frac{1}{3}$ of the cattle which thou didst entrust to me. Count for me and thou wilt find me complete.

The one algebraic problem of the Ahmes Papyrus that seems to be genuine is concerned with the strength of a solution, but it is reasonable to suppose that its subsequent use in Europe was entirely free from connection with this early case. The problem as given by Ahmes and one of its sixteenth-century versions are given below.

One *des* measure of beer, a quarter of which has been poured off. It has then been made up with water and tasted with regard to what the strength is.

A nobleman has a butt containing 12 measures of Malmsey wine. One of his servants who has but 6 days to stay in the employ of his master drinks one measure of wine from the barrel each day, and each time puts in a measure of water. How much of the wine is left at the end of six days?

Another problem from the Ahmes Papyrus was purely recreational in character although it illustrates an important algebraic concept. Peet * calls this the "inventory of a household."

* T. Eric Peet, *The Rhind Mathematical Papyrus*.

Seven houses; in each are seven cats; each cat kills seven mice; each mouse would have eaten seven ears of spelt; each ear of spelt will produce seven hekats of grain. What is the total of all these?

The early prominence that was given to geometric progressions may perhaps be traced to man's innate love of repetition, combined with the mystic properties of these rapidly increasing numbers. Many centuries later, Fibonacci (1202) gave a problem which read in much the same fashion:

Seven old women are traveling to Rome and each has seven mules. On each mule there are seven sacks, in each sack there are seven loaves of bread, in each loaf there are seven knives, and each knife has seven sheaths. The question is to find the total of all of them.

It would be interesting to know what quizzical mathematician shifted this problem into the riddle "As I was going to St. Ives."

Greek Problems. Plato's comment on the value of problem solving as he found it among the Egyptians should be considered in connection with the verbal problems of Greek mathematics. He said,

Freeborn boys should learn so much of these things as vast multitudes of boys in Egypt learn along with their letters. First there should be calculations specially devised as suitable for boys, which they should learn with amusement and pleasure, for example, distributions of apples or garlands where the same number is divided among more or fewer boys..... and again there should be games with bowls containing gold, bronze, and silver (coins?) and the like mixed together, or the bowls may be distributed as undivided units; for, as I said, by connecting with games the essential operations of practical arithmetic, you supply the boy with what will be useful to him later in the ordering of armies, marches and campaigns as well as in household management; and in any case you make him more useful to himself and more wide awake.*

The principal source of Greek verbal problems, however, is the *Greek Anthology* which was compiled by Metrodorus probably in the fifth century. This collection undoubtedly includes many time-honored questions, just as the puzzle books of to-day have drawn largely from earlier volumes.

* Quoted by Heath, *Greek Mathematics*, i, 19–20, from Plato's *Laws*.

The problems of the *Greek Anthology* are characterized by an abundance of detail and they belong, almost without exception, to the pseudo-real and recreational classes. The following problems illustrate the general tenor of the group.

The Graces were carrying baskets of apples, and in each was the same number. The nine Muses met them and asked each for apples and they gave the same number to each muse and the nine and the three each had the same number. Tell me how many they gave and how they all had the same number.

Diodorus, the great glory of dial-makers, tell me the hour since the golden wheels of the sun lept up from the east to the pole. Four times three-fifths of the distance he has traversed remain when he sinks into the western sea.

A Traveler ploughing with his ship the broad gulf of the Adriatic said to the Captain, "How much sea have we still to traverse?" And he answered, "Voyager, between Cretan Ram's Head and the Sicilian Peloris are 6000 stades, and twice two-fifths of the distance we have traversed remains till the Sicilian strait."

After staining the holy chaplet of fair-eyed Justice that I might see thee, all-subduing gold, grow so much, I have nothing; for I gave 40 talents under evil auspices to my friends in vain, while O ye varied mischances of men, I see my enemy in possession of the half, the third, and the eighth of my fortune.

Hindu Problems. The Hindu problems were fanciful and impractical but they offered interesting applications of the Pythagorean theorem, and they gave considerable practice in fractions, quadratics, and geometric progressions. Their variety is illustrated in the following cases:

A snake's hole is at the foot of a pillar, and a peacock is perched on its summit. Seeing a snake, at the distance of thrice the pillar gliding towards his hole, he pounces obliquely upon him. Say quickly at how many cubits from the snake's hole do they meet, both proceeding an equal distance? (Bhāskara.)

Of a collection of mango fruits, the king (took) $\frac{1}{6}$; the queen $\frac{1}{5}$ the remainder, and the three chief princes took $\frac{1}{4}$, $\frac{1}{3}$, and $\frac{1}{2}$ (of that same remainder); and the youngest child took the remaining 3 mangoes. O you who are clever in miscellaneous problems on fractions, give out the measure of that (collection of mangoes). (Mahāvīra.)

In the course of $\frac{3}{7}$ of a day, a ship goes over $\frac{1}{5}$ of a krosá in the ocean; being opposed by the wind she goes back (during the same time) $\frac{1}{9}$ of a krosá. Give out, O you who have powerful arms in crossing over the ocean of numbers well, in what time that ship will have gone over $99\frac{2}{5}$ yojanas. (Mahāvīra.)

Chinese Problems. A present-day problem which appears in the Chinese works on mathematics as well as in the books of Renaissance Europe concerns a tree (in the Chinese works, a bamboo shoot) broken by the wind. The original height of the tree is known and also the distance from its base to the point where the top touches the ground. The question is to compute the height of the break. Another of the Chinese problems is an interesting application of the problem of pursuit. There is considerable doubt as to the date of the various Chinese writings but this is supposed to be from a work of the sixth century. It reads:

A man who had stolen a horse rode away on his back. When he had gone 37 Chinese miles the owner discovered the theft and pursued the thief for 145 miles. He then returned being unable to overtake him. When he turned back the thief was riding 23 miles ahead of him; if he had continued in his pursuit without coming back, in how many miles would he have overtaken him?

Another problem of the same period is based on progressions. It asks for the daily journeyings of a horse who goes seven hundred miles in seven days in such a way that he covers half the distance each day that he traveled the day before.

Problems from the Early Middle Ages. The collection of problems "for quickening the mind" which is attributed by some to Alcuin,* contains a number of questions that are found in our textbooks to-day. Among these are the problems of the hound chasing the hare and the cistern problem. The author proposes the problem of the hundred animals bought for a hundred coins, giving it additional interest by placing the scene in the Orient where a camel may be bought

* This collection dates from the tenth century at the latest. It is printed in "Propositiones Alcuini doctoris Carolimagni Imperatoris ad acuendos juvenes," *Alcuini Opera Omnia*, vol. II, edited by J. P. Migne; being 101 of the *Patrologiae cursus completus*, Paris, 1863.

for five coins, an ass for one, and twenty sheep for one. He gives the problem of the man crossing a stream with a wolf, a goat, and a bundle of cabbages, and he also includes the variant of a man and wife and two children with a boat that can hold the man or his wife or the children.

Problems from al-Khowârizmî. The problems of al-Khowârizmî's algebra were largely of the "Find a number" type illustrating his theoretical work with quadratics.

From this point on, the problems will be discussed according to general tendencies rather than according to the authors in whose works they appear.

Topical Problems. Writers of all periods have sought to make their problems appear to be real and important. They have done this by the use of proper names and current dates; they have laid the scene of problems in places familiar or interesting to their readers; and they have clothed problems in new details. Köbel (1514), for example, has two men start from Oppenheim, where he lived, to go to Rome, the goal of many pilgrimages. The American writer, Pike (1788), has two men traveling from Newburyport to Providence and from Providence to Newburyport at given rates. His answer not only tells the number of miles that their place of meeting was from Providence, but it also says this was "near Ameses at Dedham." A contemporary almanac shows that Ames kept the tavern.

In some cases, new situations developed new problems. Such an instance is illustrated by an example from Sir Isaac Newton's *Arithmetica Universalis* (1707).

A Stone falling down into a Well, from the Sound of the Stone striking the Bottom, to determine the Depth of the Well.

Problems Reflecting Social and Economic Conditions. Social conditions in sixteenth-century Germany are shown in a problem given by Rudolff (1526):

Three citizens join in the hire of twelve horsemen and fifty men at arms. Each horseman receives eleven florins a month and each man at arms receives five florins a month. The first citizen pays $\frac{1}{2}$, the second $\frac{1}{3}$, and the third $\frac{1}{4}$.* Counting a year as being 13 months, how much did each pay?

Robert Recorde (*c.* 1542) gives a problem connected with the much discussed tendency of his time to enclose the commons and to turn arable land into sheep pasture.

There is supposed a Lawe made that for the furthering of tillage euerye manne that doeth keepe sheepe, shall for euery 10 sheepe eare and sowe one acre of grounde; and for his allowance in sheepe pasture, there is appointed for euerye 4 sheepe 1 acre of pasture: Nowe is there a riche sheepemayster whiche hathe 7000 acres of grounde, and woulde gladlye keepe as many sheepe as hee mighte by that statute, I demaunde how manye sheepe shall he keepe?

At a later time, Nicolas Pike (1788) gives a question regarding the division of the Federal Debt of forty-two million dollars among the states, and the establishing of a sinking fund to extinguish this debt in ten years. Another American writer (1862) gave a question regarding the number of miles of wire in the Atlantic cable.

Scientific Problems. The problem of Hiero's crown has already been mentioned as being one of the oldest of the scientific problems in our algebra, and problems relating to mixtures have also been noted previously.

Cardan (1539) was perhaps the first to introduce questions relating to the Day Line into arithmetics. He asked the number of days actually spent if a ship sailed westward on the Kalends † of January, 1517, and went three times around the earth, returning on the seventh of May, 1526. In a note to this problem he showed that the "rotation of the sun about the earth" made a difference of a day in the result for each circumnavigation of the globe.

Current medical practice is shown in another of Cardan's problems. In his day, degrees of heat or of cold were assigned to each drug and to each disease. Thus a malady hot

* This means that the ratios of the amounts were $\frac{1}{2}:\frac{1}{3}:\frac{1}{4}$. This form of expression was popular prior to the middle of the sixteenth century.

† This was the first of January.

to the fourth degree could be alleviated by a medicine cold to the fourth degree. So, over a half-century before the invention of the thermometer, Cardan wrote:

A man mixes 1 ounce of medicine warm in the third degree, 3 ounces warm in the first degree, 4 cold in the second degree, 5 warm in the second degree, 2 at temperate heat, 1 cold in the first degree, and 13 warm in the first degree. If these are mixed, what is the resulting degree of heat or cold of the mixture?

Problems Now Obsolete. Certain problems that were genuine at the time of their inclusion in mathematics textbooks have vanished because their subject matter is neither real nor important to-day.

An example of these given by Tartaglia (1556) should be noted well as it was of great importance to copyists. This problem concerned the transcribing of a book of 16 columns, each column having 60 lines and each line containing 32 letters. The new copy was to have 45 lines in a column and 36 characters in a line. The question asked both the price of the work and the price of the materials. The problem makes one realize that the invention of printing did not at once terminate the making of books in manuscript, and it suggests the importance that was given to the choice of lettering by the high cost of parchment and vellum.

Other questions that have become obsolete relate to partnerships, rent charges, agreements for the pasturing of sheep, and to the official regulation of the price of bread in accordance with the cost of wheat.

Biblical Problems. Another group of problems dealt with Biblical and theological subject matter. Early American arithmetics made occasional use of this material. The Greenwood *Arithmetick* of 1729 devoted as much space to the units of measure mentioned in the Bible as it did to those in the thirteen colonies, and Pike (1788) developed a rule for finding the tonnage of a ship and applied it to finding the tonnage of Noah's ark.

At an earlier date, Buteo (1559) computed both the number

of sheep Noah would have needed to feed his carnivorous passengers for a year, and the amount of fodder necessary to feed the sheep. Cardan (1539) discussed the question of the building of the tower of Babel to discover whether the fact that all food and building materials had to be relayed to the workers would impose a natural limit to the height that the tower could attain.

Father Clavius (1583) computed the size of the army of the Maccabees, and Tartaglia (1556) computed the number of angels in heaven, stating that his data was based on the best theological opinion.

HISTORY OF CERTAIN STANDARD PROBLEMS *

The Cistern Problem. The problem of the pipes filling a cistern appeared in the work of Heron (*c.* 50) and also in that of Diophantus (*c.* 275). In the *Greek Anthology* (*c.* 500), it had the following form:

I am a brazen lion; my spouts are my two eyes, my mouth and the flat of my right foot. My right eye fills a jar in two days, my left eye in three, and my foot in four. My mouth is capable of filling it in six hours; tell me how long all four together will take to fill it?

Its connection with the fountains which were the center of each Roman town made the problem especially vivid to citizens of the Mediterranean world even after the fall of the Roman Empire. The problem appears in textbooks to-day in the question of the pipes filling a cistern. In the early days of printing each of the many textbook writers sought as wide a variety of problems as possible. Accordingly, the fundamental idea of the cistern problem appeared as a question concerning the time it would take a lion, a leopard, and a wolf to eat a sheep if they devoured it simultaneously. In another form it asked how long it would take a number of mills to

* See David Eugene Smith, "On the Origin of Certain Typical Problems," *American Mathematical Monthly*, XXIV, 64–71. Also Vera Sanford, *The History and Significance of Certain Standard Problems in Algebra*, New York, 1927.

grind a certain amount of wheat, or how fast a ship could sail with all sails set if the first could carry the ship the required distance in 6 days, the second in 9, the third in 12. A favorite variant asked how long it would take a man and his wife to drink a certain quantity of beer, the rate of drinking being given. When applied to a number of people doing a piece of work, every sort of device was used. The men built houses, cut meadows, dug ditches, worked for varying lengths of time, etc.

The Problem of Pursuit. Problems illustrating the use of the rate-time-distance formula may perhaps be traced to the use of pace scales in the ancient world, particularly by Alexander whose official pacers measured the distance between towns and villas in mapping his empire. The marching stride of the Roman

THE PROBLEM OF PURSUIT

From Köbel, *Rechenbuch* (1564). Freely translated, this problem reads: Two citizens of Oppenheym called Heynrich-son and Contz von Treber, decided to go to Rome together. Heynrich was old and could travel no more than ten miles a day. But Contz was young and strong and could go thirteen miles a day. Accordingly, Heynrich started out from Oppenheym nine days before Contz left. The question is, In how many days will Contz von Treber overtake Heynrich-son?

legionary was so standardized that officers, knowing the required distances from their roadbooks, could calculate to a nicety just how long an army would require to march from one point to another. When these things were forgotten, the problem still appeared to be real, for it is a matter of common observation that if a person walks at a uniform rate for a given time, the distance he goes can be readily computed.

From these real origins, the problems soon passed into the pseudo-real class. Alcuin cites the case of a snail which took 246 years, 210 days to get to a banquet; Mahāvīra has a lame man walk for three and one fifth years at a time, and he pictures a snail crawling up a mountain. The men of the problem were made to travel distances increasing in geometric progression. Ships sailing at specified rates were used, and the conjunction of two planets was proposed by several sixteenth-century writers, Cardan being among their number. At a somewhat later period, this question became the well-known "clock problem."

The problem of the boat up or down stream has been variously used. It has even been applied to a steam packet moving with or against the Gulf Stream. It does not seem to have occurred in a textbook earlier than Pike's work of 1788, where it has this form:

If, during ebb tide, a wherry should set out from Haverhill, to come down the river, and, at the same time, another should set out from Newburyport, to go up the river, allowing the difference to be 18 miles; suppose the current forwards one and retards the other $1\frac{1}{2}$ mile per hour; the boats are equally laden, the rowers equally good, and, in the common way of working in still water, would proceed at the rate of 4 miles per hour; when, in the river, will the two boats meet?

The Testament Problem. Questions relating to the division of an estate have had many variants. For a long time, it was customary to give the parts into which a thing was to be divided, as fractions. When Gemma Frisius (1540) asked about the division of an estate of 7851 *aurei* so that the heirs were to receive $\frac{1}{2}$, $\frac{1}{3}$, and $\frac{1}{4}$, he meant that their shares should be in the proportion of $\frac{1}{2} : \frac{1}{3} : \frac{1}{4}$. Tartaglia was among the first to suggest a solution that has since become the answer to a popular puzzle. In dividing 17 horses among heirs who were to receive $\frac{1}{2}$, $\frac{1}{3}$, and $\frac{1}{9}$ respectively, he suggested that another horse be borrowed, making the number up to 18, so that one might take 9, another 6, and another 2, leaving the borrowed horse to be returned to his owner.

Alcuin gave an inheritance problem in which thirty flasks, ten full, ten half-empty, and ten entirely empty, were to be divided among three sons so that flasks and contents should be shared equally.

Fibonacci (1202) put an inheritance question in this form:

A man whose end was approaching, said to his eldest son, "Divide my goods among you thus: You are to have one bezant and a seventh of what is left." Then to his next son, he said, "Take two bezants and a seventh of what remains." To the third son, he said, "Then you are to take three bezants and a seventh of what is left." Thus he gave each son one bezant more than the previous son and a seventh of what remained and the last son had all that was left. Moreover, after this division, it developed that they had shared the father's property equally although they had followed out his conditions. The question is, how many sons were there and how large was the estate?

The most important of the inheritance questions is known as the Testament Problem. Based on a Roman law that made definite provisions for dower rights, the problem stated that a man left his estate to his wife and an expected child to be divided in one ratio if the child were a boy but in a different ratio if it were a girl. The question was to decide on the equal division in the case of twins, a boy and a girl. The problem was subjected to many complications, one of which was the provision of a legacy to the church, which, by the way, was paid in full before the rest of the property was divided.

Geometric Progressions. Geometric progressions appear in problems with great frequency. The chessboard problem and its variants are discussed on page 175.

Champenois (1578) made an illustration of the power of a geometric progression particularly impressive when he invented the story of the learnèd but poverty-stricken Master of Arts who offered a tailor 4888 *livres* diminished twenty times by one half for a robe that the tailor valued at 58 *livres*. The tailor accepted the offer and the scholar prudently took the robe and then showed the tailor that the price came to a trifle over twopence. He gave the tailor threepence and asked for the change. The tailor, who had lost a great deal by the transaction already, offered to gamble with him for it and lost. As a result, the scholar got himself a fine robe by means of his knowledge of a rule of arithmetic.

Problems Using Arithmetic Progressions. The standard illustrations of arithmetic progressions are the potato-race problem and the problem of the number of times a clock strikes in a day. The first is given by Buteo (1559) in a case where an ant collects grain for the winter. The grain happens to be placed with the kernels at equal distances in a straight line and the ant takes them one at a time to her hole. Of these problems Cardan's (1539) is the most interesting as a case of vicarious athletics, for a certain man places 100 stones in a straight line, each one pace from the one before, and he puts a basket one pace away from the first stone. Then he commands a servant to collect them while he looks on and calculates how far the man goes in carrying out the order.

The familiar problem of the number of times a clock strikes is given by Buteo (1559) and by Rudolff (1526). Each writer is particular to locate the problem in a country where the clock strikes the hours from 1 to 24.

The " God Greet You " Problem. One of the most popular of the problems devised to give practice with fractions has been called the "God Greet You" problem from the salutation with which it frequently begins. Humphrey Baker's (1568) version, however, is principally concerned with making the problem seem reasonable. He says:

A man hauing his eye sight somewhat altered, began to tell and reckon a certayne number of birdes to be in all 18. His Companion that had a clearer sight, beholding wel the birds, answered him, that there were not 18, but saide he, if ther were twice so many more as there are, there should be as many more abou 18, as ther be nowe lesse then 18. The question is to know how many birdes there were in all.

The Schoolmaster Problem. Another of the popular problems had many variants from men giving alms to beggars to captains arranging their men in solid squares, but one of the most frequent versions concerned a schoolmaster and his rent. Calandri (1491) gave it in these terms:

" A master has so many scholars that if each pays 8 pence he will lack 10 soldi of paying his rent, but if each pays 10 pence, he will have 20 soldi too much. How many scholars were there and what was the rent? "

Apparently any surplus above his rent would require explanation.

The Problem of the Apples and the Gatekeeper. A problem that combined skill in computation with an element of mystery is that of the apples and the gatekeeper. Fibonacci (1202) gives it as follows:

A man went into an orchard which had seven gates, and there took a certain number of apples. When he left the orchard, he gave the first guard half the apples that he had and one apple more. To the second, he gave half his remaining apples and one apple more. He did the same in the case of each of the remaining five guards and left the orchard with one apple. How many apples did he gather in the orchard?

The problem had many forms. Pacioli (1494) sent a page into a garden to fetch a single rose, but Köbel (1514) made it clear that his question concerned a lawbreaker. He said:

A thief stole a sack full of gulders from a castle. Now the castle had three gates and a gatekeeper stood at each. The thief hurried, anxious to be safely out of the castle with the stolen money. When he came to the first gate, the gatekeeper asked what he carried and said "Give me half and I'll let you go out." The thief in fear lest he be seized, gave the gatekeeper half of the money and the gatekeeper gave him back 100 gulders out of sympathy. At the second gate, the keeper demanded half his money, and out of pity returned to him 50 gulders. At the third gate, the keeper demanded half of his money, and upon receiving it, gave him back 25 gulders. When the thief got safely out of the castle he had 100 gulders in his sack. The question is, how many did he steal when he first put them into his sack?

Another variant concerned the problem of obtaining admission to a wealthy man's house. Ghaligai (1521) gave it in these terms:

A gentleman had an audience with a Signore, and according to custom, he gave each of the guards one tenth of the money he had with him as a *pourboire*. When he came, he had 100 fl. If he gave one tenth of this money to each of the ten guards, how much did he have when he departed?

Still another variant concerned a merchant or a gambler who visited various fairs and trafficked at each. Tartaglia's (1556) version is more colorful than most.

A man who had a certain capital, fell to gambling and made as many denarii as he had to start with. He then spent 20 ducats on a horse. He rode away on the horse to an inn where he gambled with the innkeeper and redoubled his money. He spent 20 ducats on a beautiful robe. He then left the inn and went on to the gate of the city where he found some people gambling. There he doubled what he had left, bought a ring for 20 ducats and found he had nothing left. How much money did he have when he started from home?

These problems appear to be highly fantastic but a little reflection shows that they contain the essence of the idea of an annuity — a fixed payment each year for a certain term of years with the capital gaining interest at a fixed rate in the mean time.

PUZZLES AND RECREATIONS

Collections of Puzzles. Certain collections of recreational and puzzle problems have already been noted in the case of the *Greek Anthology*, and the *Propositiones ad acuendos juvenes*, and mention has been made of the groups of recreations frequently given at the close of textbooks in arithmetic. A fairly comprehensive collection of puzzles was made by Bachet (1581–1638), a French writer known also for his translation of Diophantus. His *Problemes plaisans et delectables, qui se font par les nombres* was published in 1612.

This was followed by a work on the same order by Leurechon (1624) and this in turn by a similar volume by Ozanam (c. 1694). These last two far exceeded Bachet's work in popularity.

Types of Puzzles. Mathematical recreations belong to several classes: those dealing with the manipulation of objects, those dealing with the manipulation of quantities, and those involving language difficulties. Representative of the first type is the problem of the "Turks and Christians." This requires the arrangement of 15 Turks and 15 Christians in a circle in such a way that when the fifteenth man is counted out fifteen times, beginning at a given point, the Turks will be eliminated and the Christians will be left. Professor Smith suggests that this problem may be traced to a custom in the Roman armies of punishing a legion by selecting every tenth, twentieth, or hundredth man for execution. The name Josephus's problem or *Josephsspiel* is often given to it because a fourth-century writer claims that Josephus was one of the lucky ones on such an occasion. The same problem occurs in a Japanese work, that of Muramatsu (1665). Eastern problems often differ from Western ones, and in this case a woman who is trying to secure an inheritance for her children makes a mistake in arranging them, and her own family is eliminated and the step-children come into the property.

Problems involving language difficulties range from simple cases to the complexities of the question "How old is Ann?" A typical problem of the simple type, given by Tartaglia (1556), says, "A man has three pheasants that he wishes to give to two fathers and two sons, giving each one a pheasant. How can it be done?" The answer says to give them to Piero and to his son Andrea and to Andrea's son Filippo.

A more mathematical problem relates how a man bought 60 apples for 24 denarii and sold them at the price he paid and made 1 denarius profit. The solution tells that they were bought at two prices, two for a denarius, and three for a denarius. When they were bought, the larger part were bought at the lower rate.   When they were sold, the proportions were reversed.

A question based on computation of an elementary sort was given by many writers, Chuquet (1484) being perhaps the earliest to use it.   Humphrey Baker's version (1568) reads:

A mayde carieng egges vnto the market, and it happened a merrye Fellowe to meete her, who began to ieste with her in suche sorte, that he ouerthrewe her Basket, and brake all her egges; and the mayde beeing much displeased with him for breaking of the same, sayde very earnestly vnto him, ye should pay for them, the man considering with himself, that by his folly they were broken, he demaunded of her what nūber she had.   The silly poor wenche coulde not well reckon, sayde vnto him that she could not well tell him, but sayde she, when I did put them into my Basket by 2 and by 2, there remayned 1 egge: and when I counted them by 3 and by 3, there remayned 1: and when I did recken them by 4 and by 4, there remayned still 1; but when I did counte them by 5 and by 5, there remayned none.   The question is to know howe manye egges the mayde had in all?

THE PROBLEM OF THE WEIGHTS

From the collection of Professor David Eugene Smith.   Courtesy of the Museums of the Peaceful Arts, New York City.

The Problem of the Weights. A favorite recreational problem was the puzzle of finding the smallest number of weights needed to weigh any whole number of pounds up to 40. The study of weights now extant shows that the customary form was a series of little cups, each one fitting within the next larger in the denominations 1, 2, 4, 8, 16, 32... 2^n and with $\frac{1}{2}, \frac{1}{4}, \frac{1}{8}$ ..... for the fractional weights. As a general thing, the container with its cover was the largest weight of the series. It is evident, however, that weights in the series 1, 3, 9, 27.... 3^n would solve the problem if one were allowed to place the weights on both sides of the scales. Thus two pounds would be weighed by placing the 3-pound weight on one side of the scales and the 1-pound weight, with the commodity to be measured, on the other. Now that the problem has lost its connection with reality, it has reverted to the simpler form and appears in the question of finding the smallest number of bags that will hold forty silver dollars in such a way that any desired sum may be made up without opening any of the bags.

"Think of a Number" Problems. Various tricks with numbers appear in textbooks with no explanation of the reasons for their success. Köbel (1514), for example, directs you to think of a number, add half of it, add half the sum, divide by nine and tell the result. The result is one fourth of the original number. In another case, Köbel directs the reader to think of a number, divide by 3 and note the remainder, divide the original number by 5 and note the remainder, and by 7 keeping the remainder. Now multiply the first remainder by 70, the second by 21 and the third by 15. Add these numbers and subtract 105 as many times as possible. The remainder is the original number.

Rudolff (1526) gives a simple and interesting way to tell which person in a group is wearing a certain ring and on which joint of which finger. The rule is to double the number of the person in the row, add 5, multiply by 5, add the number of the finger, multiply by 10, add the number of the finger joint and subtract 250. The hundreds digit tells the person, the next digit tells the finger, and the units digit the finger joint. When the algebraic explanations of these problems are considered, it seems unfortunate indeed that this type of question is so little featured in present texts.

SUMMARY

The problems given in this chapter are only a small portion of those that could be quoted, but they will suffice to show that the problem content of texts in mathematics is dynamic, not static, adapting itself to human needs and to human interests and constantly changing to suit new circumstances.

CHAPTER VI

PRACTICAL GEOMETRY

Introduction — Egypt and Babylonia — Greece and Rome
— The Middle Ages — Modern Times — Summary.

INTRODUCTION

Origin of Geometry. Just as the early study of numbers had two aspects, one that was mystical and one that was utilitarian, so the early study of geometric form had two divisions, one æsthetic and one practical. The first of these was concerned with the decoration of pottery and fabrics. The second developed from the need of measuring land for taxation, properly orienting temples, or building canals and aqueducts.

Geometric Ornament. In the first of these uses of geometry, a definite progress is to be noted in the appreciation of geometric form. The early pottery of all countries shows crude attempts at ornamentation. This sometimes takes the form of groups of parallel lines, or of concentric circles. These gradually become designs of considerable interest showing rhythm, balance, and symmetry. But they probably never had any connection with either the practical side of geometry or with the theoretical side which was to develop as the most advanced part of the subject.

Practical Geometry. Interesting as is the study of primitive ornament, however, it will be necessary to confine this discussion to the more practical type of geometry whose study enabled men to locate the points of the compass and to cope with their environment.

This type of geometry should be interpreted to mean all parts of the subject that have practical application regardless of the means by which their formulas are derived. Had this work always depended on intuition and experiment, the progress would have been exceedingly slow. The introduction of logical reasoning from previously accepted ideas or postulates, however, placed it on a surer basis and permitted a more rapid development of the needed tools.

EGYPT AND BABYLONIA

Connection with the Temples. In both Egypt and Babylonia, practical geometry was based on formulas that probably were discovered by experimental methods. These formulas were known to the priests in both countries and although many of the rules were inaccurate, their connection with temple ritual made them sacrosanct. In spite of the fact that this connection with religion hampered the development of practical geometry, these two countries were so far in advance of the rest of the world that even after the time of Thales, Greek scholars would journey to them to learn the mathematical lore of their priests.

Both countries developed methods of placing their temples to face to the precise point of the compass demanded by the gods, which may have been done by determining the direction of the rising and of the setting sun at the equinox. A line drawn perpendicular to this line of direction would point due north and south. The Babylonians sometimes faced buildings to the intermediate points, thus showing ability to bisect an angle.

Egyptian Rope-Stretchers. In the fourth century B.C., the Greek mathematician Democritus boasted that he surpassed even the *harpedonaptae* (rope-stretchers) of Egypt in his knowledge of geometry. It has been surmised that the name "rope-stretchers" came from a rope knotted in segments whose ratios were 3:4:5, used in laying off right angles. It is highly probable that at that period, and indeed for many years before, the Egyptian surveyors understood the use of this special case of the Pythagorean Theorem. If this is not true, the use of the name "rope-stretcher" must mean simply

EGYPTIAN LAND MEASURERS (*c.* 1400 B.C.)

A scene from the Tomb of a land overseer and inspector of
the boundary stones in Thebes.   From a photograph in the
Science Museum, South Kensington, London.

a man who measured distances with a rope just as we measure
them with a steel tape.

Problems Connected with Irrigation.   Both the Babylonians and the Egyptians developed a considerable amount
of geometry in connection with irrigation projects and with
schemes to conserve their water supply.   Such work necessitated a device for running a horizontal line.   In Egypt, this
took the form of a wooden framework shaped like the letter
A.   A plumb line was suspended from the vertex where the
equal sides met.   Since the plumb line always hangs in a
perpendicular direction, the base of the isosceles triangle will
be horizontal when the plumb line hangs opposite the mid-
point of the crossbar.   Primitive as this instrument appears
to be, it was used in building canals in Mesopotamia and in
constructing the great aqueducts of Rome.   Levels of this
type are to be seen in the Museum at Cairo, and pictures of
them are carved on the tombs of Roman engineers in the
ancient cities of Arles and Nîmes in France.

Among the engineering feats of the Egyptians was the construction of a set of water gauges in the Nile Valley.   These
"Nilometers" were placed at intervals along the last seven
hundred miles of the course of the river.   The gauges still
extant have zero points below the lowest level of the water but
the important thing is that these zero points seem to lie in the
plane, which slopes from the First Cataract to the mouth of
the river.

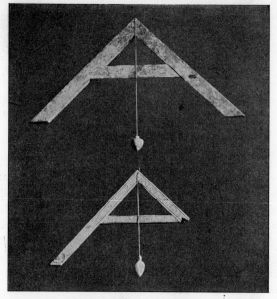

ANCIENT EGYPTIAN LEVELS

From a photograph in the Science Museum, South Kensington,
England, of the original instruments now exhibited in the Museum
at Cairo.

Surveying Problems. It has been said that "Geometry is
the gift of the Nile." The basis for this statement lies in the
fact that the annual overflow of the river obliterates land-
marks and extinguishes boundary lines. A possible beginning
of the annual survey of the flood plain was described by Herodotus in the fifth century B.C. In referring to a redistribu-
tion of land made by Rameses II (c. 1347 B.C.), Herodotus
says:

If the river carried away any portion of a man's lot, he appeared
before the king, and related what had happened; upon which the
king sent persons to examine, and determine by measurement the
exact extent of the loss; and thenceforth only such a rent was
demanded of him as was proportionate to the reduced size of his
land. From this practice, I think, geometry first came to be known
in Egypt, whence it passed into Greece.

While it is highly probable that the geometry of areas had its origin in the necessity for surveys for the purpose of taxation, this long antedated the period given by Herodotus. The Ahmes Papyrus (*c.* 1650 B.C.), for example, uses formulas for the areas of rectangles, triangles, trapezoids, and circles. These formulas were in general correct only for special cases, as in the formula for the area of a triangle: half the base times the side. Some writers interpret this to be applied to an isosceles triangle in which there is an appreciable error; others claim that this is applied to a right triangle, in which case the formula is correct. Similarly, the area of a trapezoid is given as the product of half the sum of the parallel sides and one of the non-parallel sides. The area of a circle is given as $\{(1 - \frac{1}{9})d\}^2$ which gives the value of π as 3.1605. Several volume formulas are given also but as the shape of the solid is not described, it is impossible to judge their correctness.

Trigonometry. The Egyptians had rules for building pyramids whose faces should slope at a desired angle. This work suggests a primitive trigonometry, but the subject was developed no further.

Summary. In contrast with arithmetic, in which the Egyptians showed an interest in the purely theoretical aspects of the subject, Egyptian geometry was wholly confined to practical problems. It was based on experiment, not on reasoning, and its greatest achievement was in stimulating the interest of the Greek scholars who came to the Nile to study under the Egyptian priests.

GREECE AND ROME

Early History. Although the great contribution of Thales was the creation of the theoretical subject which we know as demonstrative geometry, this philosopher used the methods of logical proof to develop ideas needed in practical work. Under his successors, however, geometry became more and more abstract, and it was not until the third century B.C. that interest in its practical side was again awakened. This re-

newed interest in the application of geometry is associated
principally with the scholars at Alexandria and later at
Rhodes, among whom were Eratosthenes, Archimedes, Heron
and Ptolemy.   In spite of the work of scholars in demonstrative geometry, popular ideas of the subject were such that
Thucydides (*c.* 399 B.C.) estimated the size of the island of
Sicily by giving the time needed to sail completely around it.

The Measurement of the Earth.   Eratosthenes undertook
to find the circumference of the earth by measuring the dis-

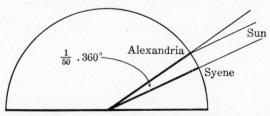

THE METHOD USED BY ERATOSTHENES IN MEASURING
THE CIRCUMFERENCE OF THE EARTH

tance between Syene near the present Assuan Dam and
Alexandria, cities which lay on the same meridian. The latitude of each city was then determined and the circumference
of the earth was calculated from these data. There is considerable doubt as to the precise length of the unit of measure
used in this work, so its accuracy cannot be estimated.

Archimedes.   Although Archimedes * (*c.* 225 B.C.) lived
in Syracuse in Sicily, he may properly be classed with the
Alexandrians.   His work in geometry was concerned with
finding the center of gravity of plane figures and solids, the
area and volume of a sphere, and the area of a triangle in terms
of the lengths of its sides.   His method of exhaustions is
discussed in Chapter X.

Heron of Alexandria.   Heron of Alexandria † is known for
certain area formulas which bear his name and also for a

* See pages 11–13.

† A.D. *c.* 50.   Heath, however, thinks he may have lived considerably
later, perhaps even in the fourth century.

manual which tells the use of an instrument called the "diop-ra." The theorem commonly attributed to Heron gives the area of a triangle whose sides are a, b, c, and whose semi-perimeter is s, as $\sqrt{s(s-a)(s-b)(s-c)}$. There is rea-son to suppose, however, that this theorem is really due to Archimedes. In any case, it furnishes a striking instance of the use of demonstrative geometry in the development of rules for surveying.

The Dioptra. Heron's instrument, the dioptra, was a straight bar fitted with sights or with a movable indicator. In a modified form, it served as a theodolite in surveying, but it was also used in astronomical work. Archimedes ($c.$ 225 B.C.), for example, used a dioptra fitted with two movable cylinders in finding the angular diameter of the sun. Sighting along the rod, he adjusted the larger cylinder so that the sun's light barely showed along its edges. The smaller cyl-inder was then moved until it just obscured the first one. Lines tangent to the two cylinders met at an angle only slightly less than that subtended by the diameter of the sun. Hipparchus ($c.$ 140 B.C.) seems to have substituted a pinhole sight for one cylinder using the dioptra as a sort of cross staff (see page 244).

Heron's manual on this instrument gives directions for measuring distance between inaccessible points, the height of inaccessible objects, and the areas of irregular plots of ground. He tells how to relocate boundary stones given a plan of the property and the location of two or three of the stones, a problem that was evidently of common occurrence in Egypt. He describes methods of finding differences in level between two points and of running a straight line from a point to another point not visible from the first. He dis-cusses the planning of harbors, the building of tunnels and of vaulted roofs, and he shows how the area of a piece of ground may be computed even though the surveyor is forbidden ac-cess to it.*

* See Heath, *Greek Mathematics*, II, 298 ff.

Ptolemy and the Quadrant. The Greek astronomer Ptolemy (*c.* 150) was a man who did a service for his science
comparable to Euclid's work in geometry. In his treatise
which was later called the *Almagest*, Ptolemy describes an

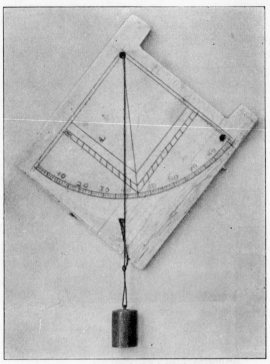

IVORY QUADRANT (18th century)

From the collection of Professor David Eugene Smith now in
the Museums of the Peaceful Arts in New York.

astronomical instrument, perhaps of his own invention, in
which a small iron tube was placed at the center of a quarter-
circle cut on a stone block. By means of this quadrant, the
angle of elevation of the sun might easily be read.

In later years, the quadrant became a square or quarter
circle of brass fitted with a plumb line; the tube became a

movable pointer fitted with sights. Writers of the sixteenth century paid considerable attention to this instrument showing how it could be used to read angles directly or to give the trigonometric functions of an angle by noting the position of the pointer with reference to the equal divisions marked on the sides of the instrument. Thus an instrument used originally for astronomy was adapted to problems of surveying. In a form that was even more simple, the observer looked through sights at the top of the instrument, reading the angle of elevation or depression from the position of the plumb line. To-day a similar instrument, called a clinometer, is sometimes used in rough work.

Rome. The Romans were interested in the practical geometry, although they neglected Euclid's work. In fact, Cicero expressed his approval of the fact that his countrymen limited their interest in geometry to the things which had practical application. It has been said, however, that this

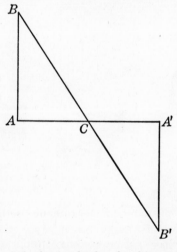

neglect of the theoretical aspects of the subject made it necessary to employ Greeks from Alexandria to plan and execute a survey of the Roman Empire in Agrippa's time.

The "Agrimensores." A considerable amount of literature relating to the Roman "agrimensores," or surveyors, is still extant. Their work was characterized by its simplicity and the rapidity with which it was executed, and the methods in use are similar in many respects to the surveying of the *Boy Scout Manuals* and the junior-high-school texts to-day. For example, one of these surveyors, Marcus Junius Nipsus by name, measured the width of a river by means of congruent triangles, as is shown in the accompanying diagram.

The Groma. As is the case with many instruments of common use in former times, no adequate ancient description of the Roman "groma" is now extant, although it seems to

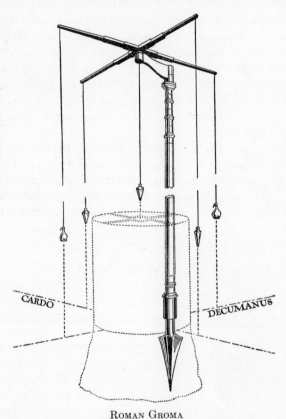

ROMAN GROMA

From *Monumenti Antichi pubblicati per cura della R. Accademia Lincei*, XXVIII. Reproduced by the courtesy of Dr. Matteo della Corte.

have been exceedingly important. Pictures of the instrument appear on the tombstones of the agrimensores together with squares, levels, and plumb lines, but these are inadequate to show its real construction. In 1912, however, the metal parts of a groma were found at Pompeii, together with the compasses, measuring rods, rules, sundial, and writing equipment of a Roman surveyor. This permitted the reconstruction of the groma which may be seen to-day in the Museum at Naples.

THE USE OF A STAFF AND CARPENTER'S SQUARE IN MEASURING
DISTANCES
From Bettini, *Apiaria*, Bologna, 1641.

The groma consisted of a wooden staff fitted with a flanged metal foot that could be thrust into the ground. This staff was probably six or seven feet long. A wooden arm swung on a pivot at the top of the staff and mounted on its outer end was a cross-shaped piece of wood whose arms of equal length were braced at right angles to each other. In using the groma the movable arm was swung so that its center was directly over a bench mark. Plumb lines hung from the extremities of the cross-pieces determined perpendicular lines through the bench mark and by rotating the cross-piece, lines might be run at any desired angle. The instrument was a practical one for use in the field, being light in weight, strongly built, and easily taken down or reassembled.*

* See Matteo Della Corte. *Monumenti Antichi pubblicati per cura della R. Accademia Lincei*, XXVIII (1922). Also a review of this article by F. W. Kelsey, *Classical Philology*, July, 1926.

The Square. Another of the instruments of practical geometry was the carpenter's square. Vitruvius notes that he has watched a stone-cutter testing a groove in a column by seeing whether the vertex of the square touches the groove when its arms are in contact with the edge of the groove.

USE OF THE CARPENTER'S SQUARE IN FINDING THE RANGE OF CANNON

From Bettini, *Apiaria*, Bologna, 1641.

The square came to have important uses in the indirect measurement of distances also. This held true even after the invention of printing, and books such as Bettini's *Apiaria* (1641) contain illustrations showing its use in measuring the heights of towers, the depth of wells, the breadth of rivers, and the like, making use of similar triangles.

Distances Measured by the Revolution of a Wheel. The direct measurement of distances by the revolution of a wheel is older than one would at first suppose. Vitruvius speaks of such a device and describes its intermeshed gears saying that at the end of each mile a pebble or counter drops into a box. This idea, which was Greek in origin, was revived by Fernel (*c.* 1535) who measured the distance from Paris to

Amiens by the revolution of a carriage wheel. The data thus obtained were used in determining the circumference of the earth, for Paris and Amiens lay on the same meridian. A century later, the device was modified and *waywisers* fitted to coaches told the number of miles and quarter miles that the vehicle traveled.

Boethius. The geometry of the Romans continued on a practical level and even Boethius, who reflected the influence of Euclid, showed a tendency to utilize the practical applications of the subject.

THE MIDDLE AGES

Gerbert. In the Middle Ages, geometry was classed as one of the seven liberal arts but the work in general was slight and ineffective. In the tenth century, Gerbert, who was then serving the abbot of Bobbio in Lombardy, discovered a copy of the *Geometry* of Boethius and a manuscript known as the *Codex Arcerianus* which gave the rules used by the Roman surveyors. Gerbert then wrote a geometry which made liberal use of these sources and which paid particular attention to surveying.

The inaccuracies of his work can be judged by the fact that he used the rule for the area of a trapezoid given by Ahmes and that he expressed the area of an equilateral triangle of side a as $\frac{1}{2}a(a - \frac{1}{7}a)$ which is equivalent to using 1.714 for the square root of 3.

After Gerbert's time, work in finding heights and distances was regularly incorporated in certain of the monastic schools, and there is evidence that actual field work was done at the monastery of Saint Gall.

Fibonacci. Fibonacci wrote on the practical side of geometry in his *Liber Quadratorum* (1220). This work dealt extensively with the use of the "quadrans" or geometric square which was a square framework with a movable pointer mounted at one corner. The instrument could be leveled by means of a plumb line and angles of elevation or depres-

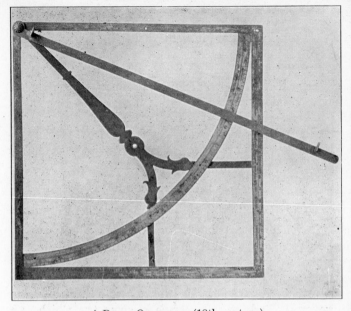

A BRASS QUADRANT (18th century)

From the collection of Professor David Eugene Smith. Courtesy of the Museums of the Peaceful Arts in New York.

sion could be found by sighting along the pointer. The sides of the square were divided in equal segments thus furnishing a simple way of computing the ratio of the unknown object.

The Astrolabe. The astrolabe, an instrument of many uses, belongs to many periods in the history of mathematics. It might properly be discussed in connection with the work of the Greeks, for the simplest astrolabe was the Greek dioptra mounted on a divided circle. The "astrolabe planisphere" was derived from the planisphere or map of the stars of the ancient astronomers. This was known in Babylonia and in Greece. Arab scholars wrote treatises on its use as did the Hebrew writer Rabbi ben Ezra (c. 1140). Toward the close of the thirteenth century, the astrolabe was used by pilots

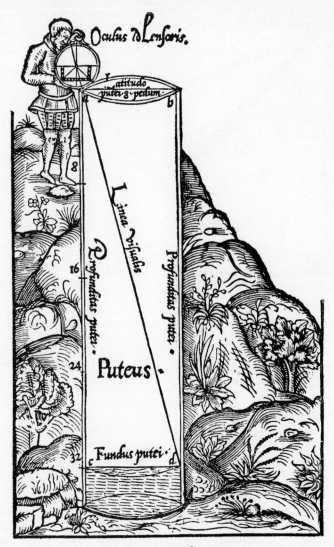

Oculus ɔ Lenſoris.

atitudo putei 3 pedum

a   b

Linea viſualis

Profunditas putei.

Profunditas putei

Puteus.

Fundus putei.

c   d

8

16

24

32

THE USE OF THE QUADRANT

From Gemma Frisius, *Les Principes d'Astronomie et Cosmographie*, Paris, 1557.

from Majorca in finding latitudes. Two centuries later, John II of Portugal was active in providing navigators with instruction in its use.

The instrument was the subject of one of the first scientific treatises written in the English language and accordingly it seems desirable to discuss it in connection with the work of the Middle Ages — the period in which this treatise was written.

Construction of the Astrolabe. Although the word "astrolabe" means "taking the stars," * the instrument was used for surveying as well as for astronomy. In its simplest form, the astrolabe consists of a metal circle with an "alidade" or pointer pivoted at its center. The instrument was hung from a ring in the top, its weight insuring its being in a vertical plane. The angle of elevation or depression of an object could be read directly from the scale on the rim of the dial and some astrolabes were engraved with a surveyor's square as well, the same pointer serving for both.

In the more complicated astrolabes, one side had the scale and alidade as described above while the other contained thin interchangeable metal plates surrounded by a movable rim called the "rete." The plates were projections of the celestial sphere on a plane, and, as each latitude had a different projection, the finer type of astrolabe had several such plates. The rete was often very elaborate. Crossing the plate from side to side was a curved piece of metal representing the zodiac. Prongs projecting from this band and from the edge of the rete gave the location of important stars. The rete was free to revolve about the plate and an alidade was mounted at its center to give the direction of the stars.†

Chaucer's Astrolabe. According to Roger Bacon's account, the astrolabes in Europe in the thirteenth century were cumbersome affairs of iron, costly to build, difficult to

---

* ἄστρον + λαβεῖν.

† See Marcia Latham, "The Astrolabe," *American Mathematical Monthly,* XXIV, 162.

AN ASTROLABE SHOWING THE DIVISIONS OF THE RIM AND THE
GEOMETRIC SQUARE

From the collection of Professor David Eugene Smith. Courtesy of the Museums of the Peaceful Arts, New York.

use, and in constant danger of rusting. He lamented that England had none of them.

By the fourteenth century, however, the instrument had been introduced into England, for an astrolabe attracted the

ASTROLABE PLANISPHERE SHOWING THE RETE AND THE MOVABLE
PLATES

From the collection of Professor David Eugene Smith. Courtesy of the Museums of the Peaceful Arts, New York.

attention of the ten-year-old son of the poet Chaucer, then
a student at Oxford. The boy asked permission to study it
and his father replied by sending him "a smal instrument
portatif aboute" and then, convinced that the existing

treatises were not reliable, he set about writing a discussion of the instrument for "litell Lowis." The title of this work was *Tractatus de Conclusionibus Astrolabii (Bred and Mylke for Childeren)*.* In the introduction to this work Chaucer acknowledges his indebtedness to other writers, saying, "I am but a compilatour of the labour of olde Astrologiens, and have it translated in myn English only for thy doctrine (instruction); and with this swerd shal I sleen envye." The book was written that Chaucer's son might learn to "knowe every tyme of the day by light of the sonne, and every tyme of the night by the fixed sterres;" to know the time of dawn and of evening twilight; to find the meridian altitude of the sun, the latitude of any place, and the points of the compass; and to measure heights and distances of inaccessible objects.

The instrument continued in use for several centuries. Brass astrolabes of wonderful workmanship were designed for the wealthy, paper ones for poorer people. Shortly before the first voyage of Christopher Columbus, the astrolabe was simplified for use in navigation and the process of finding the latitude of a ship by this means was taught to navigators by men from the observatory at Lisbon. It is not certain whether Columbus had the assistance of an astrolabe in his voyages to America, but it is known that this instrument was used by later explorers. In fact, Champlain's astrolabe was discovered in the Ottawa River in Canada in the nineteenth century.

It is interesting to note in this connection that the determination of a ship's longitude was so difficult in comparison with finding its latitude, that mariners resorted to "parallel sailing" — that is, they went north or south to the desired latitude and then followed that parallel to their destination.

The Cross-Staff. Another device used both for surveying and for astronomical purposes was the "cross-staff," which was also called the baculum, Jacob's Staff, and the arbalete.

* See W. W. Skeat, *The Complete Works of Geoffrey Chaucer*, III, Oxford, 1894.

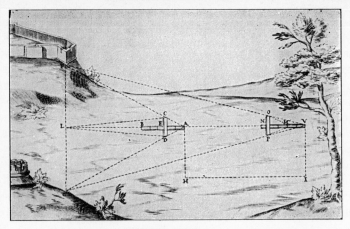

THE CROSS STAFF
From Bettini, *Apiaria*, Bologna, 1641.

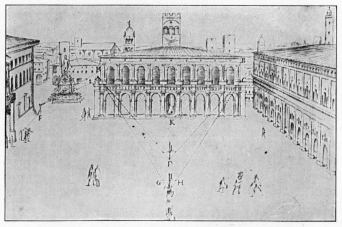

THE USE OF THE CROSS STAFF
From Bettini, *Apiaria*, Bologna, 1641.

This was a wooden rod about four feet long fitted with a cross-piece whose equal arms were always perpendicular to the staff. The observer placed his eye at the end of the staff and adjusted the cross-piece so that its extremities would just subtend the distance to be measured. The position of the cross-piece on the staff would then be noted, the observer would move to a second position on a line with his first position and with the midpoint of the distance to be measured and repeat the process. From the known distance between these stations and the known positions of the cross-piece, the desired distance could be computed.

The cross-staff was also used in astronomy in measuring the angular distance between two stars.

MODERN TIMES

The Beginning of the Sixteenth Century. During the Middle Ages, practical geometry was closely associated with

PORTRAIT BY HOLBEIN OF NICOLAS KRATZER, ASTRON-
OMER ROYAL TO HENRY VIII OF ENGLAND

astronomy, although it still maintained its identity as the subject "through which man hath sleight of length, of brede, of depth, of height," as Gower put it in 1390.

About 1464, however, Regiomontanus incorporated the applications of geometry to astronomy in his work *De triangulis omnimodis* — a treatise which was really a trigonometry, as its title indicates. From this time on, the measurement of angles tended to replace the direct measurement of lines in surveying and many portable instruments were invented to help in this work.

Surveying, however, was still considered a part of geometry, probably because many of the textbook writers, especially in Germany, acted as town surveyors. The period before the discovery of the telescope was marked by the invention of improved instruments, but it should be noted that this marks the close of the time when the instruments of elementary texts were also those of the astronomer and the surveyor.

Gauging. One of the important applications of practical geometry was in estimating the capacity of wine casks for the purposes of taxation. The subject was treated by many writers, Köbel's discussion (1514) being one of the most important. Although the topic remained in textbooks until comparatively recent times, its importance in the history of mathematics lies in the fact that, in attempting to solve the problem, the astronomer Kepler evolved a method not unlike that of the integral calculus.

The Theodolite. The modern theodolite is the invention of an Englishman, Leonard Digges (*c.* 1571). The instrument consists of a horizontal circle divided into 360 equal parts and, mounted on this, a vertical semicircle divided into 180 parts. On the vertical circle, there is a pointer with sights for measuring the angles. The theodolite was first used in estimating the range of cannon, but it was soon applied to more peaceful purposes. The name is not of Greek origin as might at first be supposed but it is a corruption from the Arabic *alhidada* through the intermediate form *athelida*. As such, it is a cognate of the "alidade," or pointer, of the earlier instruments. The theodolite was greatly improved when Ramsden (1763) invented a machine for dividing a circle more precisely than had hitherto been possible.

The Circumferentor. The circumferentor was a surveying compass perhaps invented by Tartaglia. According to the

CIRCUMFERENTOR (*c.* 1590)
From the Science Museum, South Kensington, England.

description given in Leybourne's *Compleat Surveyor* (1674 ed.), the distinctive feature of this instrument was the fact that the angle subtended by two objects could be read as the difference between the readings of the compass when the circumferentor was directed toward the two objects in turn. The instrument maintained its popularity for many years during which it was modified in various ways.

The Plane Table. The plane table, or the "Plain table" as it was sometimes called, combined the features of the theodolite and the circumferentor with certain additional advan-

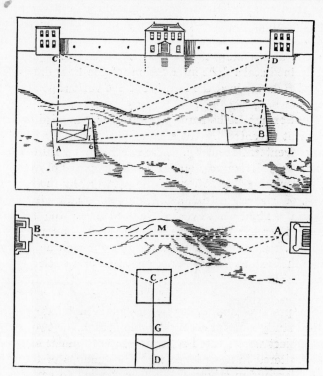

THE USE OF THE PLANE TABLE
From Le Clerc, *Traité de géométrie*, Paris, 1690 edition.

tages of great value in surveying. The instrument described by Leybourne consisted of a drawing board on which a sheet of paper might be fastened, and a movable alidade. The sights at the ends of the alidade were so arranged that a small hole in one could be raised or lowered thus permitting the reading of vertical angles. The instrument was used in map-making in the field by setting up the instrument at a point A, choosing a point on the board to represent this spot, and drawing lines through this point toward the salient points of the ground to be surveyed. The instrument was then transferred to another station B and the process was repeated, choosing the location of the second point on the map to be in the same direction from the first as B is from A and making the distance according to a previously determined scale. The intersections of the lines drawn from A and B determined the location of the various points of the map.

The Sextant. The name "sextant" was applied to an instrument invented by the astronomer Tycho Brahe in the early seventeenth century. It is referred to by Burton in his *Anatomy of Melancholy* (1628) when he speaks of examining and calculating the motions of the planets "by those curious helps of glasses, astrolabes, sextantes, quadrants." The modern sextant, however, developed from the reflecting octant invented by Newton about 1700. As the name indicate, the octant utilized an arc of one eighth of a circle while the sextant has an arc of one sixth of a circle.

SUMMARY

The practical applications of geometry antedate its theoretical study and, for a considerable period, the two parts of the subject were treated separately, the formulas of the one being altered in accordance with the findings of the other. The Alexandrian scholars, however, tended to combine the two and they wrote extensively on the use of various instruments in surveying and in astronomy. In Roman times, the study of demonstrative geometry was neglected and it practical applications were utilized in routine surveying and engineering problems. This condition continued in Europe during the Dark Ages. The revival of interest in the theoretical work began with the first translation of Euclid' *Elements* into Latin in the twelfth century. Until the seventeenth century, however, practical geometry remained as a prominent feature of works on geometry, but from that time the practical side of the work was relegated to texts for the surveyor and the engineer. The use of intuitive geometry as an introduction to theoretical work dates from about the beginning of the twentieth century, and its content as it appears in many junior-high-school courses is reminiscent both of the Egyptians who developed their geometry by observation and experiment and of later surveyors who used methods identical with those outlined in our present-day texts.

CHAPTER VII

DEMONSTRATIVE GEOMETRY

Early Greek Geometry — The Three Famous Problems — Euclid's *Elements* — Non-Euclidean Geometries — The Geometry of Conics — Modern Geometries — Summary.

EARLY GREEK GEOMETRY

Thales. The history of demonstrative geometry begins with Thales (*c.* 640 to *c.* 546 B.C.) who studied the applied geometry of the Egyptians and then took the important step of proving theorems instead of merely accepting them on the basis of intuition or experiment. Thus Thales began the work in geometry which culminated in Euclid's *Elements*, three hundred years later. The following list gives the theorems that are ascribed to Thales:

1. Any circle is bisected by a diameter.
2. The base angles of an isosceles triangle are equal.
3. When two lines intersect, the vertical angles are equal.
4. An angle inscribed in a semicircle is a right angle.
5. The sides of similar triangles are proportional.
6. Two triangles are congruent if they have two angles and a side respectively equal.*

These theorems are few in number but great in their significance. When their subject matter is compared with that of the Egyptian geometry which consisted of formulas for areas and volumes, it is evident that in founding the geometry of lines, Thales made the subject more abstract. It must be remembered, however, that Thales had practical objects in view in his theorems. One of them, for example, was used in finding the height of a pyramid from the length of its shadow, and another was needed in finding the distance of a ship from the shore.

The variety of subject matter in the theorems that are ascribed to Thales is indicative of an important characteristic

* See Heath, *Greek Mathematics*, I.

FINDING DISTANCES BY MEANS OF A RIGHT TRIANGLE

From Bettini, *Apiaria*, Bologna, 1641. The device shown here is sometimes ascribed to one of Napoleon's lieutenants, who measured the width of a river by sighting to the opposite bank along the edge of his cocked hat, and then, turning so he looked along the bank, finding the distance from his own position to the point where his gaze rested. This may also be the method used by Thales to find the distance of a ship at sea.

of the Greek geometry: many different topics were studied contemporaneously. Accordingly, when Euclid wrote his treatise he paid no attention to the chronological development of his subject matter but arranged it logically.

Pythagoras. The first philosopher to make the study of geometry a part of a liberal education was Pythagoras (*c.* 572 to *c.* 501 B.C.), who definitely broke away from the practical side of the subject which had even influenced Thales. Among the theorems discovered by Pythagoras and his followers were those relating to the sum of the angles of a triangle and of polygons. Whether the so-called Pythagorean Theorem is rightly named is open to question. The relation between the hypotenuse and the sides of certain right triangles was known in India at that time, and the Egyptians were aware that the 3–4–5 triangle was right-angled. It is probable, however, that the general theorem was due to the Pythagoreans, and that it was proved by means of similar triangles.

The Pythagoreans were the first to use geometry to express relations between quantities. The work would have been greatly simplified had they been in possession of algebraic symbolism, but even with the handicap of the clumsy expressions which this geometric algebra entailed, they were able to state important formulas and virtually to solve quadratic equations. A single example will illustrate their phraseology and method.

If a straight line be cut into equal and unequal segments, the rectangle contained by the unequal segments of the whole, together with the square on the straight line between the points of section is equal to the square on the half.

The algebraic significance of this theorem is clear if we consider a line of length $2\,a$, divided into the equal segments a and a, and into the unequal segments $a + b$ and $a - b$. The theorem then becomes $(a + b)\,(a - b) + b^2 = a^2$. In other words, the product of the sum and difference of two numbers is the difference of their squares. The geometric construction is as follows:

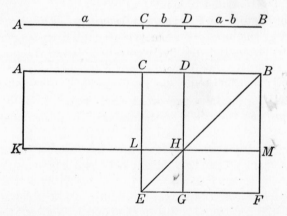

Let C be the midpoint of AB, and let D be a point taken at random on AB. Complete the square $CEFB$. Draw the diagonal EB and erect a perpendicular to AB at D cutting

EB at *H* and *EF* at *G*.   Draw *KM* through *H* parallel to *AB* cutting *CE* at *L*, and *BF* at *M*, and draw *AK* perpendicular to *AB* at *A*.

The problem now consists in showing that the rectangle *AH* plus the square *LG* equals the square *CF*, which may readily be done.

The Pythagorean Concept of a Proportion.   The Pythagorean definition of a proportion could be applied to commensurable magnitudes only.   Accordingly, when it was discovered that incommensurable numbers existed, as in the case of the diagonal of a square and its side, the entire concept of proportions was discarded, to be revived only when Eudoxus formulated a definition applicable to all cases.   Legend has it that the Pythagoreans drowned the man who first spoke of this case of incommensurable quantities outside of the society itself.   And this tale, whether true or not, illustrates the zeal with which the Pythagoreans cherished the teaching of their master and the discoveries of his followers that were gratefully attributed to him.

Other Parts of the Pythagorean Geometry.   The mysticism current in the minds of geometers prompted the suggestion by later writers that the Pythagoreans believed the universe to be composed of five elements, one for each of the five regular solids.   Thus the earth arose from the cube, fire came from the pyramid, air from the octahedron, water from the icosahedron, and the sphere of the universe from the dodecahedron.

There is probably a basis in fact for the story that the Pythagoreans adopted the mystic pentagon (the five-pointed star) as the badge of their society.   It is highly likely that the Pythagoreans could construct this figure, a task which would involve the division of a line in the Golden Section, thus introducing a new complexity, for the two segments so found are incommensurable with the line itself.

By studying geometry for its own sake, the Pythagoreans devoted considerable attention to matters of definition.

They studied the properties of parallel lines, evolved a geometric algebra based on equivalent areas, worked with the five regular solids, and developed a theory of proportion which was discarded with the discovery of incommensurable quantities.

THE THREE FAMOUS PROBLEMS

The Period from Pythagoras to Plato.   The period from the time of Pythagoras to that of Plato was characterized by great activity in geometry.   Much of the work centered about three famous problems that will be mentioned in greater detail.   Among the important mathematicians of this period were:

Hippocrates (*c.* 460 B.C.), who was the first to write a systematic treatment of geometry and who tried to square the circle (see page 258).

Zeno (*c.* 450 B.C.), whose paradoxes will be discussed in Chapter X.

Anaxagoras (*c.* 440 B.C.), who was also interested in the problem of squaring the circle (see page 257).

Hippias of Elis (*c.* 425 B.C.), who attempted the trisection of an angle.

Theodorus of Cyrene (*c.* 425 B.C.), who showed that the square roots of 3, 5, 7, ... 17 were irrational.

Democritus (*c.* 410 B.C.), who stated the propositions regarding the volume of cones and pyramids (see page 308).

Archytas (*c.* 400 B.C.), a friend of Plato, who classified geometry, arithmetic, astronomy, and music as the four mathematical sciences, and who attempted the problem of duplicating the cube (see page 265).

The progress made in geometry in this period has been summarized by Heath in this statement:

There is therefore probably little in the whole compass of the *Elements* of Euclid, except the new theory of proportion due to Eudoxus and its consequences, which was not in substance included in the recognized content of geometry and arithmetic by Plato's time, although the form and arrangement of the subject matter and the methods employed in particular cases were different from what we find in Euclid.*

The Importance of the Three Problems.   The problems of squaring a circle, trisecting an angle, and constructing a cube whose volume is twice that of a given cube occupied Greek mathematicians for upwards of three centuries.   These problems arose naturally in the course of investigations in transforming figures into others of equal area, in constructing regular polygons, and in constructing solids whose volumes were in given ratio.†

From their very beginning, these three problems have appealed to amateurs as well as to trained mathematicians.   A reference to people who try to square the circle appears in a comedy written by Aristophanes in the fifth century B.C., and from that time to the present the name "circle-squarers" has been applied to men who have attempted to do things that seem to be impossible.

It must be understood that each of these problems is beyond the limits of plane geometry, for the straightedge and compasses can be used only to solve problems involving equations of the first and second degree.   They cannot cope with transcendental numbers in the squaring of the circle, nor in solving cubic equations in the other two problems.   Accordingly, it is a waste of time to attempt to find suitable solutions using only the compasses and straightedge.

These problems may be solved, however, by means of curves drawn with other instruments or by curves that can be sketched through points located with compasses and straightedge construction.

The Quadrature of the Circle.   The first mention of the problem of squaring the circle is in connection with Anaxag-

* Heath, *Greek Mathematics*, I, 217.   Quoted by permission of the Oxford University Press.

† See Heath, *Greek Mathematics*, I, 218–70.

oras (*c.* 499 to *c.* 427 B.C.).   Anaxagoras came from a town in
Asia Minor near Smyrna, but he spent the greater part of his
life in Athens where he knew both Pericles and Euripides.
He seems to have become interested in the mathematical aspect of perspective drawing in making scenery for the plays
of Euripides, but he is chiefly remembered for his work in
astronomy.   Pericles was unpopular for a brief period just
before the Peloponnesian War, and his friends were liable to
attack by the citizens of Athens.   Anaxagoras was accused of
heresy because of his hypothesis that the moon shone only
by reflected light and that it was made of some earthly substance, while the sun, on the contrary, was a red hot stone that
emitted its own light.   He was imprisoned on this pretext, and
during this period he devoted his time to an attempt to square
the circle.   No one knows the conclusion of the story, but one
version has it that Anaxagoras was condemned to death but
that Pericles begged him off.   Another story says that he was
fined and banished, and that when he left Athens he said,
"I have not lost the Athenians, the Athenians have lost me."

The Study of Lunes.   A contemporary of Anaxagoras,
Hippocrates of Chios (*c.* 460 B.C.), succeeded in finding certain

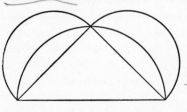

polygons which were equivalent in area to lunes,
— i.e., moon-shaped figures
bounded by the arcs of circles.

Little is known of Hip-
pocrates himself, although
a story has been told of him to the effect that he journeyed to
Athens in connection with a lawsuit about some ships that had
been taken by pirates.   This detained him in that city for a
long time, which he spent in study with the Athenian scholars
attempting to square the circle.

Hippocrates discovered that if semicircles were described
on the three sides of an isosceles right triangle, the area of the
two lunes would be equivalent to that of the triangle.   He

also discovered that if a similar construction was made on the
sides of half of a regular hexagon, the area of the three lunes
equals that of the half hex-
agon diminished by a semicircle drawn on one of the
sides of the figure.

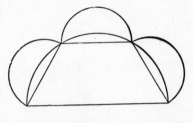

This success with an in-
scribed square and an in-
scribed regular hexagon led
Hippocrates to suppose that
he would eventually discover a polygon whose area is precisely
that of a circle.   His lack of success may have been the cause
of the discovery of another line of approach to the subject.

The Method of Exhaustion.   Antiphon (*c.* 430 B.C.) is said
to have devised the method of exhaustion whereby a regular
polygon was inscribed in a circle, the difference in area between
polygon and circle being *exhausted* as the number of sides of
the polygon was increased.   Eudoxus (*c.* 370 B.C.) carried this
further by considering both
the inscribed and the circumscribed polygons.

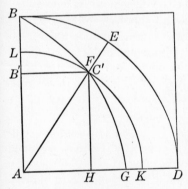

The Quadratrix. The quadratrix was a curve invented
by Hippias of Elis (*c.* 425
B.C.).   It could be used to
square the circle and also to
divide an angle into any number of equal parts.   This
curve is the locus of the intersection of the radius AE
and the line $B'C'$. The radius
rotates about the center with a constant velocity.   The line
$B'C'$ moves parallel to AD also with a constant velocity.
These rates are so timed that when AE coincides with AB,
$B'C'$ passes through B; and when AE coincides with AD,
$B'C'$ coincides with AD also.

Points on the curve may be located by drawing AE so that $\angle DAE = 45°$ and drawing $B'C'$ so that $AB' = \frac{1}{2}AB$. Then bisect $\angle DAE$ to find the new position of AE and bisect AB' to find the new position of $B'C'$. It will be noticed that if the curve is continuous, it will cut AD at a point G between A and D.

The use of this curve in squaring the circle may be due to Deinostratus (*c.* 350 B.C.), the brother of Menæchmus, or it may be due to Hippias himself. The proof is as follows: Suppose that $\dfrac{\widehat{BED}}{AB} = \dfrac{AB}{AK}$ where $AK \gtreqless AG$. If AK equals AG, the problem as solved for $\widehat{BED}$ is one fourth of the given circle and its value may be found by constructing the third proportional to AG and AB. On the other hand, if AK is greater or less than AG, the original hypothesis can be shown to be impossible. For instance, for $AK > AG$, draw a quarter circle KFL cutting the quadratrix at F and cutting AB at L. Draw FH perpendicular to AD. Then $\dfrac{\widehat{DEB}}{AB} = \dfrac{\widehat{KFL}}{AK}$ for arcs of the same number of degrees are proportional to their radii. But it was assumed that $\dfrac{\widehat{DEB}}{AB} = \dfrac{AB}{AK}$. It follows that $AB = \widehat{KFL}$. Since F lies on the quadratrix however, $\dfrac{AB}{FH} = \dfrac{\widehat{DEB}}{\widehat{DE}}$ and $\dfrac{\widehat{DEB}}{\widehat{DE}} = \dfrac{\widehat{KFL}}{KF}$. It is evident, then, that $\dfrac{AB}{FH} = \dfrac{\widehat{KFL}}{\widehat{KF}}$, and since $AB = \widehat{KFL}$, $FH = KF$, which is absurd. This rules out the hypothesis that AK is greater than AG It can also be proved that AK cannot be less than AG. The one objection to this proof is the fact that the point G cannot be located exactly. It can only be found approximately.

Later Work in Squaring the Circle. Interest in the squaring of the circle was not confined to the Greeks. Boethius (*c.* 510) said that it had been done in the period since Aristotle's time but he noted that the proof was too long for him to give.   Boethius was not unique in his illusion that the problem could be treated by the methods of plane geometry. Many other mathematicians have supposed that they have solved the problem, for unlike algebra, geometry raises no danger signal when impossible or special conditions are postulated; but each of these quadrators has been met by a critic who has demolished his argument.   The proof that the value of π is transcendental was discovered only in 1882. Prior to that, the circle-squarers were not without hope that they might attain their objective.   Now this is known to be impossible.

The Trisection of an Angle by the Quadratrix.   The ease with which any angle may be bisected and the simplicity with

which a right angle may be trisected has led many people to suppose that any angle may be trisected by a construction made with compasses and a straightedge. The proof that such a construction is impossible, however, has had no effect on amateur mathematicians, who refuse to accept this proof or who perhaps are unable to comprehend it.

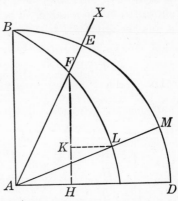

The quadratrix could be used to trisect an angle.   Suppose the given angle be $\angle DAX$.   Place this angle at the center of a circle within which a quadratrix is drawn and let AX cut the quadratrix at F and the circle at E.   Draw FH perpendicular to AD.   Then trisect FH and through K, the point of trisection, draw KL parallel to AD cutting the quadratrix at L.   Draw AL.   The angle DAL is the angle required. The proof rests on the property of the quadratrix that

$\dfrac{\overparen{ED}}{\overparen{MD}} = \dfrac{FH}{KH}.$ Since $KH = \frac{1}{3}FH$, it follows that $\overparen{MD} = \frac{1}{3}\overparen{ED}$

and since the arc ED is trisected, the central angle DAX is trisected also. It should be noted that the angle may be divided into any given number of equal parts by dividing FH in the desired ratio.

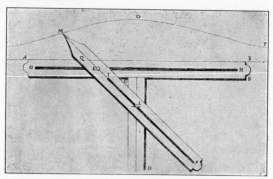

INSTRUMENT FOR CONSTRUCTING THE CONCOID
From Bettini, *Apiaria*, Bologna, 164

The Trisection of an Angle by the Conchoid. The conchoid of Nicomedes * was another curve by which the construction could be made. This is defined as a curve traced by a point P on a line l which rotates about the fixed point A, the distance from P to the intersection of l with a fixed line m being a constant. An instrument for drawing this curve mechanically is shown above. To trisect an angle, this instrument is placed so that the

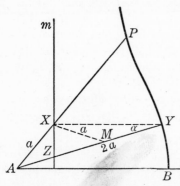

* Nicomedes (*c.* 180 B.C.) was a Greek mathematician of whom little is known. The conchoid seems to have been his only contribution to mathematics.

point A coincides with the vertex of the given angle. If l cuts m at X, then P is chosen so that $XP = 2AX$ and the curve is drawn. A line is drawn through X parallel to AB cutting the conchoid at Y. The line AY is the line required for $\angle BAY$ is equal to $\frac{1}{3}\angle BAP$.*

A Solution by Archimedes. A solution of the problem of trisecting an angle is attributed to Archimedes. It involves a new idea called a "verging" † which consisted of drawing a figure in such a way that a required line segment should *verge*

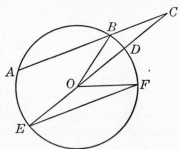

toward a specified length or position. It suggests successive trials leading to closer and closer approximations but never perhaps accomplishing the end desired.

This method of work had been described by Aristotle (*c.* 340 B.C.), and Apollonius, who was a contemporary of Archimedes, wrote two books on the subject. The method was not discussed by Euclid and it should be classed with other approximations such as the method of exhaustion.

As an example of verging, suppose that EF and AB are parallel chords of a circle whose center is O. Suppose that the diameter ED cuts AB produced at C; and suppose BC is equal to the radius of the circle. If these conditions are fulfilled, then $\angle FOD = \frac{2}{3}\angle FOB$. Accordingly, if the figure could be drawn with $\angle FOB$ equal to the required angle, the trisection problem could be solved. The difficulty lies in choosing the direction of EF and AB so that BC will *verge*

---

* The proof consists of bisecting ZY. Then since $ZY = 2a$ by construction, and since M is the midpoint of the hypotenuse of the right triangle XYZ, $XM = a$, and the triangles AXM and XMY are isosceles. But $\angle XMA = 2a$, being an exterior angle of the triangle XMY, and $\angle XMA = \angle MAX$, and $\angle XYM = \angle BAY$. Therefore $\angle YAX = 2 \angle BAY$ and $\angle BAY = \frac{1}{3}\angle BAP$.

† The Greek name for this method is *neusis*.

toward the proper length. The process suggests the difficulties that would arise if we were to attempt the accurate construction of the figures for all of the original exercises given in a plane geometry.

Another Solution. Another illustration of the use of verging, assumes a given angle XBA. The lines AC and BX are each perpendicular to BC, and AF is parallel to BC. The line BDE is drawn cutting AC at E and AF at D and having

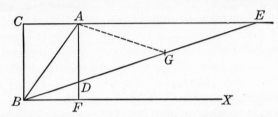

$DE = 2AB$. It follows that $\angle XBD = \frac{1}{3}XBA$. It is evident that this proof is identical with that which uses the conchoid. The difference lies in the fact that, in the case of the conchoid, the point E was located mechanically. In the problem as it is given here, it is located by having ED *verge* toward B.

Use of Conics. Pappus * (c. 300) devised a method of trisecting an angle which made use of the intersection of a

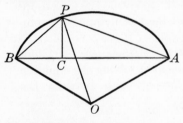

circle and a hyperbola. He placed the angle in question with its vertex at the center of a circle. He then trisected the subtended chord AB at C, and constructed a hyperbola having two thirds of the chord as its transverse axis and $\sqrt{3}$ times the transverse axis for its conjugate one. Previous work showed that points on such a hyperbola had the property that if they were joined to the ends of the

* Pappus of Alexandria wrote several commentaries on the work of various mathematicians, one being on Euclid. He also compiled a *Collection* designed to revive Greek geometry.

egment AB, one of the angles thus formed would be double
he other. Accordingly if P be the point in which the
yperbola cuts the arc AB, then $\angle PBA = 2 \angle BAP$, and
$\angle POA = 2 \angle BOP$.

The Duplication of the Cube. In a collection of solutions
f this famous problem, there appears a letter purporting to
e written by Eratosthenes (c. 230 B.C.) to the ruler Ptolemy
Euergetes who was then trying to persuade Eratosthenes to
ome to Alexandria to tutor his son. In this letter, the origin
f the problem is traced to an unknown poet who represented
n ancient king as erecting a tomb for his friend Glaucus.
Being dissatisfied with the result, the king declared it must be
oubled in size and accordingly he ordered each dimension to
e doubled. This mistake of the poet's perpetuated the
roblem and mathematicians sought to solve it.

According to another account, the Delians sought aid from
n oracle to avert a plague then raging in their city. The
racle replied that a certain altar in the city must be doubled
 size, while its shape remained a cube. At this point the
elians consulted Plato. According to Plutarch, Plato re-
used to attempt the problem but turned it over to his stu-
ents. Eratosthenes himself gives a different version, in
hich Plato said that the god in question did not really want
is larger altar but that he wished "to shame the Greeks for
eir neglect of mathematics and their contempt for geom-
ry."

Duplication by Means of Conics. Hippocrates of Chios
. 460 B.C.) had reduced the problem of solving the equation
$= 2 a^3$ to finding two mean proportionals between the
antities a and $2 a$. If these are x and y, then $\dfrac{a}{x} = \dfrac{x}{y} = \dfrac{y}{2 a}$.

king the first two ratios we have $x^2 = ay$; from the second
ir $2 ax = y^2$. But if $x^2 = ay$, then $x^4 = a^2y^2 = 2 a^3x$, and
$= 2 a^3$. From this time, then, the problem took the form
finding the two mean proportionals.

Archytas (c. 400 B.C.) found these values by means of the

intersection of three solids: a right cone, a cylinder, and an anchor ring whose inner diameter was zero.

Menæchmus (c. 350 B.C.) who was tutor to Alexander the Great, solved the problem by the intersection of two parabolas. Suppose $AO = 2OB$ and suppose AO to be perpendicular to OB. Let P be

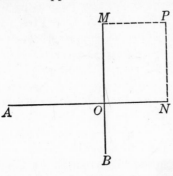

a point with PN perpendicular to AO and PM perpendicular to OB so chosen that OM is a mean proportional between AO and ON and so that ON is a mean proportional between OM and OB. The first of these last conditions means that $OM^2 = OA \cdot ON$, but if we turn this into modern notation, taking O for the origin, AO for the x axis and OB for the y axis, we have $y^2 = OA \cdot x$ which of course is a parabola. Similarly, $ON^2 = OM \cdot OB$ or $x^2 = OB \cdot y$, which is a parabola also. But since OM and ON are the coördinates of P, the point P lies on the intersection of these parabolas, and if $AO = 2\,p$ and $OB = p$, the curves are $y^2 = 2\,px$ and $x^2 = py$.

Solving these, ON is found to be the line required.*

This problem may be solved mechanically by using a framework with a movable side AM and a fixed side NB each at right angles to MN. The side OB of the cube is laid out on a line. A segment

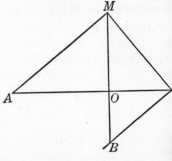

AO equal to twice OB is drawn perpendicular to OB at O. The framework is then laid on the figure with $\angle M$ on O

* This proof is abridged from that given in Heath, Greek Mathematics, 253–54.

$\angle N$ on AO and with the sides passing through A and B. By the right-angle properties of the figure, it is evident that ON is the line required.   This solution has been attributed to

Plato, but his dislike of mechanical devices makes his authorship of the device unlikely.

The Cissoid. Another solution may be obtained by using the cissoid, a curve invented by Diocles (*c.* 180 B.C.). The cissoid is obtained by the intersection of DE which is perpendicular to the diameter of a circle with a line drawn from the end of the diameter to the intersection of the perpendicular $D'E'$ such that $EO = OE'$.

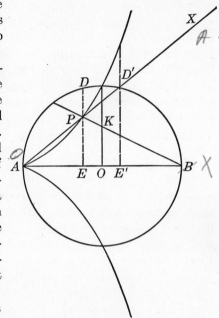

To use this curve in duplicating the cube, let OK be on a radius perpendicular to AO with OK equal to $\frac{1}{2}AO$. Let P be the point on the cissoid determined as in the accompanying figure.   Then by similar triangles, $PE = \frac{1}{2}BE$. But DE is a mean proportional between AE and EB by construction, and $\dfrac{DE}{BE} = \dfrac{D'E'}{AE'}$ by congruent triangles.   It can also be shown by similar triangles that $\dfrac{PE}{AE} = \dfrac{D'E'}{AE'}$.   Accordingly, $\dfrac{PE}{AE} = \dfrac{DE}{BE}$, but as $\dfrac{AE}{DE} = \dfrac{DE}{BE}$, it follows that $\dfrac{PE}{AE} = \dfrac{AE}{DE} = \dfrac{DE}{AB}$.   Thus AE and DE are the mean proportionals between PE and BE (or $2PE$).   Then DE is the edge of the cube whose volume is twice that of the cube of side PE.

Summary.   These three problems are justly famous for the interest they have roused on the part of mathematicians for over two thousand years.   Their value in the development of mathematics cannot be overestimated, for although none of them can ever be solved by the classical methods of plane geometry, their study prompted the invention of the method of exhaustion, a forerunner of the calculus; it increased interest in the intersection of solid figures; it fostered the study of conics; and it was the occasion for the invention and investigation of curves of higher degree.

EUCLID'S "ELEMENTS"

Euclid.   It has been conjectured that Euclid received his early training in mathematics at Athens and that there he came in contact with various attempts at reducing the subject matter of geometry to a logical basis.   About the year 300 B.C., he was teaching at Alexandria, probably at the invitation of the ruler Ptolemy, and while there, he wrote several works, the most important being the *Elements.**   Upwards of seven hundred years later, the commentator, Proclus, says that Ptolemy asked Euclid if there were not some shorter way to the study of geometry than through the thirteen books of the *Elements*, and that Euclid replied that there was no royal road to geometry.   Another commentator, Stobæus, reports that one of Euclid's students asked what he would gain from the study of geometry and that Euclid called to his servant, "Give this man three obols, since he must make gain out of what he learns."   Both anecdotes are told of other scholars and of other royal patrons and students.

The Arrangement of the *Elements*.   In the *Elements* the mathematical knowledge of Euclid's time is arranged and summarized.   Although this work is popularly supposed to

---

* στοιχεῖα.   (Stoicheia.)
The best single reference for Euclid's work is Heath, *Euclid.*

be a geometry, it also contained the theory of numbers and a considerable amount of algebra. In fact, it could aptly be called by the name "General Mathematics." Euclid seems to have contributed but little in the way of subject matter, although that little was of prime importance, but the arranging of the work would be sufficient contribution were it accompanied by nothing that was original.

Like the great literary classics of Greece and like the sacred writings of the Hebrews, the divisions of this treatise were called "books," and each was written on a separate scroll of parchment for convenience in handling.

Euclid's work was more formal than are the elementary geometries to-day. He was writing for mature thinkers who needed no introductory work to convince them of the value of the subject. Educators would say that his work lacked motivation — yet it has been the most widely used text that the world has ever produced. The concepts needed in each Book were defined at its beginning. Postulates were stated and also those generally accepted hypotheses which we call *axioms* but which Euclid called "common notions." As we have seen, the field of plane geometry had already been restricted to those figures that could be constructed by means of a straightedge and compasses. Euclid's *Elements*, accordingly, began with construction problems and the reader learned that a figure could be drawn with his instruments before he studied its properties. Each proof given in the *Elements* was stated in a standardized form: an enunciation of the problem in general terms, a statement of the conditions in specific terms (our "hypothesis"), the definition or specification of what is to be proved, the constructions needed, if any, the proof, and the conclusion. At times, this would be followed by a statement of the conditions under which the problem was impossible. These proofs were given synthetically and there was no hint of the method by which they were first devised. Corollaries were called "porisms," and were given in one of Euclid's other works. Euclid avoided proof by superposition whenever possible, but he made extensive use of the *reductio ad absurdum*. In several cases, his classification of figures or of angles indicates a conservatism that forbade his dropping customary terms even though he made no later use of them. Among such terms are rhombus and rhomboid.

The Contents of the *Elements*. The extent of the subject matter of the thirteen Books of the *Elements* is best indicated by an outline of their general bearing. Certain parts of their geometric content will then be discussed in greater detail. Other sections have been mentioned previously in Chapter II and in Chapter IV.

Book   I. Triangles, perpendiculars, parallels, areas of rectilinear figures, the Pythagorean Theorem.

Book   II. Transformation of areas, geometric algebra (see page 166).

Book   III. Circles, chords, and tangents.

Book   IV. Polygons and circles. Construction of regular polygons including the regular pentagon.

Book   V. Treatment of proportion.

Book   VI. Idea of proportion applied to similar figures.

Book VII. Theory of numbers; classification of numbers as even, odd, odd times odd — plane, solid, perfect, etc. (see Chapter XI); numerical theory of proportion.

Book VIII. Study of continued proportion.

Book   IX. Number theory, including a proof that the number of primes is infinite.

Book   X. Study of irrationals.

Book   XI. Solid Geometry corresponding to Book I for plane geometry.

Book XII. The method of exhaustion used to show that circles are proportional to the squares of their diameters, etc.

Book XIII. Regular solids.

Propositions of Book I. The most famous of the earlier propositions of Book I is Proposition 5: "In an isosceles triangle the angles at the base are equal to one another, and, if the equal straight lines be produced further, the angles under the base will be equal to one another." This is proved by extending the equal sides AB and AC to F and G respectively, making $BF = CG$, and proving the triangles AFC and ABG congruent. This proposition sometimes marked the limit of the work in Euclid in the universities in the Middle Ages. It was frequently called the *Pons asinorum* or the "Bridge of Asses," with the implication that the students could not cross it. A corollary to this implication is given in the couplet

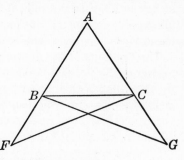

If this be rightly called the bridge of asses,
He's not the fool that sticks but he that passes.

Another interpretation would have it that the diagram of the problem resembled a bridge truss so steep that no horse could surmount it, but not too steep for an ass. Roger Bacon (*c.* 1250) gave it the name *Elefuga*, which meant, he said, the "flight of the miserable ones," but Heath suggests it may mean instead "flight from the *Elements*."

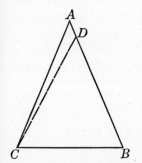

The converse problem was proved by *reductio ad absurdum*. If AB be longer than AC, then let BD equal AC. Then the triangles ABC and DBC are congruent, which is absurd.

The work on parallel lines culminated with the proposition that the sum of the angles of a triangle is equal to two right angles. The study of the subject of parallel lines is discussed in the section on Non-Euclidean Geometries pages 275 to 281.

The Pythagorean Theorem. Proposition 47, Book I, concerns the square on the hypotenuse of a right triangle. According to a legend, Pythagoras sacrificed an ox in honor of the discovery of this proposition. The case of the triangle whose sides had the ratios 3:4:5 had probably been known long before. Pythagoras investigated the question of finding rational numbers that could be made the sides of such tri-

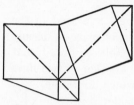

angles, and seems to have arrived at the idea that these are (1) an odd number, (2) half of the number that is one less than the square of the first, and (3) half the number that is one greater than the square of the first. It has been suggested that Pythagoras reached this formula through the study of figurate numbers, for, since the difference between two square

FIGURE FOR THE PYTHA-
GOREAN THEOREM, AS-
CRIBED TO LEONARDO DA
VINCI

numbers is an odd number (or *gnomon*), if two square numbers could be found whose difference was a square number, the problem could be solved by inspection. Thus:

Series of integers	1	2	3	4	5	6	7	8
" " squares	1	4	9	16	25	36	49	64
" " differences		3	5	7	9	11	13	15

Clearly 16, 9, 25 are square numbers that satisfy the condition, and later in the series 144, 25, 169 do also. Many different diagrams have been used to prove the Pythagorean Theorem, and many names have been applied to it: the Bride's Chair, Dulcarnon ("two-horned" or "puzzle"), the Franciscan's cowl or hood, and Pacioli's picturesque terms — the Goose's foot and the Peacock's tail. Schopenhauer spoke of the usual textbook figure for this theorem as the "mousetrap proof."

Book II. Book II contains a geometric treatment of algebra based on the equality of areas. The product of two different quantities is represented by a rectangle; the product of a quantity by itself is represented by a square. A proposition typical of this group has been discussed previously on page 166.

Book III. Book III treats of circles and the measurement of angles. It is in this Book that Euclid defines an angle of a segment as that angle "contained by a straight line and a circumference of a circle, the so-called "horn angle," evidently a relic of the older geometry but a concept that was to become important in later times.

Although Euclid's definition of an angle appeared in the introduction to Book I, it may not be out of place to discuss the matter of angles here. Euclid's definition stated that "A plane angle is the inclination to one another of two lines in a plane which meet one another but which do not lie in the same line." This should be considered in connection with the comment that appears in the Billingsley *Euclid* (1570), the first edition of Euclid to be printed in English:

> But if the two lines which touch the one the other be without all inclination the one to the other and be drawn directly the one to the other, then make they not any angle at all as if the lines *CD* and *DE* touch the one the other in the point *D*, and yet as ye see, they make no angle.

The classification of figures according to both sides and angles seems to be due to the fact that the reflex angle was not recognized as an angle until the middle of the sixteenth century. Prior to that time, the study of plane figures had included the reëntrant quadrilateral under the name of a four-sided triangle, or in the phrase of Zenodorus (*c.* 180 B.C.), a "hollow-angled" figure. And during the seventeenth century, Bettini (1641) discussed the properties of four-sided triangles (i.e. quadrilaterals containing a reflex angle).

Book IV.   Book IV requires no definitions beyond those given previously. It deals with inscribing circles in figures or with circumscribing circles about them, and it culminates in the construction of a regular polygon of fifteen sides.

The Definition of Proportion.   Book V is noteworthy for its definition of proportion, which may perhaps be due to Eudoxus and which is so phrased as to cover cases of both commensurable and incommensurable quantities. It reads:

Magnitudes are said to be in the same ratio, the first to the second and the third to the fourth, when, if any equimultiples whatever be taken of the first and third, and any equimultiples whatever of the second and fourth, the former equimultiples like exceed, are equal to, or alike fall short of, the latter equimultiples respectively taken in corresponding order.

In Book VI, the definition of proportion is put to use in the study of areas. A single case will illustrate the method. The first proposition states that triangles which are under the same height (i.e., which have the same height) are to one another as their bases. It has been proved previously that triangles having the same base and the same height are equal.

Suppose the triangles are ABC and ACD. Now produce BD in both directions, marking off to the left from B segments equal to BC, and to the right of D segments equal to CD. Join the points of division at A. Let X and Y be two points

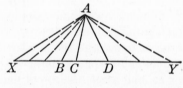

of division. Then triangle XCA is the same multiple of triangle ABC that XC is of BC and triangle ACY is the same multiple of triangle ACD that CY is of CD. Then if XC equals CY, triangle XCA equals triangle ACY; if XC is less than CY, triangle XCA is less than triangle ACY; if XC is greater, triangle XCA is greater. Thus the conditions of the definitions are satisfied and the ratio of the triangles is the same as the ratio of their bases. No mention is made of the incommensurable case for both commensurable and incommensurable numbers may form proportions according to the definition.

The Last Seven Books. Books VII, VIII, IX, and X are largely concerned with the theory of numbers, and with irrationals. Their content will be discussed in Chapter XI under the topics "Prime Numbers" and "Perfect Numbers" (see pages 331 and 334). The subject matter of irrationals has been discussed previously on pages 183 to 186.

Books XI, XII, and XIII deal with solid geometry, following the general plan of the work in plane geometry.

Popularity of Euclid's *Elements*. Although the Romans paid little attention to demonstrative geometry and although the scholars of the Dark Ages were ignorant of it for the most part, Euclid's *Elements* was one of the first works to be translated from the Greek to the Arabic under the patronage of Harun al-Rashid (*c.* 800) and of his son al-Mâmûn. Similarly, the translation of Euclid from the Arabic to Latin made by Adelard of Bath (*c.* 1120) was among the first of the translations of the twelfth-century renaissance. About a hundred and fifty years later (i.e. *c.* 1260), Campanus prepared a Latin translation of Euclid based on earlier versions and with valuable additions of his own. It was this translation that was the first to appear in print (Venice, 1482). The sixteenth century was marked by more authoritative translations into Latin and by the publication of the first version in English (1570), which is attributed to Sir Henry Billingsley who later became Lord Mayor of London. The preface to this work was written by John Dee, who may very probably have had a major share in making the translation itself. John Dee was a mathematician of considerable influence but, like other scholars of his time, he was interested in alchemy, astrology, and witchcraft as well as in more scientific studies. The revival of interest in Euclidean geometry in the universities of the sixteenth century is discussed elsewhere (see Chapter XIV), and great attention was paid the subject in England in the following century under the influence of Isaac Barrow, whose *Euclid*, published in 1655 remained the standard for many years. Legendre's *Éléments de géométrie* (1794) departed from Euclid's sequence of propositions and simplified the subject matter in many respects.

NON-EUCLIDEAN GEOMETRIES

The Parallel Line Postulate. Several definitions of parallel lines were considered by the Greeks and then discarded.

Among these was the definition that parallel lines are lines everywhere equidistant from each other, and also the definition that they were lines having the same direction from a given line. Prior to Euclid's time, the work with parallels involved many contradictions. Euclid removed these difficulties by his definition of parallels and his famous fifth postulate. He defined these lines as "straight lines which, being in the same plane and being produced indefinitely in both directions, do not meet one another in either direction. His postulate of parallels assumed "that, if a straight line falling on two straight lines makes the interior angles on the same side less than two right angles, the two straight lines, if produced indefinitely, meet on that side on which are the angles less than the two right angles." Mathematicians were not content to accept this postulate but all subsequent attempts to prove it as a proposition have failed. The authors were not always aware that this was the case, and upwards of two thousand years passed before men began to realize that this postulate was independent of Euclid's other definitions and assumptions.

Meaning of the Term "Non-Euclidean." Any system of geometry whose postulates contradict those of Euclid is said to be non-Euclidean, but the term is generally reserved for those geometries which deny Euclid's Postulate 5.

Saccheri. The Jesuit priest Saccheri (1667–1733) was the first to write on the subject of the non-Euclidean geometries, although he himself was not aware that he was dealing with this subject. Saccheri was an Italian, a brilliant teacher, and a man of such remarkable memory that he could play three games of chess at a time without seeing any of the boards. Through his teacher Thomas Ceva, brother of the discoverer of Ceva's Theorem, Saccheri met the important mathematicians of his day, among them Viviani, who called himself the last pupil of Galileo. Saccheri was thoroughly familiar with the Greek geometry but he seems to have paid little attention to the contemporary discoveries of Newton and Leibniz. His

*Euclidis ab omni naevo vindicatus,** published in 1733, the year
of his death, was an attempt to clear Euclid of the criticisms
made of the parallel line postulate and of his treatment of
proportions. Saccheri's method of vindicating Euclid's use
of Postulate 5 was to assume the postulate false and to then
show that such an assumption led to an absurdity. To do
this, he began by ignoring the postulate altogether. He considered a quadrilateral *ABCD* such that the angles at *A* and
B were right and such that the sides *A D* and *C B* were equal.

This birectangular quadrilateral was
shown to have its other angles equal.
By Euclid's hypothesis, these angles
would necessarily be right angles. If
Euclid's postulate were not accepted,
there was the possibility that each angle
was either acute or obtuse. In the
former case, the sum of the angles of a
triangle would be less than two right
angles; in the latter case the sum would be greater. Saccheri
then set himself the task of proving that each of these hypotheses led to contradictions. His work in the case of the
obtuse angle hypothesis rested on the assumption that the
length of a straight line is infinite. In the other case, he
made an illegitimate use of infinitesimals. Saccheri, however,
was unconscious of these discrepancies and at the close of his
work he declared that "The foregoing considerations seem
to me sufficient to clear Euclid of the faults with which he
has been reproached."

What Saccheri had actually accomplished, however, was
to outline the geometries that would result on the basis of the
acute and the obtuse angle hypothesis. His failure to see that

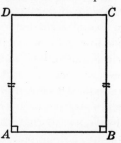

* See the translation of this work by George Bruce Halstead, published in
Chicago in 1920, with the title, *Saccheris Euclidis Vindicatus*. Translations
of excerpts from Saccheri, Bolyai, and Lobachevsky are given in the Smith
Source Book in Mathematics and should be consulted. See also H. S. Carslaw,
The Elements of Non-Euclidean Plane Geometry and Trigonometry, London,
1916.

the postulate that a straight line may be extended indefinitely was incompatible with his obtuse angle hypothesis was not surprising, for this point remained undiscovered for over a hundred years after the publication of his work.

Saccheri's book was almost ignored by his contemporaries and it was unknown to his successors, although many of them puzzled over the proof of the postulate with which it was principally concerned. In 1889, however, Beltrami hailed Saccheri as the Italian predecessor of Bolyai and Lobachevsky. This tardy recognition was characteristic of the history of non-Euclidean geometry. Outstanding mathematicians puzzled over its major issues, but the men who made the greatest contributions to the subject were ignored and their work was neglected.

Later Attempts to Prove the Postulate. The elusiveness of the problem is illustrated by several approaches made to it. Legendre (1752–1833), starting *de novo*, proved that the sum of the angles of a triangle could not be greater than two right angles, but he was unable to prove that it could not be less. His alleged proofs, however, rested on assumptions that were themselves equivalent to the hypothesis which they sought to establish. Thibaut (1809) sought to discover the sum of the angles of a triangle by the rotation of a line through each angle in turn. This idea was copied by Playfair (1813) but its validity was questioned when it was seen that the same method yielded erroneous results in the case of a spherical triangle, and Gauss showed that it virtually assumed the theorem it attempted to prove. Lagrange presented a paper on the subject of parallel lines at the French Academy, but stopped when part way through with the words, "I must meditate further on this." * Gauss, in 1817, wrote, "I am becoming more and more convinced that the necessity of our geometry cannot be proved." But mathematicians even then were unready to admit that Euclid's geometry was only one of several possible systems.

* "Il faut que j'y songe encore."

Bolyai. Toward the close of the eighteenth century, Gauss made a study of the acute angle hypothesis, which, however, he failed to carry to completion. At this time, he was in close touch with a Hungarian student named Bolyai (1775–1856) who was also interested in mathematics. Bolyai later returned to Hungary, keeping in communication with Gauss meanwhile. In 1823, Bolyai's son Janos (1802–1860) then barely twenty-one years old, wrote to his father of a new discovery, saying, "I have created a new universe from nothing." This enthusiasm was well founded, for he had developed a new system of geometry on the acute-angle hypothesis in which those theorems of Euclid that were independent of Postulate 5 still operated but in which the others were replaced by such amazing conclusions as this: that in a plane, instead of one line, two lines could be drawn through a point parallel to a given line and that through this point an infinite number of lines might be drawn lying in the angle between the first two and having the property that they would not intersect the given line. Amazing as this was in contrast to Euclidean geometry, it was equally logical. The elder Bolyai advised the immediate publication of this work, giving as his reasons, "First, because ideas pass easily from one to another, who can anticipate his publication; and, secondly, there is some truth in this, that many things have an epoch, in which they are found at the same time in several places, just as the violets appear on every side in the spring." The opportunity for publication did not come until 1832, when this study was printed as an appendix to a work by the father. Gauss was enthusiastic, saying that this publication relieved him of all necessity of continuing the work which he had begun years before; but Janos Bolyai suspected that Gauss was unwilling to admit that some one else had anticipated him and the young author questioned whether or not his father had shown the work to Gauss at an earlier date. This suspicion seems to be unfounded, as does the counter suggestion that the Bolyais had their first idea of the subject from Gauss himself.

Again, this work was almost ignored and Janos Bolyai spent the rest of his career as a mathematician studying the new geometry, always suspecting that the discoveries of others along the same line were really his own work.

Lobachevsky.   Meantime, in Russia, an obscure mathematician named Lobachevsky (1793–1856) lectured on the

NICOLAI IVANOVITCH LOBACHEVSKY
From the collection of Professor David Eugene Smith.

acute angle geometry at the University of Kasan.   His work seems to have taken form before 1826 but it was not published in translation until 1840.   Gauss was so impressed with it that he contemplated the study of Russian in order to consult Lobachevsky's other works which were available only in that language. Bolyai, of course, declared that Lobachevsky was influenced by his own work of 1832.

Riemann. Neither Bolyai nor Lobachevsky considered the obtuse angle hypothesis, a subject which was first treated by Riemann (1826–1866) at Göttingen in 1854. Riemann seems to have begun by the study of the postulate that a straight line may be infinitely long, the assumption that had convinced Saccheri and Legendre that the obtuse angle hypothesis was untenable. Discarding this postulate, Riemann developed a geometry in which all lines were of finite length, any pair of lines intersected if they lay in the same plane, and the sum of the angles of a triangle was greater than two right angles.

The Names of these Geometries. The three geometries: those of Euclid, Bolyai and Lobachevsky, and Riemann were given the names parabolic, hyperbolic, and elliptic by Klein in 1871.

Summary. For two thousand years, Euclid's geometry was held to be the only system possible. The first work based on other postulates had for its object the vindication of Euclid's ideas as the only tenable hypothesis, and the failure of Saccheri's work in accomplishing this end was not appreciated at the time. Geometries based on the acute-angle hypothesis developed almost simultaneously in Hungary and in Russia, but the development of the third type was delayed owing to the retention of the postulate that concerns the length of a straight line.

The three geometries are equally logical. For all practical purposes, work based on any of the three gives us results far within the limits of accuracy of our measurements.

THE GEOMETRY OF CONICS

Conic Sections. Although the study of the ellipse, hyperbola, and parabola was excluded from demonstrative geometry when its subject matter was restricted to figures that could be constructed by means of an unmarked straightedge and compasses, it is none the less fitting to consider in this connection the work of the Greeks and of later mathematicians in applying the methods of demonstrative geometry to conic sections.

The Greeks seem to have derived the conic sections from three types of cones each generated by the rotation of a right triangle about one of its sides. These cones were cut by planes perpendicular to an element and the resulting section was an ellipse, a parabola, or hyperbola according to whether the vertex angle of the cone was less than, equal to, or greater than a right angle.

Menæchmus. The first writer on conics, Menæchmus (c. 350 B.C.), approached the problem of the duplication of the cube by means of a parabola and a hyperbola. It had been established previously that the solution of the equation $x^3 = 2\,a^3$ might be made through the proportion $a:x = x:y = y:2\,a$. Menæchmus knew that this was equivalent to the relations $x^2 = ay$ and $2\,a^2 = xy$.

Sir Thomas Heath's reconstruction of Menæchmus's proof * is interesting in comparison with present day methods. The case of the parabola will illustrate its general bearing:

Given a cone right angled at O and having the axis OL.

Let the plane AG be parallel to the element OX, and let AG cut the axis at L. Let P be any point on the intersection of the plane AG and the

---

* See Heath, *Greek Mathematics*, II, 111–12. The abridged proof here given is reproduced by the courtesy of the Oxford University Press.

cone, and let PN be drawn through P, perpendicular to AL. Let BC be drawn through N perpendicular to OL. Draw AD parallel to BC through A, and draw DF and CG parallel to OL.

Then B, P, and C lie on a circle whose diameter is BC; and A, B, C, and G lie on another circle since the angles at A and C are right angles.

Then in the plane PBC, $PN^2 = BN \cdot NC$.

But in the plane $ACGB$, $BN \cdot NC = AN \cdot NG$ and by congruent triangles, $NG = AF = 2AL$. It follows that

$$PN^2 = AN \cdot 2AL.$$

If $AN = x$, and $PN = y$, this equation reduces to the form $y^2 = 2\,px$.

It is evident from the above that this method is equivalent to using the diameter through the vertex and the tangent at the vertex as axes.

Aristæus, Euclid, and Archimedes. Discussions relating to conics in the next half-century were given in two treatises: the one by Aristæus and the other by Euclid, and it is probable that the latter work was mainly a compilation of the contributions of preceding writers.

Archimedes (c. 225 B.C.) was particularly interested in the study of the parabola and proved a number of propositions relating to their areas * and subnormals. He also showed that all parabolas are similar.

Apollonius of Perga. Apollonius † (c. 225 B.C.) studied in Alexandria under Euclid's successors and did for the study of conic sections a service similar to that of Euclid for demonstrative geometry. His work on *Conics* seems to have been published in installments, and several of the eight Books contain prefaces addressed to individuals interested in the study of mathematics. These are of interest both for their personal touches and for their historical value. The author regrets the

---

* For the quadrature of the parabola, see page 313. For Archimedes, see Thomas Little Heath, *The Works of Archimedes*, Cambridge, England, 1897.

† See Sir Thomas L. Heath, *Apollonius of Perga*, Cambridge, England, 1896.

premature circulation of parts of his work which he had given to a certain geometer who sailed from Alexandria too soon to permit further revision at that time, and he also calls the reader's attention to sections that contain original contributions to the study.   Such notes are rare in early works in mathematics.

It is significant that, although the *Conics* of Apollonius was the subject of discussion by several commentators, the last of the eight Books is lost, the first four are known in Greek through manuscripts copied from sources formerly in Constantinople, while the other three are known only through translations into Arabic made from manuscripts obtained in Syria in the ninth century.   Latin translations of the first four Books were published in 1537 and in 1566.   Translations of the other three did not appear until 1661.

Apollonius's treatment of conics differed from that of his predecessors in several respects.   By considering the double cone, he used both branches of the hyperbola, although the single branch is frequently grouped with the other two curves while the double curve is treated separately.   He also derived all conics from the same cone by passing his planes at different angles.

His preliminary discussion of conics shows that in each case the square on the distance of a point from the tangent at the vertex is less than, equal to, or greater than the product of a parameter and the distance from the point to the diameter, the differences being constant for each curve.   Accordingly, the curves are called ellipses, parabolas, or hyperbolas from the Greek words signifying the properties noted above.   He later shows that any diameter and the tangent at its extremity may be taken as reference lines, the relation between the square of the distance from the tangent measured along a line parallel to the diameter and the distance from the point to the diameter remaining a constant.   The *Conics* contained upwards of four hundred propositions treating of the properties of the foci of ellipses and hyperbolas, the intersection of conics, the lines of greatest and least distance from a point on the diameter to the periphery of a conic, the construction of conics and normals to them.   It even foreshadows the idea of the evolute of a conic.   Its scope, considering the lack of algebraic symbolism, is amazing.

Pascal.   Mention has already been made of the conferences sponsored by the Minimite friar Mersenne at which Blaise Pascal, then only sixteen years old, presented his "Essay on Conics" which is reproduced in facsimile on page 286.   One of the two theorems of this essay was that of the Mystic Hexagram: the opposite sides of a hexagon inscribed in a conic section intersect to determine three points that lie in a straight line.   Pascal closed the essay by saying:

There are many other problems and theorems, and many deductions which can be made from what has been stated above, but the distrust which I have, due to my little experience and capacity, does not allow me to go further into the subject until it has passed the examination of able men who may be willing to take this trouble. After that if some one thinks the subject worth continuing, I shall endeavor to extend it as far as God gives me strength.*

The success of his essay on conics inspired Pascal to begin an ambitious treatise on the subject.   This, however, was never finished and the only record we have of it to-day appears in a letter which Leibniz wrote to the secretary of the Royal Society in 1676.   The secretary, Oldenburg, had heard of the treatise and asked Leibniz, who was then in France, to see whether it was still in existence.   Leibniz was fortunate in obtaining access to Pascal's papers where he found notes of the projected work which he summarized in his report to Oldenburg, but the notes themselves were never printed.   It was nearly two hundred years after Pascal wrote his statement of the theorem of the Mystic Hexagram that Brianchon, then a student at the École Polytechnique in Paris,† published a

* For a free translation of this essay, see "'Essay pour les Coniques' of Blaise Pascal," in Smith, *Source Book in Mathematics*.   The essay is reproduced in facsimile on the following page.

† This essay was published 1806.   A translation appears in Smith, *Source Book in Mathematics*.

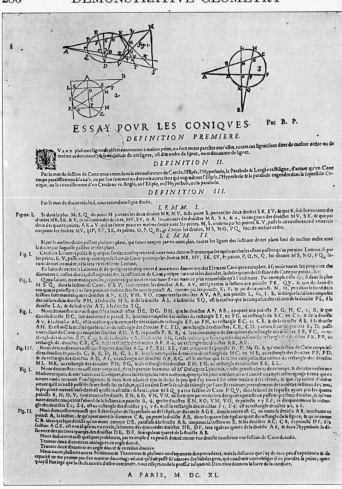

PASCAL'S "ESSAY POUR LES CONIQUES"
Courtesy of Dr. George Sarton.

statement of the allied theorem that the lines connecting the opposite vertices of a circumscribed hexagon meet in a point. Although Brianchon later became a teacher at the École Polytechnique, he made no other important contribution.

MODERN GEOMETRIES

Introduction. Although the many phases of modern geometry are beyond the scope of high-school work, it is desirable to mention certain outstanding developments lest the reader should infer that progress in recent times has been confined to the analytic and non-Euclidean geometries. This

GASPARD MONGE
From the collection of Professor David Eugene Smith.

is far from being the case, for the latter part of the eighteenth century witnessed a revival of interest in pure geometry which has had important results both in the development of new subject matter and in the philosophic study of its fundamental concepts.

Descriptive Geometry. Introductory work in descriptive geometry had been done at an earlier date, but Gaspard Monge (1746–1818) developed it independently and carried his studies far beyond the point which others had reached previously. He showed his ability in mathematics when very young and although his father was an itinerant tradesman, Monge held various important positions at an early age and ultimately became a professor in the École Polytechnique. Monge narrowly escaped being guillotined during the French Revolution, but he later became a member of Napoleon's staff on his expedition to Egypt and was the recipient of a title and of other honors which he forfeited on the defeat of Napoleon. Descriptive geometry was of great importance to the government in the science of fortification, and accordingly Monge was not allowed to publish his researches at the time when they were first made. Upwards of thirty years later this ban was removed and his *Géométrie descriptive*, based on lectures given at the École Polytechnique, was published in 1798–1799.

Projective Geometry. Gérard Desargues (1593–1662) was interested in the study of perspective and his researches in geometry led him to the use of the line at infinity, poles and polars, involution, and other such topics. His work was overshadowed by that of Descartes which was along quite different lines, and it was not really appreciated until the nineteenth century, when interest in pure geometry was reawakened. Fundamental ideas of projective geometry were used by Pascal in his study of conics and by Newton in his work with cubics.

The first half of the nineteenth century was a period of rapid progress in projective geometry. Among the important contributors to the theory were Carnot, Poncelet, Gergonne, von Staudt, and Steiner. Carnot (1753–1823) was a pupil of Monge. He became a military leader, was involved in the Revolution, and later was exiled by Napoleon. He introduced the concepts of a general quadrilateral and of negative magnitudes.

Jean-Victor Poncelet (1788–1867) developed the idea of continuity, and worked extensively with anharmonic ratios and the circular points at infinity. Poncelet also had studied under Monge. He had a commission as lieutenant of engineers in Napoleon's army and joined in Napoleon's Russian campaign. He was taken prisoner during the retreat from Moscow (1813), and although deprived of books or assistance of any kind and, as he said, distracted by his misfortunes, he devoted his period of imprisonment to the study of projective geometry, working out a treatise which he published in 1822 under the title *Traité des propriétés projectives des figures*.

Another contributor to this subject was Joseph-Diez Gergonne (1771–1859), who developed the subject of poles and polars and who was the first to discuss the "class" of a curve.

Karl Georg Christian von Staudt (1798–1867), who taught at Würtzburg, Nürnberg, and Erlangen, used only the properties of position in his *Geometrie der Lage* (1847), showing how analytic methods could be introduced without the idea of measurement.

Jacob Steiner (1796–1863) had the good fortune to catch the interest of Pestalozzi and to be taken into his school at Yverdon. He first came into Pestalozzi's notice, an illiterate boy of fourteen. Some eight years later, he entered Heidelberg and in 1834, after several years spent as a tutor and teacher, he became a professor at Berlin. His researches in geometry extended Carnot's work on the quadrilateral to a polygon in space and he also treated the properties of ranges, pencils, and curves and surfaces of the second degree.

The Geometry of the Triangle and the Circle. Properties of the triangle which apparently were unknown to the Greeks have been the study of scholars since the middle of the eighteenth century. One of the theorems of this "sequel to Euclid" was proved by Euler (1765) when he showed that the intersections of the altitudes, the bisectors of the angles, and the medians of a triangle are collinear. It was later discovered that in a triangle the mid-points of the sides, the feet of the altitudes, and the mid-points of the segments joining the intersection of the altitudes to the vertices are concyclic. The discovery of this nine-point circle seems to have been made individually by several different geometers of the early nineteenth century, among them being Brianchon and Poncelet.* Following this have come many properties relating to lines, points, and circles in a triangle. Not infrequently, the names applied to them are not those of the men who first made the discoveries.†

SUMMARY

Starting with the work of Thales, demonstrative geometry developed with great rapidity in the hands of the Pythagoreans, the members of the Eleatic school, and the Athenians. The checks imposed by the discovery of irrational numbers resulted in a new definition of proportion and the succeeding period was characterized by a general scrutiny of the subject matter and by an effort to strengthen its foundations. Plato's alleged dictum that no constructions should be allowed that required instruments other than the compasses and the unmarked straightedge had the effect of concentrating the interest of mathematicians within a narrow sector of the field.

The publication of Euclid's *Elements* served in a way to close the field of geometry to further work and little was added to the subject until the renaissance of pure geometry in the seventeenth century, when Descartes and his contemporaries developed the subject of analytics, when Saccheri began the investigation of Euclid's parallel line postulate, and when Pascal and Newton were paving the way for the modern geometry of recent years. The last two centuries have been noteworthy for the development of these various branches of geometry and for the critical study of its concepts and postulates.

---

* See "Brianchon and Poncelet on the Nine-Point Circle Theorem," and "Feuerbach on the Theorem which Bears his Name," Smith, *Source Book in Mathematics.*

† For these theorems, see Roger A. Johnson, *Modern Geometry*, Boston, 1929.

CHAPTER VIII

TRIGONOMETRY

In the Ancient World — Contributions of the East — Trigonometry in Europe — Formulas and Symbols — Summary.

IN THE ANCIENT WORLD

In Egypt. Certain problems in the Ahmes Papyrus may be interpreted to show that the Egyptians made use of trigonometric functions in building the pyramids. Indeed, the word *seked* which appears in these problems may mean the cotangent of the angle made by the face of a pyramid with its base. Considerable doubt has been cast on this interpretation, however, and all that can be said with certainty with regard to trigonometry in Egypt is that, if it existed at all, it was elementary in form and occurred only in connection with practical problems.

In Greece. The development of trigonometry was much slower than was that of demonstrative geometry. The reason lies in the wide separation made by the Greek philosophers between work that had practical application and that which was purely abstract. It is true that Thales is reported to have been a master of shadow reckoning, measuring the heights of pyramids by comparing their shadows with the shadow of an upright stick whose length is known. Except for this work, which can scarcely be called plane trigonometry, nothing was done with the subject for many years, but in the meantime spherical trigonometry developed as a tool for astronomy.

Hipparchus. It has been shown previously that the mathematicians at Alexandria were more interested in the practical applications of the subject than were the followers of Pythagoras. It happened also that the rich commercial city of Rhodes aspired to be a center of scientific activity. Her observatory was justly famous and it was there that Hipparchus (*c.* 140 B.C.) made a catalogue of upwards of eight hundred and fifty stars, placing each by its own latitude and longitude. He seems to have been the first man to make a systematic use of trigonometry. No part of his treatise on the subject is now extant, but from fragments of his other writings and from references made to his work by later scholars, it seems clear that his discussion of triangles was based on a consideration of the circumscribed circle. He calculated a table of the chords of angles inscribed in a circle of given radius, dividing the circle into 360 degrees and the radius into 60 equal parts. He knew that the sum of the squares of the chord of a given arc and of its supplementary arc was equal to the square of the diameter of the circle, a relation which reduces to our formula $\sin^2 x + \cos^2 x = 1$. This knowledge made it unnecessary to consider other functions of an angle or of its arc.

Menelaus. About A.D. 100, Menelaus, a native of Alexandria, wrote a treatise on spherical trigonometry entitled *Sphærica* which was preserved in a translation into Arabic. The first part is a spherical geometry following Euclid's sequence for plane triangles with the addition of the theorem relating to two triangles whose angles are respectively equal. The second part relates to astronomy; the third to spherical trigonometry. This includes the proof of the formula $\dfrac{\text{chord } 2\,c}{\text{chord } 2\,a} = \dfrac{\text{chord } 2\,c'}{\text{chord } 2\,a'}$, where a, a', c and c' are sides of two spherical triangles with right angles at C and C'. This formula was called the "Law of the Four Quantities." Another formula, the "Law of Six Quantities," was a relation between the segments of the sides of a spherical triangle cut by a great circle. This theorem was stated in reference to great circle arcs on a sphere, but it may be conveniently phrased as follows: If the spherical triangle ABC is cut by a great circle in the points D, E, and F, then the sines of the segments cut from the sides are proportional. An analogous formula holds for a plane triangle cut by a straight line.

Ptolemy.   The astronomer Ptolemy (*c.* 150), who also lived at Alexandria, wrote an exceedingly influential work called the *Syntaxis* or "Mathematical Collection."   In later years, this book was used as the culmination of the study of

PTOLEMY REPRESENTING ASTRONOMY
Bas-relief from Giotto's Tower in Florence.

astronomy at Alexandria and it was given the title of "megiste" * or the "greatest book."   The translation of this into Arabic was called by this nickname with the prefix of the article "al-" and the book has since been known as the *Almagest,* although this is far from its original title.   The

* From μέγιστος = greatest.   For the contributions of the Greeks to trigonometry, see Heath, *Greek Mathematics,* II.

work contains a study of the heavenly bodies, considering the earth as the center of the system.

From the point of view of mathematics, however, the most interesting part of the *Almagest* is in the work on the construction of tables. Ptolemy's object was to develop a table of chords of certain arcs, using the ancient method of dividing the radius into 60 equal parts, and expressing each chord in terms of these units and their sexagesimal divisions. Thus the chord of an arc of 60° was 60^p (that is 60 sixtieths of a radius) and the chord of an arc of 90° was $\sqrt{2}$ 60^p or 84^p 51′ 11″. He found the chords of arcs of 72 and 36 degrees by studying the sides of the regular inscribed decagon and pentagon. The chords of other arcs were derived through formulas proved in the *Almagest* that established relations:

$$\sin^2 x + \cos^2 x = 1$$
$$\sin (x - y) = \sin x \cos y - \cos x \sin y$$
$$\sin^2 \tfrac{1}{2}x = \tfrac{1}{2} (1 - \cos x)$$
$$\cos (x + y) = \cos x \cos y - \sin x \sin y$$

These formulas are proved geometrically by means of circles. A single example will illustrate the method. Suppose the chords AB and BC are known and AC is to be determined. Draw the diameter AD and connect AC, CD, and BD. In a previous proposition, Ptolemy proved that if a quadrilateral is inscribed in a circle, the product of its diagonals is equal to the sum of the products of its opposite sides. It follows that

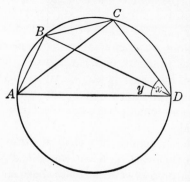

$BD \cdot AC = BC \cdot AD + AB \cdot DC$. If the circle has a unit diameter and if $x = \angle CDA$ and $y = \angle BDA$, using modern notation, this formula becomes:

$$\cos y \sin x = \sin (x - y) + \sin y \cos x$$

or $\quad \sin (x - y) = \sin x \cos y - \cos x \sin y.$

By means of these formulas and the relation $\dfrac{\sin x}{\sin y} < \dfrac{x}{y}$ for $90° > x > y$, Ptolemy computed a table of chords for arcs from 0° to 180° in steps of half of a degree. He also proved important formulas relating to a spherical triangle making extensive use of Menelaus's Law of Six Quantities. It should be noticed that relatively little had been done with the solution of a plane triangle, but that these formulas permitted the much more difficult work of solving right spherical triangles.

CONTRIBUTIONS OF THE EAST

India. Ptolemy's work was the basis for a Hindu treatise, the Sūrya Siddhānta (c. 400), which contained a table of half chords. About 510, Āryabhata called the half chord the jyā or jīva (chord). Arab translators made this into the word *gib*, which, because of its similarity in sound to their word for "fold" or "bay," confused the two meanings or at least drew no distinction between them. Accordingly, the word was translated into Latin as *sinus* (a fold) and later it became *sine*. The Hindu contributions to trigonometry were largely in the direction of the computation of tables, Bhāskara (c. 1150) giving a method for deriving sines for angles of every degree.

Arabia. Arab contributions to trigonometry comprised the addition of the ideas of tangents and cotangents, the derivation of more formulas, the construction of tables, and the transmitting of the theory of Greek and Hindu mathematics to Europe. This came chiefly through the studies of European scholars in Spain.

The Arab writers had different names for a shadow thrown on a horizontal surface and that cast on a vertical one, and in Europe this distinction was preserved in the *umbra recta* and *umbra versa* of the surveyor's instruments.

The contributions of the Arab and Persian astronomers in the computation of tables may be judged by the fact that,

considering the difficulty of computation, better and better
tables appeared within an exceedingly short time.   About
860, al-Hâsib constructed a table of tangents and cotangents.
About 920, al-Battânî found the cotangent for angles of all
degrees from 0 to 90.   Sixty years later, Abû'l-Wefâ found the
tangents for angles from 0 to 90 using intervals of 15'.   Much
later, it is true, the Persian Ulugh Beg (c. 1435) had tables
constructed giving tangents for each minute from 0 to 45° and
for every 5' for angles from 45 to 90.

TRIGONOMETRY IN EUROPE

In England.   Trigonometry seems to have been studied in
England a century earlier than in either France or Germany
for the subject was discussed by Richard of Wallingford at
Oxford in the early part of the fourteenth century.   The
practical quality of the English writing on this subject may
be judged from the introduction to an anonymous treatise of
that century: "Nowe sues here a Tretis of Geometri wherby
you may knowe the heghte, depnes, and the brede of most-
what erthely thynges."

In Germany.   After the fall of Constantinople (1452),
Greek scholars who had formerly been in that city took up
residence in Italy.   At the same time there was a growing
interest in Greek literature and science on the part of students
in other parts of Europe.   Among these men were Georg von
Peurbach (1423–1461), an Austrian who traveled to Italy to
study Greek, lectured in several Italian universities, and
finally settled in Vienna.   Peurbach began the computation of
a table of sines but died before finishing the work, leaving its
completion to his pupil Regiomontanus.

Regiomontanus.   The details of the life of Regiomontanus
(1436–1476) have been noted previously.   Like Peurbach,
he studied in Italy, and mastered Greek with a view to
translating the *Almagest*.   His treatise *De triangulis omnimodis* (c. 1464) includes both plane and spherical triangles and
it marks the beginning of trigonometry as a separate subject.

XXVI.

Data area trianguli cum eo, quod sub duobus lateribus continetur rectangulo, angulus quem basis respicit, aut cognitus emerget, aut cū angulo cognito duobus rectis æquipollebit.

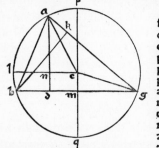

Resumptis figurationibus præcedētis, si perpendicularis b k uersus lineā a g ,p cedens, extra triangulum ceciderit, erit per ea, quæ in præcedenti commemorauimus, proportio b k ad b a nota, & ideo per primi huius angulum b a k notum accis piemus, sic angulus b a g cum angulo b a k noto duobus rectis æquiualebūt. Si ue ro perpendicularis b k intra triangulum ceciderit, quemadmodū in tertia figuratio ne præcedentis cernitur, erit ut prius a b ad b k notā habens proportione , & ideo angulus b a k siue b a g notus conclude tur. At si perpendicularis b k coinciderit lateri a b, necesse est angulum b a g fuisse rectum, & ideo cognitum, quod quidem accidit, quando area trianguli pro, positi æquatur ei, quod sub duobus lateribus eius continetur rectangulo.

THE AREA OF A TRIANGLE

From Regiomontanus, *De triangulis omnimodis*, 1533 edition.

The next important work in trigonometry by a German writer was that of Rhaeticus (1551). Rhaeticus defined the sine, cosine, and secant as functions of an angle, calling them *perpendiculum, basis,* and *hypotenusa.* He also utilized co-functions in building his tables, which read only for angles from 0 to 45°, and it should be noted that, to avoid fractions, his trigonometric tables referred angles to a circle whose radius was 10 000 000.

FORMULAS AND SYMBOLS

The Names of the Trigonometric Functions. The ideas of the sine and cosine were implied in the work of Ptolemy and Menelaus, but it was not until the twelfth century that the cosine was given a special name. The terms *umbra recta* and *umbra versa* introduced the notion of a tangent and cotangent simultaneously in medieval times, but the secant and cosecant were almost unknown until the sixteenth century.

The abbreviations for these functions were the work of the next hundred years.

TABLE SHOWING THE NAMES GIVEN TO TRIGONOMETRIC FUNCTIONS

Author	Sine	Cosine	Other Functions
*c.*1120 Plato of Tivoli		*corda residui*	
*c.*1150 Gherardo of Cremona	*sinus*		
*c.*1463 Regiomontanus		*sinus rectus complimenti*	
*c.*1542 Copernicus			*hypotenusa* (secant)
1551 Rhaeticus	*perpendiculum*	*basis*	*hypotenusa*
1583 Fincke			*secant* *tangent*
1593 Vieta		*sinus residuae*	*transsinuosa* (secant)
1620 Gunter		*co. sinus*	
1658 John Newton		*cosinus*	

TABLE SHOWING THE SYMBOLS GIVEN THE TRIGONOMETRIC FUNCTIONS *

Author	Sine	Cosine	Tangent tan	Cotangent	Secant sec	Cosecant
1625 Girard	*A*	*a*	*A*		*A*	
1631 Norwood	*s*	*sc*	*t*	*ct*	*sec*	
1634 Hérigone	sin					
1643 Cavalieri	Si.	Si.2	Ta.	Ta.2	Se.	Se.2
1647 Oughtred	S	S co arc	T arc	T co arc	se arc	se co arc
1674 Moore		cos				
1693 Wallis	S	Σ	T	τ	s	σ

Symbols. The symbols adopted for these functions varied widely. For the most part, they seem to be the product of the seventeenth century and they show a marked tendency to group the symbols for functions and cofunctions. Wallis's (1693) use of Roman letters for functions and Greek letters

* The notation for the inverse sine, cosine, etc. (sin⁻¹ ....), is due to the astronomer Herschel (1813).

for cofunctions is interesting. So too is Oughtred's use of "co arc" in denoting a cosine, cotangent or cosecant.

Formulas of Plane Trigonometry. Practically all the material needed to solve a triangle was developed prior to the year 1600. The further refinements of this work were entirely in connection with the use of logarithms, but during the seventeenth century the subject became more theoretical. Among the topics that were studied was the problem of expressing functions of nx in terms of functions of x — work which culminated in De Moivre's Theorem ($c.$ 1722) that $(\cos \phi + i \sin \phi)^n = \cos n\phi + i \sin n\phi$, where $i^2 = -1$.

The periodicity of trigonometric functions was first noticed by de Lagny, a French mathematician of the early eighteenth century, and the name radian is due to James Thomson (1871).

It should be noted that elementary textbooks avoided these analytic considerations and that their treatment of trigonometry during the eighteenth century was relatively slight. Ward's *Young Mathematician's Guide*, first published in 1706, contains "Arithmetick, Algebra, Geometry, Conick Sections, and the Arithmetick of Infinites," but it devotes only nine pages of its tenth edition to trigonometry, giving three of those to the derivation of the sines of angles taken minute by minute.

Formulas of Spherical Trigonometry. The Greeks made use of the laws of right spherical triangles but of course without stating them as formulas. Further advances were made by the Arabs and in 1614 Napier published his Rules of Circular Parts, which reduced the many laws for right spherical triangles to two statements, based on the lengths of the sides including the right triangle, the complements of the other two angles and of the side opposite the right angle. These are arranged in order as they occur in the figure. Any one of the five quantities may be called the midpart; the two next on either side the adjacent parts; and the other two, opposite parts. The Rules are: the sine of the midpart equals the product of the tangents of the adjacent parts, and the sine of

The Formulas of Trigonometry

The Relation between Trigonometric Functions:

$\sin^2 x + \cos^2 x = 1$ found implicitly in Hipparchus $c.$ 140 B.C.

$$\left.\begin{array}{l} \tan x = \dfrac{\sin x}{\cos x} \\[2mm] \sec x = \sqrt{1 + \tan^2 x} \\[1mm] \csc x = \sqrt{1 + \cot^2 x} \end{array}\right\} \qquad \text{Abû'l-Wefâ } c.\ 980$$

$$\sec x = \frac{1}{\cos x} \qquad\qquad \text{Rhaeticus 1551}$$

Functions of the Sum or Difference of Two Angles:

$$\left.\begin{array}{l} \sin (x - y) \\ \cos (x - y) \end{array}\right\} \qquad \begin{array}{l} \text{(Possibly Hipparchus)} \\ \text{Ptolemy } (c.\ 150) \end{array}$$

$\sin 2x$ Abû'l-Wefâ, $c.$ 980

$\sin 3x$ Vieta 1591

$$\left.\begin{array}{l} \sin nx \\ \cos nx \end{array}\right\} \begin{array}{l} \text{expanded in} \\ \text{series} \end{array} \qquad \text{Newton 1676}$$

$$\left.\begin{array}{l} \tan nx \\ \sec nx \end{array}\right\} \qquad \text{de Lagny } c.\ 1710$$

$(\cos \phi + i \sin \phi)^n$ De Moivre 1722

$$\left.\begin{array}{l} \tan 2x \\ \cot 2x \end{array}\right\} \qquad \text{Euler 1748}$$

$\sin \tfrac{1}{2}x$ Ptolemy $c.$ 150

Formulas Used in the Solution of Triangles:

Sine Law   Ptolemy $c.$ 150

Cosine Law   Euclid $c.$ 300 B.C.
$(a^2 = b^2 + c^2 - 2bc \cos A)$

Tangent Law:

$$\frac{\sin A + \sin B}{\sin A - \sin B} = \frac{\tan \frac{1}{2} (A + B)}{\tan \frac{1}{2} (A - B)} \qquad \text{Regiomontanus 1464}$$

$$\frac{a + b}{a - b} = \frac{\tan \frac{1}{2}(A + B)}{\tan \frac{1}{2} (A - B)} \qquad \text{Fincke 1583 and Vieta 1580}$$

Area of a Triangle $= \frac{1}{2}ab \sin C$ Regiomontanus 1464 the midpart equals the product of the cosines of the opposite parts.

Oblique spherical triangles were not studied until the tenth century, for previously all such triangles had been solved by means of a perpendicular dividing them into right triangles. The Law of Sines and the Law of Cosines of Sides appear in the work of Regiomontanus (c. 1464). The Law of Cosines of Angles and the Law of Cotangents are due to Vieta.

SUMMARY

Spherical trigonometry as a tool for astronomy developed before plane trigonometry which was a tool for surveying. The analytic side of each part of the subject is no older than the seventeenth century. The history of the subject centers first about the computation of tables and the derivation of formulas for this work. Interest then shifted to the evolving of symbolism and the study of trigonometric functions *per se*. Present textbooks in trigonometry differ from works on the subject two centuries ago in the emphasis given to the solution of triangles and the study of trigonometric identities. Like the "original" in geometry and the drill materials of algebra, this innovation is of comparatively recent date.

CHAPTER IX

ANALYTIC GEOMETRY

THE CONTRIBUTIONS OF THE GREEKS

Introduction. In tracing the development of analytic geometry, it is necessary to follow several lines of thought: the idea of coördinates, the use of geometry as an aid to algebra, and finally the geometric representation of algebraic equations. The geometric study of conics has already been discussed in Chapter VIII.

The Use of Coördinates in Surveying. The people of the ancient world who are known to have used the idea of coördinates in practical problems were the Egyptians and the Romans. It is true indeed that the Babylonians utilized axes running north and south, and east and west, in laying out their temples. But the Egyptians seem actually to have recognized a coördinate system, for their hieroglyphic symbol for land that has been surveyed is a cross-hatching of vertical and horizontal lines. The Romans laid out their towns on a rectangular plan with the two principal streets running to the cardinal points of the compass.

The Use of Coördinates in Map-Making. The use of coördinates in map-making seems to have been invented by the Greeks. Certain of the early maps had scales by which distances could be reckoned, but these were for small areas only. Maps of large areas were virtually pictures with relatively little scientific value. It is possible that the earliest use of coördinates in geography is due to Dicæarchus of Messina (*c.* 320 B.C.), a disciple of Aristotle, an orator and an historian as well as a philosopher. His map of the world was remarkable for its use of two axes directed to the cardinal points of the compass and passing through the city of Rhodes.

Distances from these axes were reckoned by a scale. The use of the equator and a prime meridian is due to Hipparchus (*c.* 140 B.C.), who adapted the idea from his Star Catalogue, which gave latitudes and longitudes reckoned from corresponding lines on the celestial sphere. Later cartographers used different meridians, generally those passing through the cities in which the maps were made. Ptolemy (*c.* 150), however, used a meridian lying beyond the Straits of Gibraltar. The choice of the Greenwich meridian on modern maps is an evidence of the growth of a spirit of scientific internationalism.

THE PERIOD BEFORE 1600

Oresme. The next contribution to the idea of coördinates in geometry was made by Nicole Oresme (*c.* 1323–1382), a Norman writer who taught at the Collège de Navarre in Paris and who later became dean of Rouen and then bishop of Lisieux. In his *Tractatus de uniformitate et difformitate intensionum* he discusses a series of points whose *longitudines* and *latitudines* are changing quantities. The terms are suggestive of the use of coördinates in map-making. Although Oresme gave the name *forma* to a series of points, he does not seem to have ever drawn a curve through them.

Geometry as an Aid to Algebra. Euclid's use of geometry in solving problems which we would express algebraically has been previously noted, and al-Khowârizmî's use of geometry in substantiating his rules for solving equations has also been discussed. The Hindu writer Bhāskara (*c.* 1150) occasionally gave both algebraic and geometric solutions for the same problem, and the books of the sixteenth century make frequent use of geometry in connection with algebra.

ANALYTIC GEOMETRY

Fermat's Work. The French mathematicians Fermat and Descartes seem to have arrived at the idea of analytic geometry almost simultaneously. Fermat's claim to priority rests on a letter to Roberval written in 1636,* in which he

---

* A translation of this letter appears in Smith, *Source Book in Mathematics.*

says that he first had the idea seven years earlier.   Descartes published *La Géométrie* in 1637, stating that he had been developing the subject for some eighteen years.   Fermat's work, published subsequently, contains the equation of a general straight line and of a circle, and it discusses hyperbolas, ellipses, and parabolas.

Descartes.   The *Geometry* of Descartes is divided into three books.   The first deals with the product of numbers represented by lines, the second with tangents and normals, the third with the roots of equations.   In the first section,

RENÉ DESCARTES

From a mezzotint in the collection of Professor David Eugene Smith, made from the portrait by Franz Hals in the Louvre.

Descartes shows how to multiply two numbers represented by line segments by laying off a unit line and one of the factors on one side of a triangle beginning at the vertex and laying off

Des. minimes de Paris

L A

GEOMETRIE.

LIVRE PREMIER.

Des problesmes qu'on peut construire sans
y employer que des cercles & des
lignes droites.

Ous les Problesmes de Geometrie se
peuuent facilement reduire a tels termes,
qu'il n'est besoin par aprés que de connoi-
stre la longeur de quelques lignes droites,
pour les construire.

Et comme toute l'Arithmetique n'est composée, que
de quatre ou cinq operations, qui sont l'Addition, la
Soustraction, la Multiplication, la Diuision, & l'Extraction des racines, qu'on peut prendre pour vne espece
de Diuision : Ainsi n'at'on autre chose a faire en Geometrie touchant les lignes qu'on cherche, pour les pre-
parer a estre connuës, que leur en adiouster d'autres, ou
en oster, Oubien en ayant vne, que ie nommeray l'vnité
pour la rapporter d'autant mieux aux nombres , & qui
peut ordinairement estre prise a discretion, puis en ayant
encore deux autres, en trouuer vne quatriesme, qui soit
à l'vne de ces deux, comme l'autre est a l'vnité, ce qui est
le mesme que la Multiplication ; oubien en trouuer vne
quatriesme, qui soit a l'vne de ces deux, comme l'vnité

Commēc le calcul d'Ari-thmeti-que se rapporte aux ope-rations de Geome-trie.

P p   est

FIRST PAGE OF DESCARTES'S "LA GÉOMÉTRIE" (1637)

the other factor on the other side. A line parallel to the line segment that joins the end point of the unit line to the end point of the second factor cuts off a segment equal to the product of the lines. Square roots are extracted by means of a semicircle erected on the original number increased by unity, the root being the length of the perpendicular drawn to the point where the unit segment joins the other line.

Descartes gives explicit directions for solving problems by means of lines:

If, then, we wish to solve any problem, we first suppose the solution already effected, and give names to all the lines that seem needful for its construction, — to those that are unknown as well as to those that are known. Then, making no distinction between known and unknown lines, we must unravel the difficulty in any way that shows most naturally the relations between these lines, until we find it possible to express a single quantity in two ways. This will constitute an equation, since the terms of one of these two expressions are together equal to the terms of the other.

We must find as many such equations as there are supposed to be unknown lines, but if, after considering everything involved, so many cannot be found, it is evident that the question is not entirely determined. In such a case we may choose arbitrarily lines of known length for each unknown line to which there corresponds no equation.*

In these paragraphs, then, Descartes gave a statement of the essence of analytic geometry: the application of algebra to the study of geometric relationships.

After a little more explanation, Descartes stops his discussion with remarks that are typical of his writings in this essay, for he frequently leaves work for the reader to finish for himself. He says:

But I shall not stop to explain this in more detail, because I should deprive you of the pleasure of mastering it yourself, as well as of the advantage of training your mind by working over it, which is in my opinion the principal benefit to be derived from this science.

Descartes then discusses a theorem studied by Euclid and Apollonius which neither of these writers could solve completely. The problem was to find a curve traced out by a

* Smith-Latham, *Descartes*, 6, 9, quoted by permission of the Open Court Publishing Company.

point so situated that if lines were drawn from it making fixed angles with three or more fixed lines, the segments of the lines cut off from the point should have a certain relation to each other. In the case of three given lines, the rectangle of the segments should equal the square of the third; for four lines, the rectangle of one pair should equal the rectangle of the other pair; for five lines, the parallelopiped of three should have a given ratio to the rectangle of the other two, etc. The discussion of this problem is involved and difficult to follow, but it led to important results — namely, the idea that a curved line can be expressed algebraically in terms of an equation involving the perpendicular distance of a general point to two perpendicular reference lines. Descartes then discussed the equation of lines that are tangent and normal to a curve and the curvature of lenses that have a given focal length.

In Book III there are given certain considerations concerning the roots of an equation which belong more properly to algebra than to analytic geometry. It also contains the use of a parabola and a circle in finding two mean proportionals between two given quantities (the old problem of the duplication of the cube), and the trisection of an angle by similar means.

The book closes with the words: "I hope that posterity will judge me kindly, not only as to the things which I have explained, but also to those which I have intentionally omitted so as to leave to others the pleasure of discovery."

Later Developments of Analytic Geometry. The further developments of analytic geometry are in general beyond the scope of this work. It should be mentioned, however, that the names "coördinates," "abscissa," and "ordinate" were contributed by Leibniz (1692); that Newton gave an almost exhaustive treatment of cubics which Plücker completed in 1828; and that the idea of other types of coördinates was not developed until toward the close of the eighteenth century, Fontana, an Italian mathematician, being responsible for the use of polar coördinates.

Solid Analytic Geometry. Solid analytic geometry was mentioned by several writers including Descartes, but the first work on this subject was written by Parent (1700). Euler attempted the classification of certain types of surfaces. Monge (c. 1800) introduced the idea of a "ruled surface," i.e., a surface such as a cone or a cylinder which is generated by a straight line, but the later development of this subject is also beyond the scope of this work.

SUMMARY

The history of analytic geometry had its origin in topics that were apparently unrelated. The initial work on the practical side was developed by surveyors and cartographers while the theoretical study of conics was due to the Greek mathematicians. The men of the Middle Ages made small contributions to it, and, prior to the seventeenth century, all of the work was concerned with particular problems. The creation of a general method which used geometry as an aid to algebra and conversely was due to Descartes and Fermat.

CHAPTER X

CALCULUS

Early Ideas of the Calculus — The Method of Exhaustion — The Use of Mechanics by Archimedes — Later Uses of Mechanics — The Study of Indivisibles — Applications of the Calculus — Newton's Predecessors in England — Newton and Leibniz — Later Developments of the Calculus — Summary.

EARLY IDEAS OF THE CALCULUS

Democritus.   The first record of the ideas of the calculus occurs in the history of Greek mathematics at an early date. The first writer mentioned by Archimedes in his summary of this movement is Democritus (*c.* 460 to *c.* 357 B.C.), who is supposed to have stated the theorems that relate to a cone and a cylinder, and to a pyramid and a prism whose bases and altitudes are respectively equal.   According to Archimedes, Democritus was unable to prove these theorems.   Little is known of Democritus himself except that he was an untiring worker who spent his fortune in travel and study.   It is he who boasted that he excelled even the Egyptian "harpedonaptae" with whom he lived for five years.   Plato ignored him; Aristotle praised him.   He seems to have been exceedingly vain, but for some reason which is not now known, he was given the name of the "Laughing Philosopher."

In the course of his work, Democritus had occasion to consider a cone as being made up of infinitely many cross sections cut parallel to the base.   This concept of a solid as being composed of planes resulted in a dilemma; for if two adjacent sections were of the same size, the solid would be a cylinder, not a cone.   On the other hand, if two neighboring sections were of different areas, the surface of the figure would be broken into a series of many small steps, which Democritus realized was not the case.

Zeno of Elea.   About the time of Democritus, or perhaps slightly earlier, Zeno of Elea (*c.* 496 to *c.* 429 B.C.), proposed

four questions or paradoxes dealing with the concept then
current that a line is composed of an infinite number of points.
It is clear that this is closely related to the idea which had
troubled Democritus.

The first of Zeno's paradoxes stated that there can be no
motion, for in order to traverse any distance whatever, it is
necessary to reach the mid-point of that distance before reaching the end, and to do this, one must traverse half of the
half-distance before reaching the mid-point, and so on, *ad in-
finitum.* It is said that one of his auditors tried to refute
this argument by walking about the lecture room to prove
that motion does exist.

The second paradox related to Achilles and the tortoise.
Even though Achilles were to run faster than the tortoise, if
the tortoise were to start first, he would never be overtaken,
for by the time that Achilles reached the spot *A* where the tortoise was a moment ago, the tortoise would be at *B*, a little
further along. When Achilles reached *B*, the tortoise would
be at *C*, and so on.

The third paradox showed that a moving object is always at
rest, for at any instant it is in a fixed position, that is, it is at
rest. Since this is true at every instant, it is true for all
instants and the arrow never moves.

The fourth paradox stated that if the points on the line *A*
were moving to the left and those on *C* to the right while
those on *B* remained stationary, then in traversing any given
distance a point in *C* passes twice as many points in *A* as it
does in *B*. In other words, a unit length of one line may have
on it twice as many points as a unit length of another line.

The general bearing of these paradoxes, then, was that if a
quantity is infinitely divisible its parts become zero, and the
sum of these parts is zero also; for otherwise the individual
parts have definite size and the sum of an infinite number of
them is infinity.*

* See Florian Cajori, "The History of Zeno's Arguments on Motion,"
American Mathematical Monthly, xxii; also "The Purpose of Zeno's Arguments on Motion," *Isis,* iii.

Interpretations of Zeno's Paradoxes. Zeno's purpose in these paradoxes has been variously interpreted. Plato suggested that Zeno was attempting to show the fallacies that followed from a notion of philosophy then popular. Certain modern writers think that he was combating the idea that a point was a unit having position. Bertrand Russell reads into it a statement of the idea that every possible value of a variable is a constant.

The Effect of the Paradoxes. Whatever Zeno's motive, the effect of his work was to exclude infinitesimal quantities from geometry. They might, indeed, be used in discovering a theorem, but they might not be used as a part of the proof of the theorem so discovered. Zeno also showed that numerical ratios could not be used to express continuous quantities. It was to avoid these difficulties that Archimedes formulated his famous postulate that if a and b are any two line segments, some multiple ma of a will exceed b.

It was not until the fifteenth century that a mathematician stated that rules framed for finite quantities lose their validity when applied to infinite ones.* Two hundred years later, Descartes considered mathematical infinity as being mysterious but not impossible.

THE METHOD OF EXHAUSTION

Antiphon. The enunciation of Zeno's paradoxes blocked further study of infinitesimals; but before the close of the fifth century B.C., another forerunner of the calculus was invented. This was the method of exhaustion, due in all probability to Antiphon (*c.* 430 B.C.). This method was developed in connection with the quadrature of the circle. It consisted of doubling and redoubling the number of sides of a regular

---

* This statement was made by Nicholas Cusanus (1401–1464), the son of a fisherman from the town of Cues, near Treves. He became a bishop and then a cardinal. He is described as an original thinker in many lines, and his library which has been kept intact in his native town is interesting from many points of view. In mathematics, he was known for work in the theory of numbers, in the squaring of the circle, and for the discussion of the notion of infinity mentioned above.

inscribed polygon, the assumption being that, as this process continued, the difference in area between the circle and the polygon would at last be exhausted.

Eudoxus. The mathematician Eudoxus (*c.* 370 B.C.) put the method of exhaustion on a more rigorous footing by consider- ing the area of a circle as lying between that of the inscribed and the circumscribed polygons. He proved the two theorems stated by Democritus by a *reductio ad absurdum*, a method which was frequently used in later days to avoid the difficulties that arose when infinitesimals were involved in a discussion.

This proof was substantially as follows: — Let V be the volume of the cylinder and C that of the cone, then $V = 3C + E$, or $V = 3C$, or $V = 3C - E$. Suppose that the first of these hypotheses is true. Inscribe a prism in the cylinder making its base of such size that the volume of the prism P will be greater than $V - E$. Then construct a pyramid having the same base and the same altitude as the prism. The volume of the pyramid will then be less than that of the cone, but it will be equal to one third of the volume of the prism. It follows that P is less than $3C$, but P was constructed in such a way that P is greater than $3C$. Thus the hypothesis that $V = 3C + E$ leads to an absurdity for it means that the difference between V and P is both greater and less than E. The use of circumscribed pyramids and prisms proves that the third hypothesis is false also. Accordingly, V must equal $3C$.

THE USE OF MECHANICS BY ARCHIMEDES

Method of Discovery. In 1906, a hitherto unknown letter of Archimedes was discovered in Constantinople. The manuscript is important for the information which it gives on the methods which Archimedes used in the discovery of his theorems. The purpose and general bearing of this work may be best judged from parts of the text itself:*

* See J. L. Heiberg, *Geometrical Solutions derived from Mechanics, A Treatise of Archimedes*, translated by Lydia Robinson and edited by David Eugene Smith, Chicago, 1909, 7–8. Quoted through the courtesy of the Open Court Publishing Company.

Archimedes to Eratosthenes, Greeting:

Some time ago I sent you some theorems I had discovered, writing down only the propositions because I wished you to find their demonstrations which had not been given........

Since I see, however, as I have previously said, that you are a capable scholar and a prominent teacher of philosophy, and also that you understand how to value a mathematical method of investigation when the opportunity is offered, I have thought it well to analyze and lay down for you in this same book a peculiar method by means of which it will be possible for you to derive instruction as to how certain mathematical questions may be investigated by means of mechanics. And I am convinced that this is equally profitable in demonstrating a proposition itself; for much that was made evident to me through the medium of mechanics was later proved by means of geometry because the treatment by the former method had not yet been established by way of a demonstration. For of course it is easier to establish a proof if one had in this way previously obtained a conception of the questions than for him to seek it without such a preliminary notion. Thus in the familiar propositions the demonstrations of which Eudoxus was the first to discover, namely that a cone and a pyramid are one third the size of that cylinder and prism respectively that have the same base and altitude, no little credit is due to Democritus who was the first to make that statement about these bodies without any demonstration. But we are in a position to have found the present proposition in the same way as the earlier one; and I have decided to write down and make known the method partly because we have already talked about it heretofore and so no one would think that we were spreading abroad idle talk, and partly in the conviction that by this means we are obtaining no slight advantage for mathematics, for indeed I assume that some one among the investigators of to-day, or in the future will discover by the method here set forth still other propositions which have not yet occurred to us.

The method consists of considering each area as being composed of extremely narrow rectangles and each volume as being made up of exceedingly thin plinths. The area of a figure is discovered by balancing the elements of this figure against those of a figure whose area is known. The centers of gravity of the given figure and of the figure of known area are determined and the position of the fulcrum of the system is also known. Since the areas are inversely proportional to their distances from the fulcrum, the area desired may be computed.

In finding the area of a segment of a parabola, the chord AC is bisected at D, DE and AF are drawn each parallel to the axis of the parabola, CF is a tangent and CH bisects AF. The point H is chosen so that $HK = KC$. It is then shown geometrically that if K be taken as a fulcrum, any line OM drawn parallel to DE is balanced by the line OP, provided that this segment is placed with its center of gravity at H, for by a property of the parabola, $OM : OP = AC : AO$. It follows that the area of the segment has the same ratio to the area of its circumscribed triangle that $\frac{1}{3}KC$ has to HK.

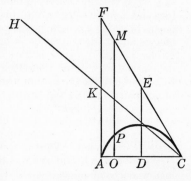

In other words, the area of the parabola is one third that of the triangle ACF. It should be noted that Archimedes developed the theorem that the center of gravity of a triangle lies on its median for use in this connection. This theorem is stated in his work *On Plane Equilibriums*. It followed from this theorem that the center of gravity of a triangle lies at the intersection of two medians, and Archimedes assumes that this is a trisection point without further proof.

Method of Proof. The preceding discussion shows how aptly the French mathematician Chasles could say that Archimedes founded the geometry of measurements. It must not be inferred, however, that Archimedes allowed the truth of a theorem to rest on considerations from mechanics. These were merely the means of arriving at the statement of a theorem which he would subsequently prove by more rigorous methods.

In finding the area of the segment of a parabola, for example, he showed that the area of the circumscribed triangle was less than three times the sum of the areas of trapezoids circumscribed about the figure and greater than three times the sum of the areas of the inscribed trapezoids. Using a *reductio ad absurdum*, he then proved that the area under the curve was one third that of the triangle. By similar methods, Archimedes developed formulas for the surface of a sphere and of its segments, for the volumes of hyperboloids of revolution, for the segment of a spheroid, and for the area under a spiral.

The important point that must be kept in mind with reference to this work is that although Archimedes used infinitesimals as a means to finding the statement of his theorems, he did not use them in establishing the truth of these statements.

LATER USES OF MECHANICS

Influence of Archimedes. A translation of the works of Archimedes was made about 1450, the source being a ninth-century copy of manuscripts then at Constantinople. This translation was later revised by Regiomontanus and the work was printed in 1540. A second translation appeared a few years later.

Stevin. The first writer of modern times to use methods comparable to those of Archimedes was Stevin. His work appears in treatises on statics and hydrostatics published in 1586. In finding the center of gravity of a triangle, however, he inscribes parallelograms within the figure and shows that by doubling their number, the difference in area between the triangle and the parallelograms will be cut in half. He states that the difference in area may thus be made less than any given area no matter how small it may be. He then says that when two weights differ, a weight can be found that is less than their difference, but that in this case there is no weight that is less than the difference of the weights involved. Accordingly, the weights of the quantities are equal.

In his work on hydrostatics, Stevin finds the pressure of water against a dam in two ways: by "mathematics" and by "numbers." The second of these proofs is the more interesting for our purposes. The author supposes that the dam is a square with an area of one square foot. He divides it into four rectangular strips of equal area and imagines these strips to be rotated so that they lie in a horizontal plane. The pressure against the first strip will be zero if it is at the top of the dam, but one sixteenth of the weight of a cubic foot of water if it be one fourth of the way down. The true pressure, then, lies between 0 and $\frac{1}{16}$. Similarly, the pressure against the next strip lies between $\frac{1}{16}$ and $\frac{2}{16}$, and the pressure against the four strips is between $\frac{6}{16}$ and $\frac{10}{16}$ of the weight of a cubic foot of water. If the supposed number of strips be increased, these limits converge, and a formula is developed equivalent to showing that the lower limit is $\frac{1}{n^2} + \frac{2}{n^2} + \cdot\cdot \frac{n-1}{n^2}$ or $\frac{1}{2} - \frac{1}{2n}$, while the upper limit is $\frac{1}{2} + \frac{1}{2n}$. By increasing the number of the strips, it is seen that the difference between the weight against the dam and the weight of half a cubic foot of water may be made less than any assigned weight. Accordingly, the pressure against the dam is that of a prism of water whose base is a square foot and whose height is half a foot.*

THE STUDY OF INDIVISIBLES

Cavalieri. The Jesuit priest Cavalieri (1598–1647) was a pupil of Galileo, and to him he owed his contact with the work of the astronomer Kepler. Cavalieri made extensive use of the idea of *indivisibles*, that is, of considering a surface the smallest element of a solid, a line the smallest element of a surface, and a point that of a line. This concept was the foundation of Cavalieri's famous theorem which reads as follows:

If between the same parallels, any two plane figures are constructed, and if in them, any straight lines being drawn equidistant from the

* See H. Bosmans, "Le Calcul Infinitésimal chez Simon Stevin," *Mathesis*, XXXVII.

parallels, the enclosed portions of any one of these lines are equal, the plane figures are also equal to one another; and if between the same parallel planes any solid figures are constructed, and if in them, any planes being drawn equidistant from the parallel planes, the included plane figures out of any one of the planes so drawn are equal, the solid figures are likewise equal to one another.

BONAVENTURA CAVALIERI
From the collection of Professor David Eugene Smith.

Cavalieri's methods were unscientific but they enabled him to derive a theorem that was equivalent to finding the area under a curve in the form $y = x^n$. Criticisms of his first work prompted him to produce a more rigorous treatment, which was printed posthumously in 1653.

The French mathematician Roberval (1602–1675) also made considerable use of indivisibles and developed a method for drawing a tangent to a curve.

APPLICATIONS OF THE CALCULUS

Gauging. One of the problems in which ideas of the calculus found early application was in gauging, i.e., finding the volume of wine casks for the purposes of taxation. The problem had been given an unscientific treatment at an earlier date and various rules for solving it were current. Rudolff and others had published treatises on the subject, and Stevin devoted a section of his work on decimals to their use by gaugers.

In 1612, the grape harvest in Austria was particularly fine and the quantity of wine produced was correspondingly large. The problem of measuring the casks attracted the attention of the astronomer Kepler (1571–1630) who had previously assisted Tycho Brahe in Prague and who was then serving as court astronomer to the Emperor. Of the various rules for gauging, Kepler's are the most scientific and perhaps the least practical.

Kepler's Laws of Planetary Motion. Kepler developed a crude type of integration in finding his laws of planetary motion: that planets move in elliptical orbits with the sun at one focus of the orbit, the velocity of any particular planet being such that the areas swept out by its focal radius in equal intervals of time are equal.

Maxima and Minima. Kepler had seen that the increment of the dependent variable becomes very small in the neighborhood of a value that is a maximum or a minimum point. Fermat (1608–1665) followed this line of thought and developed a procedure equivalent to finding the value of x which makes the limit of $\dfrac{f(x+h) - f(x)}{h}$ equal to zero as h approaches zero.

The Cycloid. Many discoveries relating to the calculus were made in connection with the study of the cycloid, i.e., the curve traced by a point on the rim of a wheel that rolls along a straight line. The French mathematician Fermat, for example, was particularly interested in this subject, but the greatest contribution to it was made by Pascal. Pascal's essay on the cycloid was written in 1658 after he had abandoned the study of mathematics for some years. He says that the idea came to him when he was suffering with a toothache, but at that moment the toothache stopped. Interpreting this as a sign of divine permission to continue, Pascal devoted several days to the study of the cycloid, carrying the subject far beyond the point it had reached previously in the hands of other workers, and solving problems equivalent to integrating $\sin \theta$, $\sin^2 \theta$, and $\theta \sin \theta$.

NEWTON'S PREDECESSORS IN ENGLAND

Wallis. John Wallis (1616–1703) was the first Englishman to make a notable contribution toward the calculus. He generalized the formula for the area bounded by the curve $y = x^m$, the x-axis, and the line $x = h$, even applying his generalization to fractional values of m. This work appeared in his *Arithmetica Infinitorum* (1658). Wallis also attempted to find the value of π by finding the area of a semicircle by a method similar to the one which he had used to evaluate the area under the curve $y = x^m$. He derived a formula for the area under the curve $y = (1 - x^2)^m$ for integral values of m, but he was unable to extend this formula to the case where $m = \frac{1}{2}$, which was necessary in order to find the area of the semicircle. It was to assist in the solution of this problem that Newton undertook his work with the Binomial Theorem (see page 179).

Barrow. Isaac Barrow (1630–1677), who was Newton's teacher at Cambridge, was the author of certain lectures on geometry in which he discussed constructions for finding lengths, areas, and volumes which are now usually derived by the methods of the calculus. Indeed, his "differential triangle" seems closely akin to the differential calculus, but when considered separately, it is evident that the lack of symbolism and the neglect of algebraic analysis make it impossible to attribute the invention of the calculus to Barrow himself.*

NEWTON AND LEIBNIZ

The Invention of the Calculus. It is a matter of frequent occurrence in the history of scientific thought that preliminary work approaches so nearly to the final product that the critic,

* For these lectures, see *The Geometrical Lectures of Isaac Barrow*, translated by J. M. Child, Chicago, 1916.

surveying it in retrospect, is astonished that the implications, plain to him by virtue of his foreknowledge, were not perceived by earlier workers, and he is surprised that the final steps in the discovery were so long delayed. Thus in the history of the calculus, it is difficult for the reader to keep from interpreting Barrow's "differential triangle" in the light of later knowledge gained through the work of Barrow's successors, and it is also difficult to give true weight to the work of Roberval, Pascal, and the others.

Although only a master mind could utilize this material as the foundation for a new departure in mathematical thought, it is evident that in the latter half of the seventeenth century the times were ready for this to take place. According to English mathematicians of the following century, this new interpretation was due solely to Sir Isaac Newton. According to continental mathematicians, the credit should be paid to Leibniz. It is highly probable that each worked independently of the other, but the controversy as to the priority of the invention was so important in its later influence as to make it desirable to give an outline of its course and of its issues.

Fluxions. Newton's work in the calculus was largely founded on the concept of *fluxions*.* Curves were considered as being generated by moving points, the change in the position of a point in an infinitely short time was called its *moment*, and the ratio of the moment to the change in time was the *fluxion* or velocity of the point. In his notation, if x is the variable quantity and o the change in time, then $\dot{x}$ is the fluxion and $\dot{x}o$ the moment.

Newton began his study of fluxions in 1665, the year of his work with the Binomial Theorem, but instead of publishing it at that time, he merely made it known to his friends. His *Methodus fluxionum*, written in 1671, was published posthumously in 1736. He spoke of his work in a letter to Oldenburg,

---

* See Florian Cajori, "Newton's Fluxions," in Brasch, *Sir Isaac Newton,* 191–200.

the secretary of the Royal Society, in 1676; he gave its principal concepts in the *Principia* (1687), but without giving its notation; and he contributed a supplement to Wallis's *Algebra* in 1693 in which he used his notation and described his theory. Newton's tract on fluxions, *De Analysi per Equationes numero terminorum infinitas*, written in 1669, was not published until 1711. During this interim, Newton's ideas underwent important changes, a fact not generally recognized by the critics of the next generation.

Limits. It is evident that Newton was dissatisfied with his first theory of fluxions, which involved the rejection of infinitely small quantities. Accordingly, he later introduced the concept of limits, computing the ratio of the increments of the variable x and of its function x^n. It should be noticed that he was concerned with the ratio of two quantities each of which was approaching zero, but that he had not reached the point of considering the limit of the ratio of these quantities. His work on limits appeared in his *Tractatus de Quadratura Curvarum* (1704), which also contained integration as the inverse of differentiation.

Thus Newton's work showed a steady development from the idea of infinitesimals used in the *Principia* (1687) through the concept of fluxions to a treatment by means of limits in which the infinitesimals figure to only a slight degree. Much of the controversy into which Newton was drawn resulted from the tardy publication of his work and from the failure of his readers to appreciate the fact that his work of 1704 was much more rigorous than were his earlier contributions.

Newton's work was distinguished from that of his predecessors by being a general method, applicable to many cases, by its algebraic character, its rigor, and its notation.

The Newton-Leibniz Controversy. Meantime, the German mathematician Leibniz (1646–1716) was developing a form of the calculus also. This was different in several important respects from Newton's work and it is of especial historical importance because of its use of the dx, dy, and $\int$ notation.

n his instinct for form, Leibniz was superior to Newton: in
athematical rigor, Newton was superior to Leibniz.

According to his own account, Leibniz began his work in
ne calculus about 1674. Correspondence with Oldenburg in
676 informed him of the existence of Newton's work, and in
ne following year Newton transmitted to Leibniz the infor-
nation that the problem was to find the fluxion of a given
quation and conversely, but this statement was hidden in a
ipher in which only the letters were given as so many a's, so
nany c's, etc., the recipient being expected to arrange the ana-
ram for himself. Shortly after this, Leibniz explained his
otation and concepts to Oldenburg, giving both in full. He
dmitted that he had been greatly influenced by the work
f Pascal, but in 1691 Jacques Bernoulli hinted that Leibniz
ad gotten his ideas from Barrow. In speaking of this pe-
iod, Ball says,† referring to l'Hospital ‡ (1661–1704), that
t seems strange, but it is substantially true, that a knowledge of the
ifinitesimal calculus and the power of using it was then confined to
Tewton, Leibniz, and the two elder Bernoullis — and it will be
oticed that they were the only mathematicians who solved the more
ifficult problems then proposed as challenges. There was at that
ime no textbook on the subject, and the credit of putting together
he first treatise which explained the principles and use of the
nethod is due to l'Hospital.

t appears that Jean Bernoulli had spent some time in Paris
utoring l'Hospital in the new branch of mathematics, and,
ccordingly, it is likely that it is his ideas that are reflected in
he preface of l'Hospital's book. After summarizing the work
f Archimedes, Vieta, Descartes, Pascal, and Barrow, the
uthor says of Leibniz:

'hat learned Geometer began where Barrow and the others left off.

* For an account of the contributions of Leibniz, see J. M. Child, *The Early
Mathematical Manuscripts of Leibniz*, Chicago, 1920.

† *A Short Account of the History of Mathematics*, sixth edition, London, 1915,
69, quoted by the courtesy of Macmillan & Co., Limited.

‡ The name is also sometimes spelled l'Hôpital. Guillaume François An-
oine de l'Hospital was a precocious mathematician who solved difficult prob-
ems at an early age and who wrote on algebra and mechanics as well as on the
alculus.

GUILLAUME FRANÇOIS ANTOINE DE L'HOSPITAL
From the collection of Professor David Eugene Smith.

His calculus took him into regions hitherto unknown where he made discoveries that were the wonder of the ablest mathematicians of Europe. The Bernoullis were the first to perceive the beauty of this calculus: and they carried it to a point which enabled them to surmount difficulties which they had never ventured to attempt before.

.   .   .   .

In addition, I wish to acknowledge a great debt to the insight of the Bernoullis, especially to the young professor at Groningen.* I have made use of their discoveries and those of M. Leibniz without ceremony. Accordingly, I agree to their claiming all that pleases them, contenting myself with whatever they wish to leave to me.

* Jean Bernoulli was given this appointment in 1695. He was then twenty-eight years old.

It is in justice to the learned Mr. Newton that I say, as M. Leibniz himself has done (Journal des Sçavans du 30 Aoust 1694), that he also has found something similar to the differential calculus as is evident in his excellent book entitled *Philosophiae naturalis principia Mathematica* which he gave us in 1687 and which is almost entirely made up of the calculus. But the notation (*caractéristique*) of the calculus of M. Leibniz makes work much more easy and expeditious besides being a marvelous aid in many problems.

With such opinions being held on the continent, it was not surprising that in 1699 Fatio de Duillier, a Swiss mathematician living in London, claimed that Leibniz had appropriated Newton's ideas. Supposing that this attack had the approval of the Royal Society, Leibniz appealed to its president and was assured that the accusation had been made without the sanction of the society. Not content with leaving matters in this state, Leibniz printed an anonymous review of Newton's *Tractatus de Quadratura Curvarum* which appeared in 1704. In this, Leibniz referred to himself as the inventor of the calculus, but he later disclaimed all connection with the review. In answer to the assertion made in this article, a Scotchman, John Keill, who was a professor at Oxford, repeated Fatio de Duillier's statement. Leibniz had made his former appeal to the Royal Society while Wallis was its president. Wallis had died in the mean time, and when Leibniz inquired whether the attack made by Keill was approved by that society, he was answered by the appointment of a committee of eleven whose duty was to examine the archives and whose implied purpose was to defend Newton, who, it should be remembered, had been president of the society since 1703. The committee consisted largely of Newton's friends, Halley and De Moivre being among its members. No one was the official representative of Leibniz, although the Prussian Minister served on the committee. The report of the committee, presented in April, 1712, after a month's research, supported Keill's claim and the papers involved were published that year under the title *Commercium Epistolicum*. Leibniz made no reply but Jean Bernoulli countered with an attack on Newton's character. Finally, Newton presented his case in a letter to a mutual friend, and Leibniz replied by a communication of great length. The controversy was terminated by Leibniz's death in 1716, and although he was considered wholly at fault in the judgment of contemporary Englishmen, he was zealously defended by De Morgan in 1852,[*] and critics to-day are disposed to admit the possibility that both Newton and Leibniz worked independently in making their discoveries.

The effect of the controversy was virtually to separate the work in mathematics in England from that on the continent for a long period.

The Calculus in England Prior to 1734. In the first half of their existence, the fluxions and the dot-notation of Newton and the infinitesimals and d-notation of Leibniz were applied to problems of the same type and a tremendous confusion resulted. For example, in England, John Craig, who has been described as an "inoffensive virtuous man," used the concepts and notation of Leibniz in 1685, but upwards of thirty years later he discarded these and used Newton's fluxions entirely. On the other hand, De Moivre used the Newtonian ideas and symbols in a work published in 1695. Professor Cajori notes [†] that prior to 1734 English writers applied the notation of Newton to the infinitely small quantities of the Leibniz calculus, thus putting "a home label on goods of foreign manufacture."

Controversies in England. Following the Newton-Leibniz controversy over the priority of invention of the calculus came notable discussions in England regarding the validity of the subject. As has been noted above, mathematicians were confused in their handling of the concepts and notations of New-

[*] "A Short Account of Some Recent Discoveries in England and Germany Relating to the Controversy on the Invention of Fluxions," reprinted in *Essays on the Life and Works of Newton*, edited by Philip E. B. Jourdain, Chicago, 1914.

[†] *A History of the Conceptions of Limits and Fluxions in Great Britain from Newton to Woodhouse*, Chicago, 1919.

ton and Leibniz, the situation growing more and more serious
until the publication of an essay by Bishop Berkeley (1684–
1753) in 1734. George Berkeley was an Irish clergyman who
as Dean Berkeley spent several years in the colony of Rhode
Island in connection with a project for establishing a mis-
sionary college in Bermuda. While in America, he interested
himself in Yale College, and he was a warm friend of Samuel
Johnson who later became President of King's College (now
Columbia University) in New York. On his return to England, Berkeley was made Bishop of Cloyne (1733) and he
spent much of his time in London where he knew Swift, Steel,
Addison, and Pope. With such a history, it is clear that
Berkeley was no mean opponent. The title of this work was
*The Analyst: or a Discourse addressed to an Infidel Mathema-
tician,** Wherein it is examined whether the Object, Principles,
and Inferences of the Modern Analysis are more distinctly
conceived, or more evidently deduced than religious Mysteries
and Points of Faith.* Berkeley was one of the cleverest
debaters of his time, and his attack on the methods of the
calculus may well be compared with Zeno's attack on the concept of infinitesimals. In fact, Zeno's paradoxes may be
closely compared with Berkeley's *Analyst* in regard to their
bearing on the latter idea. Berkeley says:

Our Sense is strained and puzzled with the perception of objects
extremely minute, even so the Imagination.... is very much strained
and puzzled to frame clear ideas of the least particles of time, or the
least increments generated therein; and much more so to comprehend the moments or those increments of the flowing quantities in
statu nascenti, in their very first origin or beginning to exist, before
they become finite particles. And it seems still more difficult to con-
ceive the abstracted velocities of such nascent imperfect entities.
But the velocities of the velocities — the second, third, fourth, and
fifth velocities, etc. — exceed, if I mistake not, all human understanding.

He later adopted the postulate that if an assumption is made
by virtue of which certain conclusions follow, and if this as-

* Probably Halley.

sumption is later rejected or destroyed, the conclusions must be discarded also. According to this postulate, he argues:

But it should seem that this reasoning is not fair or conclusive. For when it is said, let the increments vanish, *i.e.* let the increment be nothing, or let there be no increments, the former supposition that the increments were something, or that there were increments, is destroyed, and yet a consequence of that supposition, *i.e.* an expression got by virtue thereof, is retained. Which, by the foregoing lemma, is a false way of reasoning.

At a later point, he attacks the idea of fluxions in other terms and using an expression that has become almost a classic one. The phrasing is that of an orator who has reached the climax of his argument.

And what are these fluxions? The Velocities of evanescent increments. And what are these same evanescent increments? They are neither finite quantities, nor quantities infinitely small, nor yet nothing. May we not call them the ghosts of departed quantities?

Replies to the *Analyst* were written by the physician James Jurin and by John Walton who was professor of mathematics at Dublin. Neither of these was an effective rejoinder, but in the next eight years much progress was made in banishing infinitely small quantities and in developing the concepts of limits.

In the year of the publication of the *Analyst*, Colin Maclaurin * wrote to James Stirling saying:

Upon more consideration, I did not think it best to write an answer to Dean Berkeley but to write a treatise of fluxions which might answer the purpose and be useful to my scholars.... I am not at present inclined to put my name to it. Amongst other reasons there is one that in my younger years I have not perhaps come up to that accuracy which I may seem to require here. When I was very young I was an admirer too of infinites; and it was Fontenelle's † piece that

* 1698–1746. Maclaurin was a mathematical prodigy who entered the University of Glasgow at the age of 11, and who taught at a college in Aberdeen at 19. It is said that his death resulted from a cold caught at the battle of Preston Pans when the Young Pretender was making his last attempt to seize the throne of England.

† Bernard le Bovier de Fontenelle, 1657–1757, the nephew of the famous Corneille, and himself a writer, poet, and philosopher. It is not clear just which of his many works is referred to in this letter.

ave me a disgust of them or at least confirmed it together with
eading some of the ancients more carefully than I had done in my
ounger years. I have some thoughts in order to make this little
reatise more compleat to endeavor to make some of Mr. De Moivre's
heorems more easy which I hope he will not take amiss as I intend to
ame everybody without naming myself." *

n the course of the next eight years, the "little treatise"
ecame a monumental *Treatise of Fluxions* and Maclaurin so
ar forgot his early misgivings as to publish his work under his
wn name in 1742. Berkeley was effectively answered, but
he unfortunate effect of this publication was to further the
solation of English mathematicians and their adherence to
he ideas of fluxions rather than to those of the differential
alculus.

The discussions regarding the calculus gave rise to great
opular interest in the subject. Local mathematics clubs
ere started for the benefit of those who wished to study the
ubject. Private tutors gave instruction to many who felt
he inadequacy of their knowledge. The *Ladies Diary* and
ther journals had departments devoted to answering the
ueries of their readers, and Thomas Simpson and others
dded to their incomes by replying to these questions.

Thus the Berkeley controversy resulted in a popular in-
erest in the calculus on the one hand, and in its development
o a high point of logical precision on the other. But by the
eginning of the nineteenth century, a reaction began and
Woodhouse at Cambridge advocated the "d-ism" of Leibniz
ather than the "dot-age" of Newton.

Work on the Continent. In the meantime, mathematicians
n the continent were attempting to reconcile the Leibniz
alculus with the theory of limits. There was great confusion
n the concepts and notations of works published prior to 1784,†
he year in which Lagrange persuaded the Berlin Academy to
ropose a prize for a satisfactory explanation of the calculus.

* See Frances Marguerite Clarke, *Thomas Simpson, Mathematician and
Educator*, Baltimore, 1928, p. 69. Quoted by permission of the author.
† See Florian Cajori, "Grafting the Theory of Limits on the Calculus of
eibniz," *American Mathematical Monthly*, xxx, 223.

SUMMARY

The history of the calculus is remarkable for the way i which its methods were developed in connection with practica problems so that many cases were met by use of this branch o the subject before the validity of the work had been estab lished. Few parts of mathematics are associated with s many incidents of human interest, and more than any oth branch of the subject, the history of the calculus shows th influence of critics who, though not necessarily in sympath with the subject itself, were in the end its actual benefactor

CHAPTER XI

THE THEORY OF NUMBERS

The Greek "Arithmetic" — The Theory of Numbers in the
Middle Ages and in Modern Times — Summary.

THE GREEK "ARITHMETIC"

The Scope of the Subject. Certain topics that were once included in the Greek arithmetic are now studied in elementary
mathematics. Among these are "odd and even" numbers,
irrational numbers, problems of the "Find a number" type,
and the work in proportions that is given in demonstrative
geometry. Other parts of the subject are now treated by
higher analysis. In other words, the theory of numbers has
points of contact with a wide range of mathematical subject
matter and it appeals alike to the research worker and to the
amateur. So although the simpler parts of the theory of
numbers are discussed in other chapters, certain points should
be given brief treatment here despite the fact that these topics
do not appear in elementary mathematics as it is now taught.

Thales and Pythagoras. Work in the theory of numbers
seems to have begun with Thales, who came in touch with the
number mysticism of the Egyptian priests while he was studying their applied mathematics. Pythagoras duplicated this
Egyptian experience and may even have traveled to other
Eastern centers of learning. It is reasonable to suppose
that these contacts stimulated both scholars to investigate
the properties of numbers on a rational basis. It is certain,
at any rate, that Pythagoras distinguished between computation and the theory of numbers. His followers are known to
have studied figurate numbers and they made researches in
other parts of the theory of numbers also.

Figurate Numbers. The Pythagoreans used symmetric
arrays of dots to represent specific numbers, deriving the

properties of various series of numbers from these diagrams. The addition of consecutive integers beginning with 1 made the triangular numbers 3, 6, 10, etc. The sum of consecutive

Triangular Numbers

Square Numbers

Heteromecic Numbers

odd integers gave the square numbers 4, 9, 16. The sum of consecutive even integers made the oblong or heteromecic numbers 6, 12, 20. This system was extended to include polygonal numbers, which were really arithmetic progressions with the first term 1 and the common difference 3, 4, 5, etc. Solid numbers were made in a similar style and they may be visualized as symmetrical piles of marbles or of cannon balls.

Classification of Numbers by Their Factors. The subject of factors included the classification of numbers as defective, perfect, or abundant, according to whether the sum of their aliquot parts was less than, equal to, or greater than the number itself. For example, since the parts into which 6 may be divided are 1, 2, and 3 whose sum is 6, the number 6 is called a perfect number. On the other hand, the parts of 12 are 1, 2, 3, 4, and 6 whose sum is 16, hence 12 is an abun-

dant number. This topic also included prime numbers —
that is, numbers that have no factors other than themselves
and one.

The location of prime numbers has challenged the atten-

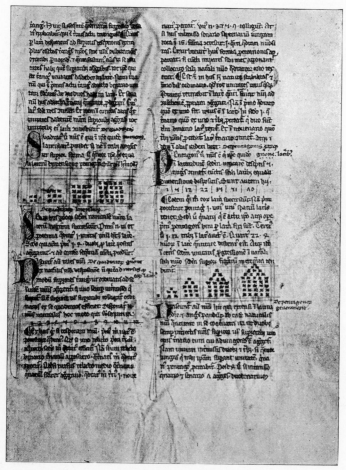

FIGURATE NUMBERS

From a manuscript of Boethius (c. 1294), now in the collection of Mr. George
A. Plimpton, and reproduced with his kind permission.

tion of many workers. Eratosthenes (*c.* 230 B.C.) invented a device called a *sieve* for locating them. This scheme consisted of writing down all the odd numbers and canceling every third one after 3, every fifth one after 5, and so on. The method is laborious, but no algebraic formula for locating all the prime numbers has ever been discovered.

Euclid. Euclid devoted three books of the *Elements* to the consideration of the theory of numbers. His work was more general than was that of the Pythagoreans, for instead of discussing particular numbers, he dealt with any pairs of numbers. Since he had no symbolism to represent them, he was forced to use a line segment for a number and a rectangle for the product of two numbers. Book III in the traditional arrangement of plane geometry illustrates his methods of treating the relations between pairs of numbers.

Euclid's theory of numbers begins with a geometric discussion of the highest common factor of two quantities. This consisted in representing the numbers by line segments and laying off the length of the smaller segment on the larger as many times as possible. The remaining segment of the longer line was then measured off on the shorter one and the process was repeated until there was a unit remainder, in which case the numbers were prime to each other, or until there was no remainder whatever. In this case, the last remainder represented the greatest common factor of the two numbers. The proof that this was actually the greatest of their common factors rested on other theorems that had previously been established. When applied to specific numbers, the division of the larger by the smaller replaces the subtraction of the segments. Under the name of the "Euclidean Method," this version of the theory lingered in textbooks in arithmetic until recent years.

Euclid then continued with the proof of various laws of proportions. For example, Proposition 11, Book VII, reads: "If, as a whole is to a whole, so is a number subtracted to a number subtracted, the remainder will also be to the remainder as whole to whole." That is, if a, b, c, and d are so chosen that a is greater than c and b greater than d and if $a : b = c : d$, then $(a - c) : (b - d) = a : b$. In another theorem, he shows that the order in which factors are multiplied is immaterial. His propositions on prime numbers include such statements as: "If two numbers be prime to one another, the number which measures the one of them will be prime to the remaining number." In other words, if two numbers are prime to each other, no factor of one can be a factor of the other also.

Euclid discusses composite numbers, square and cube numbers, and plane and solid numbers, the last of these groups being the product of two and three numbers respectively. Similar plane or cube numbers are ones in which the sides are proportional.

The climax of Euclid's work with prime numbers is the important theorem that "Prime numbers are more than any assigned multitude of prime numbers." The proof consists in assuming that A, B, C ..... represent the assigned group of prime numbers. Then their least common multiple is found and this number is increased by unity. The resulting number may or may not be a prime number. If the first possibility is true the theorem is proved. If the second is true, then this number has a factor that is a prime number, as has been proved in a previous theorem. If this prime number is one of the original assemblage A, B, C, ... it will necessarily be a measure not only of their least common multiple but also of the difference between this quantity and other numbers of which it is a factor. In other words, the prime number will be a factor of 1 which is absurd. Thus the number of primes is infinite.

Euclid's work with odd and even numbers includes the theorem that the sum of any number of even numbers is an even number and that the sum of an even number of odd numbers is also even. The difference of two odd numbers is even, and so on. His concluding theorems deal with geometric progressions and with perfect numbers:

If as many numbers as we please be in continued proportion, and there be subtracted from the second and the last numbers equal to the first, then as the excess of the second is to the first, so will the excess of the last be to all those before it.

That is, in the geometric progression $a, ar, \ldots ar^n$,

$$\frac{ar - a}{a} = \frac{ar^n - a}{a + ar + \ldots + ar^{n-1}}.$$

If we now substitute the sum of n terms, in the denominator of the second fraction, and clear of fractions, the equation becomes

$$(r-1)S_n = ar^n - a \text{ or } S_n = \frac{ar^n - a}{r - 1}.$$

If as many numbers as we please beginning from a unit be set out continuously in double proportion (i.e., $1, 2, 2^2, 2^3 \ldots 2^{n-1}$) until the sum of all becomes prime and if the sum multiplied into the last makes some number, the product will be perfect.

In modern notation, if $2^n - 1$ is prime, then $2^{n-1} (2^n - 1)$ is a perfect number. It has been shown that every *even* perfect number is in Euclid's form; no *odd* perfect number is known.

Nicomachus. About four hundred years after Euclid's work, the existing knowledge of the theory of numbers was summarized by Nicomachus of Gerasa.* No proofs are given in his *Introduction to Arithmetic*, and the contrast between this volume and Euclid's may be judged from the verbose quality of the following passage:

It comes about that even as fair and excellent things are few and easily enumerated, while ugly and evil ones are widespread, so also the superabundant and deficient numbers are found in great multitude and irregularly placed…. but the perfect numbers are easily enumerated and arranged in suitable order; for only one is found among the units, 6, only one among the tens, 28, and a third in the ranks of the hundreds, 496, alone, and a fourth within the limits of the thousands, that is below ten thousand, 8128.†

* c. 100. See *Nicomachus of Gerasa*, D'Ooge, Robbins, Karpinski. New York, 1926.

† *Ibid.* Quoted by permission of the editor of the *Michigan Humanistic Studies*.

It happens, however, that this generalization is not true, for there is no perfect number between 8128 and 33 555 336.

The work of Diophantus might be cited here, but, as his discoveries are more closely tied to algebra as we know it to-day, his contributions have been discussed in that connection.

THE THEORY OF NUMBERS IN THE MIDDLE AGES AND IN MODERN TIMES

In the Middle Ages. The *Arithmetic* of Nicomachus was preserved in the Middle Ages through the writings of Boethius (*c.* 510) which were widely studied.

One of the ideas perpetuated through this work was that unity is not a number. This idea persisted until the close of the eighteenth century. An outstanding argument against this point was presented by Stevin (1585). He stated that since a part is of the same nature as the whole, and since unity is a part of a number, then unity must be a number, just as a slice of bread is bread. An antagonist objected to his fundamental postulate saying that although a semicircle is part of a circle, it cannot be said to be a circle itself.

Relatively little was added to the theory of numbers during the Middle Ages although a great deal of attention was paid to it. For example, in a play written by Hrotsvitha, a German nun who lived in the tenth century, Wisdom gives the ages of her daughters as follows:

The age of Charity is a defective evenly even number; that of Hope a defectively evenly odd one; and that of Faith an oddly even redundant one.

In Modern Times. Since the close of the sixteenth century, the subject has developed rapidly, due to improved symbolism and to modern methods of analysis. The content of this newer part is beyond the scope of high-school mathematics but brief mention must be made of one of the most notable contributors.

Pierre de Fermat (*c.* 1608–1665) owed his interest in mathematics to the work of Diophantus which came to his attention in the translation recently made by Bachet. Stimulated by this, Fermat followed various lines of investigation, publishing none of his discoveries, merely writing them to other math-

PIERRE DE FERMAT
From the collection of Professor David Eugene Smith.

ematicians or leaving them in rough notes. Fermat had the unfortunate habit of omitting to give the proofs of important theorems. In one case, for example, he states that the equation $x^n + y^n = z^n$ cannot be satisfied for integral values of

x, y, and z, and n when n is greater than 2. His comment reads: "I have found a truly wonderful proof for this but the margin is too small to hold it." Fermat had previously proved that his theorem was true for $n = 4$. Later mathematicians have discovered proofs for other particular exponents, but no one as yet has developed a proof for *any* integral value of $n > 2$.*

SUMMARY

While many of the concepts and propositions of the theory of numbers seem entirely without practical application, they provide a vivid illustration of the fact that the mysterious properties of numbers are fascinating to scholar and layman alike. The latter is astonished and awed while the former is challenged to discover the laws which govern these phenomena. It is no exaggeration to state that the theory of numbers has the same rôle in relation to the student of higher mathematics that number recreations and puzzles have to an inquiring school boy.

* For a detailed discussion of this topic see L. E. Dickson, *History of the Theory of Numbers*, Washington, 1919–1923.

CHAPTER XII

CALCULATING DEVICES

Introduction — Napier's Rods — Sector Compasses — The Slide
Rule — Calculating Machines — Summary.

INTRODUCTION

Early Computing Instruments. Proportional compasses
were known in classic times and so should rank among the
oldest calculating devices. They were made of two bars
divided by a pivot in a fixed ratio. By spreading the points
at one end of the legs of these compasses to span a given
distance, the points at the other end would spread a distance
which had the same ratio to the first that the segments of the

ETRUSCAN COMPASSES AND PROPORTIONAL COMPASSES

From the collection of Professor David Eugene Smith. Courtesy of the Museums
of the Peaceful Arts, New York City.

legs had to each other. Roman compasses, divided in the
ratio of 1 to 3, have been found at Pompeii. Others may be
even older. About the year 1500, Leonardo da Vinci used
adjustable proportional compasses and the instrument is still
manufactured for architects and engineers.

The abacus should properly be mentioned as an important
aid in calculation, but although this instrument simplified
computation by reducing it to a counting process, it did not
provide a mechanical way of finding a result. Accordingly,
a description of this instrument appears in the discussion of
arithmetic rather than here.

Computation in 1600. At the beginning of the seventeenth century, computers were still making use of the abacus. In England, according to Glaisher,* writers on arithmetic were devoting their attention to mechanical contrivances rather than to perfecting rules for computation. It was not surprising that Napier's rods, sector compasses, and the slide rule were invented within a quarter of a century of each other, and that they were soon followed by Pascal's calculating machine.

NAPIER'S RODS

Construction. Napier's rods were a device to facilitate multiplication. In many ways they resembled the gelosia framework (see page 99) for this process, and their popularity for over a half-century after their invention in 1617 is an index of the need which people felt for such a device.

Unlike modern calculating machines, whose cost limits their use, these rods could be made by any one and so could be used by every one. Some copies still extant are made of wood, others are of paper. Those of wood are sets of rectangular prisms of square cross section. These are divided into nine cells, one for each of the first nine multiples of the digit that appears at

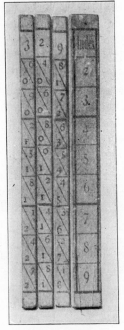

NAPIER'S RODS OR "BONES"

From the collection of Professor David Eugene Smith. Courtesy of the Museums of the Peaceful Arts, New York City.

the top of the rod. In each case, a slanting line separates the tens digit from the units figure.

In multiplying two numbers, the multiplicand was laid out by placing the rods marked with the proper figures side

* "Logarithms and Computation," *Napier Memorial Volume.*

by side.   The numbers in the top row gave the product of the
number and 1; those in the second row gave the product of the
number and 2; and so on.   In finding these products, a num
ber to the left of the slanting line on one rod was added to the
number to the right of the line on the next rod.   Let us sup
pose that the multiplicand is 329, and that the multiplier is
192.   The partial products 658, 2961, and 329 may be read
directly from the rods, and these partial products would then
be written down and added as:

$$
\begin{array}{r}
658 \\
2961 \\
329 \\
\hline
63168
\end{array}
$$

The rods thus made it possible to multiply mechanically
without memorizing any tables whatever.

A Similar Device in China.   A somewhat similar device
was described by a Chinese writer about fifty years after the
publication of Napier's account of his rods.   These Chinese
computing rods are thought by some to be of Chinese inven
tion, dating perhaps from the thirteenth century.   Other
investigators believe that knowledge of Napier's rods was
taken to China by Jesuit missionaries and that these rods are
an adaptation of Napier's idea.

SECTOR COMPASSES

Construction.   One of the most important calculating de
vices of the seventeenth and eighteenth centuries was invented
by the Italian physicist Galileo about 1597.   Galileo's sector
compasses were based on the similarity of certain triangles
whose vertex angles are equal.   The instrument was made of
brass, but it may be reproduced by using two long narrow
pieces of cardboard fastened together at one end so that they
are free to move about a pivot.   On each arm of the com
passes, a line is drawn radiating from the pivot.   These lines
are divided into equal parts with the zero at the point where

the arms are fastened together. The number of divisions should be at least 200 and at least every tenth one should be numbered.

The Use of the Line of Equal Parts. It is evident from the accompanying figure that if $OA = OA'$ and if $OB = OB'$, then $\dfrac{OA}{OB} = \dfrac{AA'}{BB'}$. Thus if the length of OA is one unit, the number

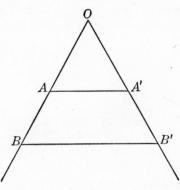

of units in BB' will be equal to the product of those of OB and AA'. Accordingly, two numbers may be multiplied by spreading the compasses so that the distance AA' measured by a pair of dividers is numerically equal to one factor. Then if OB is the other factor, the distance BB' will represent the product. A little study will show that the scale of AA' and BB' need not necessarily be that of the scale of OA and OB.

Division is accomplished by opening the compasses so that the distance between the two divisor numbers is equal to the dividend. The quotient is measured between the 1's. In a similar way, it is possible to solve problems in per cent and to calculate foreign exchange.

The fourth proportional to three numbers is found by making the distance OA equal to the first number, AA' equal to the second, and OB equal to the third. The distance BB' will then be the required number.

Galileo wrote a full discussion of the uses of his invention and, among other applications, he showed how it could be used in compound-interest problems, which were very difficult to solve before the invention of logarithms.* His problem asks the amount of money that should have been invested five

* A translation of this work appears in Smith, *Source Book in Mathematics.*

years ago at 6 per cent compounded annually to amount t
150 scudi to-day. The solution is to make the distance fror
106 to 106 on the two arms of the compasses equal to 15(
The distance from 100 to 100 will then be the amount of th
investment one year ago. Repeating this process using th
new quantity for the distance between 106 and 106, gives th
amount two years ago and three additional repetitions of th
process give the sum required.

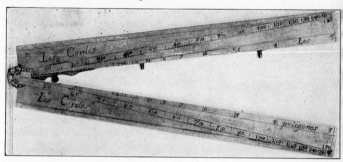

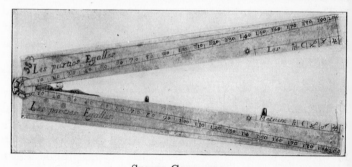

SECTOR COMPASSES

From the collection of Professor David Eugene Smith. Courtesy of the Museums
of the Peaceful Arts, New York City.

Other Lines of the Compasses. Besides the lines of equa
parts, the sector compasses had other pairs of lines. On
of these was marked according to the squares of the number
involved. These lines were used in finding squares, squar

roots, and the like. Another set were marked according to the cubes of the numbers, and these were called the "lines of volumes." Still another set gave the chords of arcs of any specified number of degrees of a circle of unit radius. This last device enables an engineer to use the compasses as a protractor, for by setting the arms of the compasses on the arms of the angle to be measured, the angle can be read by the distance between the 60° marks, this distance being the chord of the included angle which could then be measured. Conversely, to set the compasses at an angle of any required number of degrees, it was only necessary to open them so that the chord of the required angle just reached between the 60° marks.

Another addition was a "line of metals" where the medieval symbols for gold, silver, iron, etc., were spaced according to the densities of these materials. This made it possible to use the compasses to solve such problems as finding the diameter of a sphere of iron whose weight is equal to that of a given sphere of copper.

Thus sector compasses were used for many purposes and they kept their popularity for two centuries at least, but it must be admitted that they are by no means so accurate nor so easy to manipulate as is the slide rule.

THE SLIDE RULE

Gunter. The logarithmic scale was applied to mechanical computation very shortly after the publication of Napier's *Descriptio* in 1614 and its translation from Latin into English in 1616. The first man to make use of logarithmic scales seems to have been Edmund Gunter (1581–1626). Gunter belonged to the interesting group of English clerics who spent their leisure time in mathematical pursuits. It is said that he aspired to appointment as Savilian Professor of Geometry at Oxford, but that when he appeared before Sir Henry Savile he brought his instruments and "fell to resolving of triangles and doeing a great many fine things. Said the grave knight, 'Doe

you call this reading of Geometrie?   This is showing of tricks,
man!' and so dismissed him with scorne, and sent for Henry
Briggs of Cambridge." Gunter had an opportunity to teach,
however, for when Briggs * left Gresham College in London
for the Savilian Professorship at Oxford, Gunter was given
an appointment at Gresham.

Oughtred.   Another of the mathematicians important in
this connection was William Oughtred (1574–1660),† an
English clergyman who devoted most of his energy to the
study of mathematics.   He is reputed to have been a "pittiful
preacher" but his sermons improved rapidly when the Puritan
Revolution was gathering headway and when he seemed to be
in danger of losing his living.   His biographer stated that he
died of joy on hearing of the restoration of Charles II, but
De Morgan remarks, "It should be added, by way of excuse,
that he was eighty-six years old."

Oughtred seems to have been content to stay in his parish
in Surrey, studying, writing, teaching, and receiving visits
from other mathematicians to the amazement of his neighbors
who failed to appreciate his ability.   John Wallis and
Christopher Wren were among his pupils.   His most important work was the *Clavis mathematicæ* (1631), a key to arithmetic and algebra, which popularized the use of the sign ×
for multiplication; but he was generally reluctant to publish
the results of his research, and his delay in doing so was probably the cause of the controversy over the priority of the invention of the slide rule.

The Invention of the Slide Rule.   Gunter made a logarithmic scale in 1620, but instead of using two scales sliding on one
another as is the case in the modern slide rule, he marked a
single line in segments proportional to the logarithms of his
numbers and added these segments by means of a pair of
dividers.   He claimed to have been the first to use the double
scale also, but there is considerable reason to suppose that

* The mathematician who suggested 10 as the base of the system of
logarithms, see page 196.

† See Florian Cajori, *William Oughtred*, Chicago, 1916.

WILLIAM OUGHTRED
From the collection of Professor David Eugene Smith.

Oughtred made his device in 1621 — eleven years earlier than Gunter's second invention. Gunter's circular slide rule was invented in 1632, but Delamain, a pupil of Oughtred, claimed prior discovery. Delamain capitalized his work at once by sending King Charles a slide rule and a copy of his book which described it. In his address to the king, the author said that his invention was "fit for use.... as well on Horse backe as on

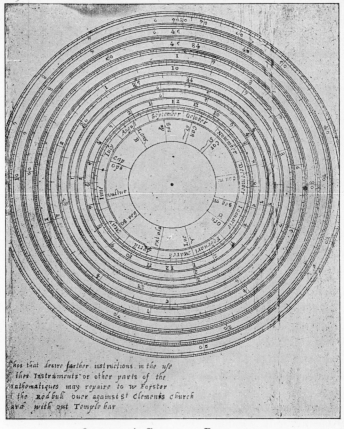

OUGHTRED'S CIRCLES OF PROPORTION

From Oughtred, *The Circles of Proportion and the Horizontal Instrument*, translated into English by William Forster (1632). Courtesy of the Science Museum, South Kensington, England.

Foot." The pamphlet consisted of thirty pages with the following title and description: *Gramelogia or, The Mathematicall Ring. Shewing (any reasonable Capacity that hath not Arithmeticke) how to resolve and worke all ordinary operations of Arithmeticke. And those which are most difficult with greatest facilitie: The extraction of Roots, the valuation of Leases, &c.*

The measuring of Plaines and Solids. With the resolution of Plaine and Sphericall Triangles. And that onely by an Ocular Inspection and a Circular Motion.* In return for these courtesies, the king gave Delamain a government appointment and, just before the Civil War in England, granted Delamain's widow a pension for herself and her large family.

It is of little importance to know whether Oughtred or Gunter invented the straight slide rule and whether Gunter or Delamain is responsible for the circular one. But the incident has a valuable bearing on the history of mathematics, for it shows how several men, working perhaps independently but animated by the same stimulus, may reach similar conclusions at the same time.

Early Slide Rules.† The circular slide rule described by Oughtred in his work *The Circles of Proportion and the Horizontal Instrument* (1632) was a brass disk with two pointers mounted at its center. These pointers were virtually a pair of compasses which could be spread to any desired span and which were held by friction so that they could be revolved while maintaining any set angle with each other. A specimen of this type of slide rule dated 1635 may be seen in the Ashmolean Museum in Oxford. It is marked with the logarithms of sines, tangents, and numbers and with scales giving the natural functions also. An early example (1654) of a slide rule of the straight form is now in the Science Museum at South Kensington in London. This rule is about two feet long and it has a square cross-section. The slide, shaped like a Greek cross, moves between four corner pieces that are fastened together by metal bands. The four sides of the instrument are

* This was printed in 1630. For further details, see Professor Cajori's article in Smith, *Source Book in Mathematics*, and also by the same writer, *History of the Logarithmic Slide Rule*, New York, 1909, and, "On Gunter's Scale and the Slide Rule during the Seventeenth Century," *University of California Publications*, I, no. 9, 187 ff.

† For descriptions of early slide rules, see D. Baxandall, *Catalogue of the Collections in the Science Museum, South Kensington — Mathematics*, 1. *Calculating Machines and Instruments*, London, 1926; also R. T. Gunther, *Historic Instruments for the Advancement of Science*, London, 1925 and *Early Science at Oxford*, Part II, *Mathematics*, London, 1922.

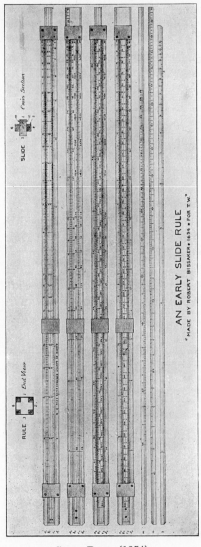

SLIDE RULE (1654)

From the Science Museum, South Kensington, England.

marked with lines of numbers, tangents, and sines, the lack of a runner making much duplication of scales necessary.

Special slide rules were made for particular problems, as for instance for measuring timber(1662). This work attracted the attention of Samuel Pepys. He found the slide rule "very pretty for all questions of arithmetick," and he made the following notation in his famous *Diary*:

Abroad to find out one to engrave my tables upon my new sliding-rule with silver plates, it being so small that Brown who made it, cannot get one to do it. So I got Cocker,* the famous writing master, to do it, and sat an hour beside him to see him design it all, and strange it is to see him, with his natural eyes, to cut so small at his first designing it, and reading it all over, without any missing, when, for my life, I could not with my best skill, read

* Edward Cocker, the writer of one of the most popular arithmetics ever published.

one word or letter of it (10 Aug. 1664). On the next day comes Cocker with my rule, which he hath engraved to admiration for goodness and smallness of work. It cost me 14s. the doing.*

Improvements in the Slide Rule. Although Sir Isaac Newton suggested the use of a runner for the slide rule, in 1675, none was invented until a century later. In 1815, Roget invented the log log scale, and in 1850 the French army officer Mannheim standardized the modern slide rule. Meantime, however, logarithmic scales had a wider use than has commonly been supposed, as is attested by the slide rules and Gunter's Scales that are preserved in the collection at Oxford University and at the South Kensington Museum in London.

The Slide Rule in Textbooks. Various opinions were held as to the value of the slide rule. John Ward, whose *Young Mathematician's Guide* was widely used in England and in this country, says that a gauger should

be ready at computing the contents of any Vessel, and casting up his Gauges by the Pen only, *viz.* without the Help of those Lines of Numbers upon Sliding Rules, so much applauded, but too much practis'd, which at best do but help to guess at the Truth; I mean such Pocket-Rules as are but nine Inches (or a Foot) long, whose Radius of the double Line of Numbers is not six Inches; and therefore the Graduations or Divisions of those Lines are so very close, that they cannot be well distinguished. 'Tis true, when the Rules are made two or three Feet long (I had one of six Feet) there they may be of some Use, especially in small Numbers; altho' even then the Operations may be much better (and almost as soon) done by the Pen.†

On the other hand, John Potter devoted three pages of his *System of Practical Mathematics* (London, 1753) to a description of the slide rule with the comment, "Though in large Numbers we cannot come to the Degree of Exactness necessary in some Things, yet it may be of great Use to correct a Mistake." And Nicolas Pike in the third edition of his *Arithmetick* (1808) gives the proper setting of the "Sliding

* R. T. Gunther, *Early Science in Oxford*, II, 70. Quoted by permission of the author.

† *Young Mathematician's Guide*, 10th edition, London, 1758, 533.

Rule" after each problem in his section on Mensuration. Pike also tells the method of solving each of these "by Gunter's Scale" but he evidently assumed that the construction of these instruments was familiar to his readers for he does not seem to give descriptions of either of them.

The reason for the omission of the slide rule from textbooks during the greater part of the nineteenth century and the early years of the twentieth may perhaps be explained on the basis of opinions such as that of Ward that the instrument was good only for approximate work or else on the grounds that mechanical instruments have no place in the study of pure science.

CALCULATING MACHINES

Addition Machines. The first calculating machine was devised by Blaise Pascal * in 1642. The elder Pascal was engaged in auditing the government accounts at Rouen at that time, and his son, who was still in his teens, invented a machine to help in this work. Its principle was the now familiar device of a series of wheels each having ten gear teeth, one for each unit from 0 to 9. At each complete turn of any wheel, the next higher one was turned through one tenth of a revolution. The invention was so novel that Pascal was given a royal privilege for manufacturing it. Subsequently several machines of similar character were invented in England and elsewhere.

Modern adding machines operate on the same general plan, with the additional feature in some instances of typing the addends on a strip of paper as the work proceeds.

Multiplication Machines. Machines designed primarily for multiplication were developed almost simultaneously in England and in Germany. In 1671, for example, Leibniz made a computing machine in which the ten teeth on each

* The calculating machines mentioned in this section are described in the *Encyclopædia Britannica* and also in Baxandall's catalogue, see page 347 above. See also articles on the Pascal machine and the Leibniz machine in Smith, *Source Book in Mathematics*.

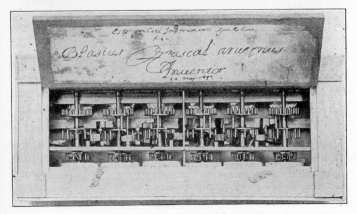

PASCAL'S CALCULATING MACHINE

From a replica of this machine now in the Science Museum, South Kensington,
England. The original machine is in the Conservatoire des Arts et Métiers in Paris.

wheel were of different lengths. His machine proved impractical, however.

In 1820, Thomas de Colmar made a machine which operated on the same principle, but his work seems to have been wholly independent of that of Leibniz.

The invention of a practical machine for multiplication bears striking resemblance to the circumstances of Pascal's work. Léon Bollée, a French boy then in his eighteenth year, designed a machine to help his father in the involved computation that was necessary in casting bells. This invention was made public in 1889. It is interesting to note that the comparison between Bollée and Pascal stopped at this point, for Pascal, as we have seen, became interested in philosophy and theology while Bollée devoted himself to the development of automobiles.

Three years after Bollée's invention was announced, Otto Steiger in Switzerland made a machine, later called the "millionaire," by which any multiplication whatever can be performed by entering both numbers on the machine and giving the handle one turn.

One of the sad figures in the history of mechanical computation was Charles Babbage, who worked from 1820 to 1856 in an attempt to develop machines that would solve highly complex mathematical problems. Unfortunately, before one machine was finished, Babbage would abandon it and devote his attention to another which seemed to offer greater promise. As a result, he made many beginnings, none of which were developed to a useful machine.

SUMMARY

Calculating devices may be considered in three categories: those which are little more than tables, those which require mathematical skill in their operation, and those which are purely mechanical. No one would advocate the revival of the use of Napier's Bones to-day, although they were popular for a century and more after their invention. The sector compasses are less easy to manipulate than is the slide rule and, accordingly, they have disappeared from use, although they had certain features not duplicated by the slide rule. The slide rule itself is more convenient than is Gunter's Scale — and it and the various machines for computation are of lasting value.

CHAPTER XIII

WEIGHTS AND MEASURES

General Survey — Units of Measure — The Metric System —
Coinage — Time and the Calendar — Summary.

GENERAL SURVEY

Natural Units of Length. The early units of length have a
natural origin. Primitive man undoubtedly measured small
objects by the length of his foot, the width of his hand, or
perhaps the length of his thumb joint. These measures were
later standardized as the foot, the palm, and the inch. Again,
a man might use the greatest stretch of his hand (the span),
the length from his elbow to his finger tips (the cubit), the
length of his arm (the yard), or the total stretch of his arms
(the fathom). Short distances were gauged by the pace.
Longer distances were the bowshot and the league, the latter
being the distance a man can see on a level plain. This type
of unit survives to-day in the German *Stunde*, which means
the distance a man can walk in an hour (that is, about $2\frac{1}{2}$
miles). Similar measures of length are seen also in the
Hollander's "three pipes" and the Southern mountaineer's
"two whoops and a holler."

Labor Units. Another type of unit is found in the furlong,
which probably means the length of a furrow, and the acre,
which represents a morning's plowing. In a somewhat similar way, a Babylonian measure of area was based on the
amount of grain needed to sow the ground.

Duplication of Units. A prime requisite in the devising
of a unit of measure is that it shall be possible to reproduce
that unit at any later time independently of existing standards. This led to the old English statute that an inch should
be considered as the total length of three barleycorns taken

from the middle of the ear. It prompted Köbel (1514) to give the following rule for the length of a rod:

> To find the length of a rod in the right and lawful way, and according to scientific usage, you should do as follows: Stand at the door of a church on Sunday, and bid sixteen men to stop, tall ones and small ones, as they happen to pass out when service is finished: then make them put their left foot one behind the other and the length thus obtained shall be the right and lawful *rod* to measure and survey land with, and the sixteenth part of it shall be a right and lawful foot.

The necessity of being able to duplicate units led the French scientists who devised the metric system to take for their unit of length a distance which they supposed to be a ten-millionth part of a quadrant of a meridian, thus basing their unit on an invariant distance where Köbel and his followers had used the mean of a random sampling of variable quantities. Another attempt to attain a standard that might readily be duplicated was concerned with the length of the second's pendulum at sea level in a given latitude. A modern development of this nature is Michelson's determination of the length of the meter as a multiple of the wave-length of a certain line in the spectrum of cadmium. This last piece of work is accurate to one part in ten million.

The extension of units to interstellar magnitudes has only begun, but two units that are in common use by astronomers are the "light year," that is, the distance light travels in a year, and the "parsec," the distance at which the radius of the earth's orbit subtends an angle of one second.

Thus the determination of units has passed from those based on the human body to those based on terrestrial magnitudes, and finally to the cosmic phenomena revealed by the spectroscope or connected with the speed of light. These measures are more and more objective, but unlike as they at first appear, the determination of the inch from the three barleycorns and of the meter from the line in the spectrum are only the extremes of the same tendency.

Standardized Units an Economic Asset. Uniform weights

and measures constitute an important asset in commercial transactions. The use of the same standards tends to unite a country. The use of several different units within a country indicates lack of union or even discord. Thus W. Flinders Petrie observes that the independence of the traders of ancient Phœnicia as reflected in the bad workmanship and variability of their weights shows the lack of centralized national authority.

Recognition of the importance of agreement in these matters led Solon (c. 594 B.C.) to discard the standards which Athens had previously used, which were those of her enemy Ægina also, and adopt the standards of Chalcidia with whom he hoped to establish favorable trade relations. This act occurred at the beginning of the increase in the power of Athens, and it is highly probable that there was a close relationship between them. In the third century B.C., similar considerations may have prompted the Achæan League to bind its member cities to the use of the same measures, weights, and money. A similar idea appears in the introduction of the metric system to replace local units in Italy in 1861 and in the North German Confederation which later became the German Empire, in 1868. In each case this action was a step in the unification of the country under discussion, and in each case it was associated with the establishing of a strong central government.

On the other hand, the weakening of central authority has, in the past, been the occasion for the exercise of a short-sighted independence and localism in this matter. For example, in feudal times, continental Europe exhibited many different systems of measures, each legalized by the lord of a manor or the council of a town. England never came under the feudal system to the same degree as did France and Germany, and in her great charter of liberties — *Magna Carta* (1215) — there appears the provision that

There shall be one measure of wine and one of ale through our whole realm; and one measure of corn, that is to say the London quarter; and one breadth of dyed cloth..., that is to say, two ells within the lists (that is, between the selvages); and it shall be of weights as it is of measures.

In France, over two hundred different feudal units were in use at the beginning of the French Revolution. The barrier which this diversity offered to commerce can readily be imagined. Accordingly, in presenting the idea of the metric system to the Estates General in 1792, the advocates of the new measures emphasized the point that these units were symbolic of democracy as opposed to the feudal units which were connected with autocracy.

The Preservation of Standards. Standard units of measure that cannot be redetermined with accuracy, must be safeguarded against fraudulent alteration. Accordingly, in ancient times the standard measures were intrusted to the priests. Thus the Roman standards were kept in the Temple of Castor and Pollux. The standard weight of the Hebrews was called the "Shekel of the Sanctuary." The Roman measure of length was chiseled into the base of the statue of Vespasian in the Roman Forum, just as to-day a meter is engraved on a tablet on the Department of Justice building in the Place Vendôme in Paris and just as the yard is marked on the base of the Nelson monument in Trafalgar Square in London. In a similar way, standard units of volume were cut into a block of stone in the portico of the forum at Pompeii.

Prior to the Norman conquest, the English kept their standard measures in the city of Winchester. They were later moved to Westminster following the change of the capital.

In medieval days, the standard measure of length for a town was often recorded in the distance between two iron prongs set in the city wall; and later, when great trading companies were organized, standard weights were preserved at the headquarters of the organization. Such a set is shown in the Hall of the Merchants Adventurers at York, and each weight bears the initial of the monarch in whose reign

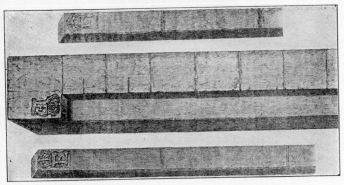

The Exchequer standard yard and ell of Queen Elizabeth.

The Exchequer standard avoirdupois
pound (bell shape) of
Queen Elizabeth.

ENGLISH STANDARDS OF
LENGTH, WEIGHT, AND
VOLUME

(15th and 16th centuries)

From the *Seventh Report of the Warden of the Standards* (Great Britain)
for 1872–73. Reproduced by the courtesy of the Standards Department of
the Board of Trade of England, and
the Controller of H.B.M. Stationery
Office.

it was compared with the English standard.

In Roman times the work of seeing that the measures in use were legal became the responsibility of the government. Juvenal, for instance, speaks with contempt of "the threadbare magistrate who decides the cases that arise about fraudulent measures and who breaks the containers below the standard size at the empty town of Ulubrae."

Exchequer standard Winchester bushel
of Henry VII.

The Discovery of Ancient Standards. The value of early standards in modern units has been discovered in various ways. For example, several ancient Egyptian cubit rods have been found — rods that probably were being used by master builders and that were lost in the crevice between two walls.

A Greek bas-relief now in the Ashmolean Museum at Oxford shows a man with arms outstretched measuring the fathom, while the imprint of a foot gives another unit for the sake of comparison. It has been suggested that this illustrates the measures of Egypt and Greece.*

Many actual weights have been discovered, especially in the ruins of the commercial cities of the Nile delta. The archeologist W. Flinders Petrie, has made a study of these, applying correction factors for losses through the wearing of the edges and corners of these weights and for accretions due to the oxidation of the metal. He gives a graph showing the frequency of the various weights and estimates the value of the units from the high points of the graph.

Starting on the hypothesis that the dimensions of a building in its ground plan and in its mouldings and cornices will yield information regarding the units used in its construction, Petrie claims that "Out of eleven units found in Asia Minor, eight are historically known to have been used by the nations that ruled there and the other three are connected with the units of adjacent countries." He goes on to show that the ruins at Stonehenge belong to a building planned on the Phœnician foot,† but conclusions of this sort are open to question.

Variation of Standards. Although local usage showed wide variability, the standard Egyptian cubit changed by less than one part in one hundred and seventy in several thousand years; the Italian mile has not altered by one per cent since

* R. T. Gunther, *Early Science in Oxford*, Part II, *Mathematics*, London, 1922, p. 76.

† W. M. Flinders Petrie, *Inductive Metrology*, London, 1877.

Roman days, and the English foot has not changed by one third of one per cent in three hundred years.

UNITS OF MEASURE

Arbitrary Nature of Units. Although many units of length had a natural origin, the actual standards were chosen somewhat arbitrarily. Tradition has it that the origin of the "Black Cubit" of Arabia was the arm length of al-Mâmûn's favorite slave. The yard as standardized in the reign of Henry I of England is supposed to be the length of that monarch's arm.

The Mile and the Pace Scale. The mile was originally a thousand double paces, and it seems to have been closely connected with the trained runners who acted as messengers in the ancient world. In the days of Alexander the Great, official pacers traveled from one end of the empire to the other. They furnished data as to the distances from villa to villa in the Nile Valley and they provided scientists with the necessary material for a map of the world as it was then known.

The marching stride of the Roman legionary was so well standardized that an officer could tell from his road book exactly how long it would take to go from one army station to another and "Rome's race, Rome's pace" became a proverb. Interestingly enough, the step of the Roman soldier was the same as the "Scout pace" of to-day.

The Yard. The principal use of the English yard has been in the measuring of cloth. This was difficult to standardize, for unscrupulous merchants would stretch the fabric as they measured it off. Accordingly, the legal yard for cloth measures for many years prior to the fifteenth century was a standard yard and a handful, that is, 40 inches in all. In 1439, this was replaced by a yard and a thumb, roughly 37 inches, and about a century later (1553) this was reduced to the standard yard.

Measures of Weight and Volume. Units of volume and of

weight are ordinarily defined in terms of the units of linear measure and of the weight of a unit volume of some common commodity. In former days, this might be grain, wine, or pure water. The study of the relation between these units gives convincing evidence that the definitions were devised long after the units themselves had come into use, an exception to this, of course, being the metric system, which was planned on a logical basis before being offered to the public.

The English units of weight — the Troy pound and the avoirdupois weight — differed in origin. The first was the weight used in checking the value of coins at the fairs of Troyes in France. The pound avoirdupois was used, as its name indicates, to weigh heavy goods. Both were used side by side, the Troy weight being the more popular until the sixteenth century, when the lighter pound being less convenient was given up for all uses but those of the goldsmiths.

Pike's *New and Complete Arithmetick Composed for the Use of the Citizens of the United States* (1788) gives the following measures with others: For linear measure, the Perch, Pole, Furlong; for Wine Measure, Gallons, Anchors of Brandy, Runlets, Hogsheads, Pipes, and Tuns; for Ale-Measure, there were Firkins, Kilderkins, Barrels, Hogsheads, Puncheons, and Butts, with a note that Milk is sold by the Beer Quart; and Dry Measure included the Pottle, Gallon, Peck, Bushel, Strike, Coom, Quarter, Chaldron, Wey, and Last. Equivalent cloth measures were given for the Ell Flemish, English, French, and Scotch, and for the Spanish Var. Among the special tables, it appears that a Tod is 28 pounds, and a Sack is 13 Tod. De Morgan observes that this measure is convenient for the spinners, since a pound of wool a day would mean a sack used a year.

THE METRIC SYSTEM

Early Schemes for the Metric System. The problem of devising a system of weights and measures that should be convenient to use had been considered by many people for long period before the work on the metric system began. The Flemish writer Stevin made an attempt to solve the question in 1585. In the appendix to his book on decimals he suggested that the unit of length, however long it might be, be divided into tenths and hundredths for convenience in computation. He also suggested that the units of square and volume measure be similarly divided into tenths and hundredths called Primes and Seconds. In this way, all tables would read alike:

10 Seconds (of a unit) = 1 Prime (of that unit)
10 Primes   = 1 Unit

The system was unfortunate in that, although the side of a square equal to a unit of area was itself a unit of length, the side of a square whose area was one Prime would be $\sqrt{10}$ times the Prime of a unit of length. Stevin also urged that measures and coinage be put on a decimal basis, and he closed his discussion with the optimistic observation that:

Even though these (reforms) are not put into effect so soon as we might wish, we have the consolation that if the men of the future are like those of the past, they will not long neglect a thing which would be so convenient for them.

It should be noticed that Stevin paid no attention to the original determination of the units.

In the latter part of the seventeenth century two schemes were proposed, each of which had the merit of using a unit which could be redetermined at any time. One of these units was the length of the pendulum that beats half-seconds. This was sponsored by a group of scientists: Sir Christopher Wren who built Saint Paul's in London, Picard who measured the arc of a meridian, and Huygens who was particularly interested in the pendulum. It developed, however, that the length of this pendulum varied slightly in different latitudes. Accordingly, later proposals suggested that the length of the second's pendulum at the equator be used.

Simultaneously with the pendulum suggestion (1670), Gabriel Mouton, a cleric at Lyons, proposed a decimal system based on the length of an arc 1' long on a great circle of the earth. Investigations made in Peru (1735) and in Lapland in 1746, however, showed that the earth was flattened at the poles as Newton had conjectured it to be. Gabriel Mouton's suggestion, then, would have failed in its purpose unless a particular great circle were specified.

Official Interest in New Standards. The French government was not blind to the need of instituting uniform measures; but Necker, who was minister of finance under Louis XVI, stated his opinion in these terms:

> I have set myself to examine the means one must employ to make weights and measures uniform throughout the realm. But I still doubt whether the usefulness of the new standards will be proportional to the difficulties of all sorts which this operation entails — witness the changes of values which it would make in a multitude of contracts of sales, feudal dues, and deeds of every sort.

The thing which the French monarchy despaired of doing because of its cost, was undertaken by the revolutionists and brought to a finish by Napoleon.

Work on the Metric System.* The French Revolution began in 1789. The following year, the Legislative Assembly authorized the appointment of a committee to devise new standards. The scheme finally adopted entailed the determination of the weight of a given volume of distilled water to link units of weight and volume, and the comparison of the standard meter with the length of the second's pendulum. The majority of the great mathematicians and physicists of France took part in this work at one time or another. The project of making triangulations from Dunkirk on the north to Barcelona just across the boundary of Spain would have been difficult under any circumstances, but with the changing governments, the chronic lack of money, and the interference of local officials, the task was an exceedingly hard one. The work was sponsored by the French *Académie des Sciences*, and its plans were meticulously laid before Louis XVI in 1791.

* See G. Bigourdan, *Le système métrique*, Paris, 1901.

The interview was largely between the astronomer royal Cassini and the monarch. Representatives of the Cassini family had held the post of astronomer royal for over a century. The king referred to this and inquired how it was that the man before him presumed to think he could better the surveys made under his grandfather's direction. Cassini disclaimed any suggestion that he was superior to his ancestors, but maintained that the new survey would have the advantage of the improvement in instrument-making in the mean time. The king appeared greatly interested in the new project, but this was probably an assumed enthusiasm, for on the following day he attempted to escape from France and the revolutionists. The flight to Varennes and the imprisonment of the royal family that followed their capture are too well known to require repetition.

Four Sections of the Work. The base line for the measurement of the meridian was surveyed by Méchain and Delambre in 1791, the determination of the length of the pendulum was entrusted to Borda and Coulomb with the assistance of Cassini, and the determination of the weight of a known volume of water was undertaken by Lavoisier and Haüy. Still another commission was given the task of assembling the measures current in the different provinces for the preparation of conversion tables based on the new standards.

Provisional Meter. The work on the metric system seemed unnecessarily slow to the legislators in Paris, and in 1792 they adopted a temporary standard to facilitate the marketing of crops, choosing for this a unit based on the measurement of the earth made fifty years before.

The Great Survey. The Académie des Sciences was suppressed in 1793, but the work on the metric system was continued under a temporary committee, the excuse for this appointment being, as has been mentioned previously, that the new system would be a weapon against feudalism. Later in that year the committee was purged of some of its most valued members on the plea that it should consist only of

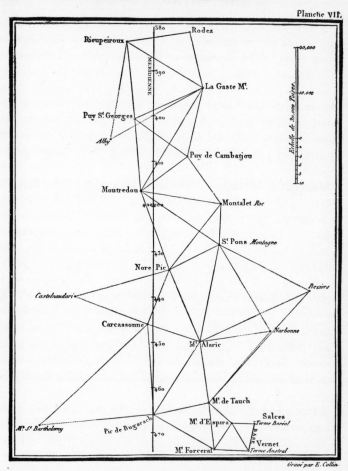

Planche VII.

PART OF THE GREAT SURVEY SHOWING THE BASE LINE
From Méchain and Delambre, *Le Base du systéme métrique décimal*, Paris, 1806.

men "worthy of trust because of their republican virtues and their hatred of kings."

As the government of France passed through kaleidoscopic changes, the men who were conducting the survey for the metric system were hampered by the depreciating currency, they were arrested for lack of proper passports, and they were imprisoned on the pretext that their theodolites were guns of a new type. The character of these delays is illustrated by an occasion on which it was necessary to increase the visibility of a target placed on a tower by wrapping it in a white sheet. The revolutionists were incensed, because the recently executed monarch had used a white flag for his banner; but the commissioners hastened to prove their patriotism by sewing on strips of red and blue cloth, making their target into a tricolor.

Méchain's Mistake. Méchain was given the task of determining the latitude of Barcelona. While his work was in progress, Spain declared war on France. Méchain was permitted to continue his investigations but was forbidden to return to his own country. After sending copies of his computations to Delambre, Méchain discovered a mistake amounting to $3''$ of a degree of latitude. He attempted to rectify this mistake but died of yellow fever before completing the work. Meantime, his erroneous results were used by the committee. Méchain's error can be condoned in view of his many difficulties, but his failure to acknowledge it has made posterity forget his ability as a mathematician and remember him, if at all, as the man who made the mistake in the metric system.

Adoption of the Metric System. The standard meter and kilogram were formally presented to the French Government in June, 1799, but they did not come into general use. In fact, in 1811, Laplace found it necessary to enlist Napoleon's interest by suggesting that the new units be called the Napoleonic Measures. After the fall of Napoleon (1815) even France abandoned the system to a great extent, and it did not become obligatory in that country until 1840.*

The United States and the Metric System. The fact that

* The dates of the adoption of the metric system in the other European countries were: Belgium, 1816, Greece, 1836, Spain, 1849, North German Confederation (later the German Empire), 1868, Sweden, 1878.

the United States did not adopt the metric system was due to apprehension of the consequences of subscribing to units fostered by a questionable government rather than to lack of appreciation of the system itself.   In fact, Jefferson made a thorough investigation of the matter in 1793 while work on the system was still in progress, and John Quincy Adams made a further study of it in 1821.   These measures have been legal in the United States since 1866, and they are generally used in scientific laboratories.

COINAGE

Money Substitutes.   Where coins are scarce or non-existent, commodities of recognized value are used instead. An example of this is reckoning in terms of the value of cattle. Tradition has it that Theseus struck money and stamped an ox on it.   A foundation for this story exists in the copper and iron ingots shaped like an ox hide that have been discovered in Crete.   An Egyptian wall painting shows the use of these ingots in commerce with Mycenæ and a tablet at Knossos seems to show the equivalent of these ingots in talents of a different metal.*   The Romans also seem to have used cattle as a standard, for their word for money, *pecunia*, is derived from *pecus* (cattle), and early Roman coins stamped with the figure of an ox are still extant.   In the early days in New England, bargains were struck in terms of beaver skins or strings of wampum; and in Virginia, tobacco was the medium of exchange.   The " Forty-niners " in California reverted to the customs of their ancestors when they used sacks of gold dust instead of coins.

War conditions always bring a scarcity of hard coin.   Thus during the Civil War, paper money was printed in even the small denominations.   Besides these "shin-plasters," small change was provided by one- and two-cent postage stamps in transparent containers.   Postage stamps were used in a

* See C. T. Seltman, *Athens, Its History and Coinage before the Persian Invasion*, Cambridge, England, 1924.

similar fashion in Europe during the World War while "local money," sponsored by the various chambers of commerce, was not legal beyond a very restricted area.

Early Coinage. When precious metals were first used as a medium of exchange, coins had not been invented and the gold or silver was weighed out to the required value. The metal was in bars or in some cases in flat rings. Thus the Biblical talent stood for a weight as well as for a sum of money, and the value of the English pound was that of a pound weight of silver.

Early coins were made in Asia Minor in the seventh or eighth century B.C. These were irregularly shaped pieces struck with a die and marked with crude devices.

Rods of iron were used as currency in certain localities of Greece, and for a time at least strips of copper 29.6 cm. long (i.e., a Roman foot) passed as currency in Rome. This monetary unit was called the *as*, and its twelve equal divisions were the *unciae* to which reference has been made previously

Alligation. Coins were struck by free cities and by small principalities in the Middle Ages and this resulted in great diversity in value. The problem of the amount of base metal that might be used in an alloy was consequently of enormous importance, and questions related to these matters appeared in textbooks in connection with the rule of alligation (or mixtures). A single example from Fibonacci's work (1202) will show their general purport although the problems appeared in many forms.

A man has seven pounds of silver from which he wishes to coin money having two ounces of silver to the pound. He wishes to know how much alloy he should add.

When the coining of money became the prerogative of a central authority, the rule of alligation still appeared in textbooks being applied to questions of mixing groceries and the like. Robert Recorde's (*c.* 1542) comment on the matter seems to have been personal rather than academic. He said,

It hath great vse in composition of medicines, and also in myxtures of metalles, and some use it hath in myxtures of wines, but I wshe it were lesse vsed therin than it is now a daies.

Money of the United States. The importance of standards of weights, measures, and coinage was recognized at an early period in the history of the United States. The Articles of Confederation (1777) stipulated that: "The United States in Congress assembled shall have the sole and exclusive right and power of..... fixing the standard of weights and measures throughout the United States." Accordingly decimal coinage was adopted by the Confederation in 1786. The Constitution made similar provisions. It should be remembered that for many years people referred to "*these* United States" rather than to "*the* United States." The doctrine of states rights was the favorite weapon of minorities, whether in the North or in the South. Under such circumstances, it was not strange that the different commonwealths exercised considerable independence in their coinage, as is shown by the fact that even the third edition (1808) of Nicolas Pike's *Arithmetick* devoted many pages to changing Federal Money into the currency of four groups of States: New England and Virginia; New York and North Carolina; New Jersey, Pennsylvania, Delaware, and Maryland; and South Carolina and Georgia. The value of a dollar as given in this work varied from 4*s*. 8*d*. in South Carolina, to 8*s*. New York money.

In the preface to this edition of Pike's work, the publishers stated that:

The most important improvement in this Edition, is the introduction of examples in the Federal Currency under each rule; and while this was considered necessary in order to extend the knowledge and use of that currency, it was thought important not to omit examples in pounds, shillings and pence, which are, and will continue to be, the basis of many arithmetical questions; and therefore an acquaintance with them will always be useful.

The somewhat ambiguous expression "arithmetical questions" might be interpreted to mean problems given in arithmetics, for at that period English texts or American editions of those texts were used to a wide extent.   Indeed, Cajori is of the opinion that the popularity of these books had much to do with keeping the words pound, shilling, and penny in ordinary speech.   To say you did not care a *penny* for anything was to use a more aristocratic and cultured expression than to say you did not care a *cent* for it.   On the other hand, a problem from the second edition of Pike's work (1797) shows that the arithmetical questions might be of considerable importance to New England shipowners whose vessels sailed to many ports.   It should be noted that the problem includes coins from three nations, England, Portugal (the half jo), and the United States.   It reads:

Shipt for the West indies 223 quintals of fish, at 15*s*. 6*d*. per quintal; 37000 feet of boards at 8⅓ *dolls.* per 1000; 12000 shingles at ½ *guin.* per 1000; 19000 hoops at 1½ *dolls.* per 1000, and 53 *half joes*; and in return, I have 3000 gallons of rum at 1*s*, 3*d*. per gallon; 2700 gallons of molasses, at 5½ *d*. per gallon; 1500 lb. of coffee at 8½ *d*. per lb. and 19 *cwt.* of sugar at 12*s*. 3*d*. per *cwt.* and my charges on the voyage were 37£ 12*s*., pray, did I gain or lose, and how much by the voyage?

The above example shows the use of an abbreviation instead of the dollar sign.   The sign itself does not seem to have appeared in print much before that time.   In the same edition of Pike's work, $223.50 is given as D.223 50*c*. or as D. 223.50.

TIME AND THE CALENDAR

Natural Units.   Unlike the measurement of lengths, weights, and volumes, whose units may be chosen arbitrarily, the length of a fundamental unit of time, the year, is determined by the nature of the solar system and man's efforts can operate only in the closer approximation to this constant in terms of the other fundamental unit, the day.   The divisions of the year and of the day are somewhat more arbitrary, although the passage of the moon around the earth forms a natural basis for a month of approximately twenty-eight days. There was room for much confusion in the problem of when the year should begin, how years should be numbered, how many days should constitute a year, and how a year should be divided into months. There was further confusion in the questions of whether a day should begin at sunrise, sunset, or at midnight; and of whether the divisions of the day should divide the time from sunrise to sunrise in equal parts or whether the length of the hour should be so adjusted from season to season that there would be twelve hours of daylight each day throughout the year.

Gnomons and Sundials. One of the earliest astronomical instruments for measuring time was the gnomon, a rod or a stone shaft standing on a level surface. Such a pillar casts a shadow whose length varies from day to day and from hour to hour. The shadow has its least length for any day when the sun is at its highest, that is at noon; and in the northern hemisphere it has its least length for a year at the summer solstice, when the sun reaches its highest point in the sky. The gnomon, then, acted both as a calendar and as a clock. Thus in a comedy of the Greek writer Aristophanes, two men plan to meet when the shadow of a particular gnomon is ten feet long.

The gnomon was used in China, in Babylonia, in Egypt, and in Greece, but contrary to a popular impression, the Egyptian obelisks were not used for this purpose. They were too close to the temples, and the refraction of the sunlight about their sharply pointed tops caused a blurring of the tip of the shadow. Consequently the gnomons were capped with a spherical block of stone. In the hands of the Arab astronomers, the spot of light cast through a hole in a wall replaced the round-topped gnomon.

In the Middle Ages, this scheme was adopted in Europe also, and to-day one occasionally sees perpetual calendars of this type in churches or in the north side of a cloister. In one such case, light from a tiny hole in the stonework between two arches falls on a line running north and south along the floor and up the outer wall of the cloister. Transverse marks tell the day of the year on which the light will cross the line at certain points and, owing to the direction of the line, the time of crossing is always noon. A similar device is sometimes to be seen to-day in the "noon mark" of old farmhouses in New England. In these cases, the edge of a window frame acts as the gnomon.

When the gnomon was to operate as a clock, a number of hour lines for the different seasons were traced on the ground at its foot. The one farthest from the base was for use in winter months, that which lay closest was for the summer. The position of the tip of the shadow varied with the hour and with the season. Since the shadow was exceedingly long at sunrise and at sunset, gnomons were sometimes set on a concave surface so that the tip of the shadow would always lie within reasonable bounds. It was but a short step from this to the invention of a portable instrument in which the shadow was cast by a bead hung in the center of a hemispherical globe which bore the hour circles on its inner surface. Like the gnomon, these sundials required adjustment of the lines for different latitudes. Yet although a sundial was made for the city of Athens in the time of Pericles, and although one was brought to Rome as booty about 200 B.C., it was not until 164 B.C. that a dial was designed for that city.

The step from the sundials such as the gnomon with a vertical pointer to those with a pointer directed toward the north star was in all probability slow in coming, but the great advantage of this move was that a single set of hour lines on a vertical or a horizontal plane was all that was necessary. It was this type of dial that the boy Newton set up on his mother's house in Woolsthorpe.

Another type of dial was a metal ring with a conical hole drilled at a point 45° from the point at which it was hung. The inner surface of the ring opposite this hole was marked with the hours of the day so the beam of sunlight passing through the hole acted as the hand of a clock or as the shadow of the gnomon.*

Water Clocks. Among the devices used to measure the passage of time at night or in dark weather were the water clocks or "clepsydra," which were similar in principle to the hourglasses of Colonial America, the trickling of water through a tiny hole being analogous to the passing of the sand from one part of the hour glass to the other. These instruments were known to the Greeks and to the Romans. Until recently, a clepsydra stood in one of the towers of the walls of the city of Canton in China, and it is recorded that Charles the Bald received one as a gift from the caliph Harun al-Rashid.

Nocturnal Dials. Shadows cast by the sun provide the hour hand of the sundial while the relation of the "pointers" of the Great Dipper act as the hour hand of a nocturnal clock as they rotate about the North Star. Nocturnal dials were invented to utilize this fact. These dials were set for the day of the year. Then the instrument was held so that the North Star was visible through a hole in the center. A movable pointer was then directed toward the stars in question. Thus the position of the stars in relation to the North Star is duplicated by the position of the pointer with relation to its center. The time is then read from the hours marked on the instrument. Such dials were in use in the sixteenth century or perhaps earlier. For convenience they were often fitted with raised knobs that permitted reading the instrument without a light.

Clocks. Clocks driven by weights are much older than are those regulated by a pendulum. In fact Boethius (c. 510) is said to have invented one. But although many of the medieval cathedrals boasted of the elaborate mechanism of their clocks, it was a long time before the invention of portable instruments that could be trusted as timekeepers. Navigation required the use of an accurate chronometer for determin-

* For descriptions of these dials, see R. T. Gunther, *Historic Instruments for the Advancement of Science*, London, 1925, pp. 31–48.

ing longitude. Prior to the invention of a portable clock that would keep time despite the motion of the ship, mariners had been obliged to use the astrolabe and the hourglass. In fact the problem of determining time and longitude was so difficult that Columbus was able to find his longitude with accuracy only once, that being on an occasion when a lunar eclipse occurred during one of his later voyages. The pendulum clock, largely the work of Huygens, was developed about 1657, but the French Academy used sundials as well as clocks in 1666.

Several prizes were offered for the invention of a reliable ship's clock. In 1714 the British government, for example, made an offer of £20,000 to stimulate this work, but the prize could not be awarded for a half-century when, in 1761, John Harrison made a clock so perfect that it lost less than a minute a month; but, despite this invention, it is reported that the ships of the British navy were equipped with hourglasses until after the battle of Trafalgar (1805).

The Year. Although the Chaldean astronomers in Babylonia had computed the length of the year to a high degree of accuracy, this knowledge did not become universal. The early Roman calendar, for example, had a year of only 304 days. This was remedied by various corrections, but in the course of time the first of spring on the calendar was considerably earlier than the actual occurrence of the equinox. Julius Cæsar undertook a reform of the calendar (46 B.C.) in which he first added the needed eighty days to the current year and then instituted a year of 365 days with an extra day added to every fourth year. This system continued in use until the sixteenth century, when Pope Gregory XIII (1582) reformed the calendar by ordering the leap-year day to be omitted in all century years when the number of the year could not be divided by 400. The Gregorian calendar replaced the Julian one in the Roman Catholic countries at once. It was adopted by the English in 1752, distrust of the innovation being registered by processions of workmen carrying placards marked "Give us back our eleven days," for the calendar had been shifted by that number of days to reconcile the civil and the astronomical years. This is the origin of the O.S. (old style) and N.S. (new style) sometimes written beside dates. The Julian calendar continued in use in Russia until the recent Revolution.

The Beginning of the Year. In his reform of the calendar, Julius Cæsar had decreed that the first of January should be chosen as the beginning of the year, but with the beginning of counting dates according to the Christian Era other days were used in various parts of Europe. Among these were March first, the old Roman date, September first, March twenty-fifth,* Christmas Day, and Easter Day. The reason for a shift from the Julian Calendar is probably to be found in the association of pagan rites with the beginning of the Roman year. The diversity of new year's days, however, caused great confusion in the chronology of the records of the Middle Ages. The return to January first was made gradually, England accepting it only with her acceptance of the Gregorian calendar in 1752. Prior to that, the English year began on March twenty-fifth. Accordingly, dates falling between January 1 and March 25 are reported with the two year numbers, as Feb. 12, 1731/32.

Numbering the Years. In general, each nation of the ancient world numbered the years from a starting point of a date of great historical importance. Thus the Romans counted their years from the supposed date of the founding of the Eternal City, and they referred to a year numbered from this point as *anno urbis conditae*, abbreviating it as A.U.C. In later times the Mohammedans reckoned their era from the Hejira, that is, from the year of their leader's pilgrimage to Mecca. A similar idea appears in the dating of Thanksgiving Proclamations and the like "in the —— year of the independence of the United States."

It was not until the sixth century of our era that an abbot, Dionysius Exiguus, proposed numbering the years as being

* The Feast of the Annunciation, popularly called Lady Day. For the medieval calendar, see Reginald J. Poole, "Medieval Reckonings of Time," *Helps for Students of History*, London, 1921.

so and so many A.D., that is, since the birth of Christ. It is a generally accepted fact, however, that the abbot began his chronology too late, but his estimate was accepted at the time and it was gradually adopted throughout Christendom. The amount of this error has been variously estimated. The astronomer Kepler observed that Jupiter, Saturn, and Mars were repeatedly in conjunction in 1603–1604. The brilliance of this phenomenon suggested the story of the star of Bethlehem. Kepler's subsequent computations showed that the same phenomenon occurred in the years 7–6 B.C. Historical research places the death of Herod in the year 4 B.C. and puts a census of the Roman world in 9–8 B.C. These considerations have led critics to believe that the birth of Christ took place in the year 8 B.C.*

The Month. The division of the year into twelve months of varying lengths has been characteristic of many calendars. The Egyptians, for example, had eleven months of thirty days each and one month of thirty-five. Julius Cæsar added two months to the old ten-month Roman calendar, preserving an alternation of thirty-one and thirty day months, February having but twenty-eight days except in the newly instituted leap year, and keeping the old numbering of the months counting from March, the fifth to the tenth months being called Quinctilis, Sextilis, September, October, November, December. The first of these was changed to Julius in honor of Julius Cæsar and the second to Augustus in honor of his successor.

The difficulty of remembering which months had thirty days and which thirty-one led to various memoriter devices. Latin versions of the rhyme, "Thirty days hath September," are found very frequently in manuscript collections, one of these being credited to the fourth-century writer Ausonius.†

* See George A. Barton, *Jesus of Nazareth*, New York, 1926.

† One such version reads:
> " Junius, aprilis, september et ipse
>   nouember
> Dant triginta dies reliquis
>   superadditur unus,
> De quorum numero februarius
>   excipiatur."

The Week. The Romans considered that the seven planets (so called) Saturn, Jupiter, Mars, the Sun, Venus, Mercury, and the Moon ruled the hours of the day in turn. Thus since the first hour of Saturday was sacred to Saturn, the first hour of Sunday to the Sun, Monday to the Moon and so on, from these they derived names for the days of the week. In a somewhat similar way, the English names for the days of the week are derived from the names of the sun, the moon, and various Norse gods and goddesses.

The Divisions of the Day. The ancient practice had been to divide the time from sunrise to sunset into twelve hours of equal length. Thus the length of an hour differed with the season. This gave rise to apparent inconsistencies. For example, in his account of the Gallic War, Cæsar speaks of the fact that at a certain point on the French coast a fortified town was cut off from the mainland by the high tide which occurred twice in twelve hours. The explanation lies in no strange phenomenon. It is simply that in June, when Cæsar made his observations, the daylight lasts fifteen of our hours in that locality. Accordingly, the tide might easily be high twice in that interval. Clocks, however, marked hours of equal length throughout the year. In contrast to the old hours of varying length, the hours by the new timepieces were called so and so many *o'clock*. It should be noticed also that the scheme of numbering the hours from 1 to 24 must have been prevalent in sixteenth-century Italy, for we find frequent references in problems of that period to the number of times an Italian clock strikes in telling these hours.

The Computi. The calendars of several races have been marked by holy days that depended on the phases of the moon, and the computation of the proper dates for these festivals has been the occasion of important work with the calendar. In fact, the computing of the calendar of the Christian year was the chief mathematical activity of the monasteries in the Dark Ages. Manuals telling how the date for Easter might be calculated were called *computi*. Such works were written by Bede, Alcuin, and others, and the subject often formed a chapter in the early printed arithmetics.

The Day Line. It was not until the first circumnavigation of the globe (1519) that people were obliged to decide on a day line. Cardan's problem about the number of days taken to go once around the earth (see page 214) is a clear indication of the perplexity caused by the apparent loss of a day on a westerly voyage, or the apparent gain of a day on an easterly one.

It might be said that the day line of the Romans reached westward from the farthest point of the Spanish peninsula to the farthest point known to the east. Navigators contracted this a bit by the discovery of the Azores and the Canary Islands. Columbus narrowed it still further. The Philippine Islands, being settled by men who rounded Africa, pushed the area of separation between days farther to the east. Eventually when the Greenwich meridian had been agreed upon as the zero line for map-making, the 180° meridian was taken as the day line. It has well been said, then, that the history of discovery is registered in the narrowing of this line.

SUMMARY

The history of the units of weights, measures, and time is the story of the gradual approach to recognized standards which in the case of the weights and measures may be reproduced *de novo* if occasion arises, and which in the case of the units of time may be redetermined by astronomical observations. The units in use to-day are far fewer in number than those of even a hundred years ago, and each step in simplification means greater economic progress. The human race may conceivably be on the verge of a further simplification. Astronomers have long made use of Greenwich Mean Time, but laymen have used the standard time of the capital of their country if it be small, or the time of a time zone if it be large. The radio and the transoceanic telephone, however, may quite conceivably result in the popularizing of Greenwich Time as a "World Time" in the not too distant future.

CHAPTER XIV

THE PLACE OF MATHEMATICS IN THE SCHOOL CURRICULUM

In the Ancient World — Schools and Universities of Europe — Schools and Colleges in America — Summary.

IN THE ANCIENT WORLD

Introduction. Our information regarding the subject matter which has been considered as essential to a liberal education at various periods lacks detail at many points, and any statements made regarding it are generally applicable only to restricted areas and to short periods of time. In spite of these limitations, however, it seems desirable to present briefly the part which mathematics has played in formal education in the past in the Western world as a background for the tendencies of the present.

Mathematics in Greek Education. There is evidence to show that addition and multiplication were taught to Greek boys early in their education. The popularity of games played with knuckle bones and with dice indicates a knowledge of elementary arithmetic, and references to counters and to finger computation in Greek literature show familiarity with simple reckoning.

Plato considered that free-born citizens should study calculation and the theory of numbers, mensuration, and astronomy — the first for its utility in the managing of a household or the administration of civil government, and the last to make possible the understanding of the calendar. There is evidence that Plato's critics objected to the emphasis he laid on mathematics, giving as reasons that these subjects are soon forgotten and that they should be replaced by others that are of greater value in everyday life. It may have been in answer to arguments such as these that Plato is reported to have had carved above the door of his Academy the words, "Let no one ignorant of geometry enter here." Heath summarizes the comments of Isocrates on these diverse points of view as follows: *

True, those who specialize in such subjects as astronomy and geometry get no good from them unless they chose to teach them for a livelihood; and if they get too deeply absorbed, they become unpractical and incapable of doing ordinary business; but the study of these subjects up to a proper point trains a boy to keep his attention fixed and not to allow his mind to wander; so, being practised in this way and having his wits sharpened, he will be capable of learning more important matters with greater ease and speed.

Aristotle whose word was to become a law to the schools of the Middle Ages, mastered elementary mathematics and held its discipline in high regard.

It is unfortunate that we know so little of the place of mathematics in the education of the period in which Euclid's *Elements*, the greatest textbook of all times, was written.

Mathematics in Roman Education. The Romans were neither a race of shopkeepers nor a race of philosophers. Mathematics was valued by them principally for its use in engineering, although Quintilian believed that the study of geometry was a means of acquiring skill in oratory. Cicero, however, declared his thankfulness that his countrymen did not spend their efforts on abstract mathematics.

SCHOOLS AND UNIVERSITIES OF EUROPE

The Dark Ages. During the years from the fall of Rome to the close of the first millennium A.D., education was largely in the hands of the monks; and although some attention was paid to the theory of numbers, the principal mathematical activities of the students were in connection with the study of the calendar. There were infrequent times when learning flourished, these generally occurring when a country was somewhat secure in its external and internal relations. These

* Heath, *Greek Mathematics*, i, 21. Quoted by permission of the Oxford University Press.

conditions obtained in England during the lifetime of Bede, and a like state existed in France when Alcuin established his school in Charlemagne's palace and later when he taught at Tours.

The Universities. The founding of the great universities in the twelfth century marked the beginning of a period when the status of a subject as a part of a liberal education might be judged by the place awarded to it in the curriculum. Work in the medieval universities centered about the seven liberal arts: the *trivium* (grammar, rhetoric, and logic) and the *quadrivium* (arithmetic, astronomy, geometry, and music). The content of this work in mathematics as it was given at Oxford is outlined by R. T. Gunther as follows: *

By Arithmetic was meant at that time (the twelfth and first half of the thirteenth century) the study of the proportions of numbers; and particularly of ratio, proportion, fractions, and polygonal numbers. It did not include the art of practical calculation, so that the abacus, the instrument upon which calculations were then generally performed, was not required for the academic curriculum. For the modicum of Geometry that was necessary, Boethius and Gerbert were read. They supplied enunciations of the first book of Euclid and a few selected propositions from Books III and IV. Some practical applications to the determination of areas were usually added in the form of notes. But even this was too advanced for most students, and few if any of the residents at Oxford had mastered more than the definitions and enunciations of the first five propositions of Euclid, Book I.†

It must not be supposed that all students gained a real mastery of these topics — Roger Bacon, for example, said that people studied geometry only under compulsion.

During the fourteenth century, Merton College at Oxford was the center of mathematical knowledge in Christian Europe, one of the most noted of its scholars being Thomas Bradwardine, who was familiarly known as "Doctor Profundus." At the same time, the German universities, one by

* *Early Science at Oxford, Part II, Mathematics*, London, 1922, 8–9. Quoted by permission of the author.

† This would take them to the Pons Asinorum, see page 271.

one, were requiring that candidates for higher degrees be familiar with certain sections of Euclid. This was true in the University of Paris also, but the requirements of the Italian universities were less rigorous. Scarcity of texts led to the student's preparing notebooks based on the lectures of the instructor or copied from his notes. These were supplemented by discussion or disputations. The notebook method of teaching persisted until long after printed texts were available for the students.

The epidemic called the Black Death checked the progress of education in Europe in the fifteenth century. In the early part of this century the only mathematics required for a bachelor's degree at Oxford was a little arithmetic and a knowledge of the computus, while by the middle of the century the mathematics required for a master's degree included only two books of Euclid and a little astronomy. It should be noted that Regiomontanus found no fellow students in geometry at Leipzig, and that Widman's lectures on algebra at that institution in 1484 were evidently an innovation.

The Study of Geometry.* In the sixteenth century, the German universities seem to have taught geometry with success. In France, several practical texts were written in the vernacular in the same century, but in succeeding years the subject was neglected in many of the schools. This gives credence to the story that Pascal reached the age of sixteen without having seen a geometry. It should be remembered that Newton, at about the same age, considered Euclid a "trifling book" and studied it later only at Barrow's urgent request.

By 1730, geometry was taught in the French colleges which later became the lycées, but it was not stressed in the universities until 1789.

In England, after a burst of interest in the twelfth century, the study of geometry lapsed until the sixteenth. About

* See Alva Walker Stamper, *A History of the Teaching of Elementary Geometry*, New York, 1909.

1570, Sir Henry Savile lectured on Greek geometry at Oxford, but he carried the subject only through the first part of the first book of Euclid. The Savilian professorship, which he founded in 1619, marked the beginning of serious work in geometry in that university; and this, coupled with the founding of a similar chair in Cambridge in 1663, had a great share in making the period to about 1730 a time when Greek geometry was at its height in England.

Geometry, however, was slow in getting a foothold in the secondary schools. From being "lightly glanced at once a week" by the seniors at Harrow, it was made a required subject in 1837; but it was not required at Eton until 1851, although military schools in France had been teaching it since the time of the French Revolution.

SCHOOLS AND COLLEGES IN AMERICA

Elementary Mathematics in the Colleges. In the early days of the American colleges, it was customary to publish lists of statements which candidates for degrees were to defend as part of their commencement exercises.* Arithmetic and geometry appear in the earliest of these lists for Harvard that are now extant (namely, those of 1653), but algebra does not enter until 1721, although conics appeared in 1711 and fluxions in 1719. The earliest Yale list (1718), however, pays considerable attention to algebra.

In 1788, at Harvard, the Hollis professor of Mathematics was instructed to carry his classes "as far as through affected quadratics and infinite series." † At King's College (later Columbia University), the freshmen studied algebra to quadratics in 1785 and the sophomores studied higher branches of the subject.

Geometry was required of second-year students at Yale in 1744 and at Harvard in 1787. It was put into the Harvard

---

* For these theses and for other points in this connection, see Lao Genevra Simons, *Introduction of Algebra into American Schools in the Eighteenth Century*, Washington, 1924.

† *Ibid.*, 46.

course for freshmen in 1818, and it was required for entrance in 1844.

A comment on the work in mathematics at Dartmouth in the latter part of the eighteenth century may be biased, but it probably has some basis in fact:

> I remember hearing one of the older graduates say that the first lesson of his class in mathematics was twenty propositions in Euclid, the instructor remarking that he should require only the captions of the propositions, but if any doubted the truth of them he might read demonstrations, though for his part his mind was perfectly satisfied.*

College Entrance Requirements.†   An understanding of common arithmetic was required for admission to Yale in 1745.   Princeton put a similar requirement in 1760, increasing this in 1813 to include the Rule of Three.   King's College stipulated that students entering after 1755 be expert in the subject.   Other institutions made similar requirements — Pennsylvania in 1758, Brown and Williams in 1793, and Harvard in 1807.

Algebra was required for Pennsylvania in 1758, by Harvard in 1820, Columbia, 1821, Yale, 1847, and Princeton, 1848. Plane geometry was on the list of work prescribed for entrance to the University of Pennsylvania in 1758, Harvard in 1844 (elementary concepts only), Yale, 1856 (two books), Princeton, Michigan, and Cornell, 1870.

Mathematics Outside of the Universities.   In the United States as in England, however, private masters were engaged in tutoring pupils in mathematics, and the small amount of the subject taught in the secondary schools and colleges should not be interpreted as showing complete lack of interest.   In this connection, a letter written by John Adams to Waterhouse, a professor at Harvard, should be noted.   The future president was speaking of the work accomplished by his son

---

* Florian Cajori, *The Teaching and History of Mathematics in the United States*, Washington, 1890, 74.   Quoted by permission of the author.

† Edwin Cornelius Broome, *A Historical and Critical Discussion of College Entrance Requirements*, New York, 1903.

John Quincy Adams, who then intended to go to Harvard before beginning the study of law. He says:

In Mathematicks I hope he will pass muster in the Course of the last Year, instead of playing Cards like the fashionable world I have spent my Evenings with him. We went with some Accuracy through the Geometry in the Praeceptor, the Eight Books of Simpsons Euclid, in Latin and compared it Problem by Problem and Theorem by Theorem with Le Pere Dechalles in french, We went through plain Trigonometry and plain Sailing, Fennings Algebra, and the Decimal Fractions, arithmetical and Geometrical Proportions, and the Conic Sections in Wards Mathematicks. I then attempted a Sublime Flight and endeavored to give him some Idea of the Differential Method of Calculation of the Marquis de L'Hospital, and the Method of Fluxions and infinite Series of Sir Isaac Newton. But alas it is thirty years since I thought of Mathematicks, and I found I had lost the little I once knew, especially of those higher Branches of Geometry, so that he is as yet but a Smatterer like his Father, however he has a foundation laid which will enable him with a Years Attendance on the Mathematical Professor, to make the necessary Proficiency for a Degree.*

SUMMARY

These statements indicate that even among the Greeks, mathematics was subject to as severe criticism as it has met in recent years. One should also note that with the production of texts suitable for young children, work in elementary mathematics has made its way from the university into the secondary schools, until from being a subject for college seniors, it is generally required for college entrance work. There is no reason for supposing that this shifting has reached its end, and a considerable change may be anticipated as the result of the demand of modern science and economics that the student be prepared to make constant use of the tools and concepts of mathematics.

* "John Adams As He Lived, Unpublished Letters to Dr. Benjamin Water-house, Professor of Physic at Harvard College," *Atlantic Monthly*, 139, May, 1927, 611. Quoted by permission of the publishers. This letter was written from Auteuil, April 23, 1785.

GENERAL HISTORIES OF MATHEMATICS

THE following histories of mathematics should be consulted for greater detail than could be given in this volume and for differing points of view. The list has purposely been made a short one, since the use of bibliographic references in connection with particular topics in the text makes their repetition unnecessary here.

Ball, W. W. Rouse: *A Short Account of the History of Mathematics,* sixth edition, London, 1915.

Cajori, Florian: *A History of Elementary Mathematics*, New York, 1917.

A History of Mathematics, second edition, New York, 1919.

Cantor, Moritz: *Vorlesungen über Geschichte der Mathematik*, 4 vols., Leipzig, 1880–1908.

Smith, David Eugene: *History of Mathematics*, 2 vols., Boston, 1923–1925.

A Source Book in Mathematics, New York, 1929.

Tropfke, J.: *Geschichte der Elementar-Mathematik in systematischer Darstellung*, 7 vols., Leipzig, 1922.

c. 600 B.C.			Thales
c. 540			Pythagoras
c. 450			Zeno
c. 380			Plato
c. 300			Euclid
c. 225			Apollonius, Archimedes
c. 140			Hipparchus
c. 100 A.D.			Nicomachus, Menelaus
c. 150			Ptolemy
c. 275			Diophantus
c. 510			Boethius, Āryabhata
c. 628			Brahmagupta
c. 820			Al-Khowârizmî
c. 850			Mahāvīra
c. 1000			Gerbert
c. 1120-40			Adelard of Bath, Robert of Chester
c. 1150			Bhāskara
c. 1200-25			Fibonacci, Jordanus Nemorarius
c. 1260			Campanus
c. 1360			Oresme
c. 1460-70			Peurbach, Regiomontanus
1480 - 1500			Chuquet, Widman, Pacioli
c. 1545			Cardan, Tartaglia
1614			Napier
1637			Descartes
1650			Pascal
1680			Newton, Leibniz
1720			De Moivre
1740			Maclaurin
1750			Euler
1800			Gauss, Laplace

Greek Mathematics

Hindu Mathematics
Arab Mathematics
Dark Ages

Period of Transmission

Modern Times

CHRONOLOGICAL OUTLINE

INDEX

In this index, the first reference after a *name* is the biographical note in case one is given: the first reference after a *topic* is, in general, its fullest treatment. In bibliographical references, only the first appearance of a book or essay is listed, and on the page referred to is given the full title together with the abbreviation in case one is used in subsequent pages. While it is impossible to give in small compass a key to the pronunciation of the various proper names, the accent of the Greek names has been indicated, and it should be remembered that the *ā* in Hindu names and the *â* in Arabic ones are to be pronounced as is the *a* in *father*, the *ī* and *î* as in *pique*, the *û* as in *rule*.